MAINTAINING THE WHOLE

This course is dedicated to the memory of Dr Richard Holmes, a Senior Lecturer in Biology (1971–1993) and former Pro-vice-chancellor for Student Affairs at the Open University. Richard's vision was an inspiration in laying the foundations for *Human Biology and Health*.

SK220 Book 3
Science: a second level course

MAINTAINING THE WHOLE

HUMAN
BIOLOGY
AND HEALTH

BOOK 3

Edited by Jill Saffrey and Michael Stewart

The SK220 Course Team

Course Team Chair

Michael Stewart

Course Manager

Verena Forster

Course Team Secretary

Dawn Partner

Academic Editors

Brian Goodwin (Book 1)
Michael Stewart (Books 2 and 3)
Jill Saffrey (Book 3)
Frederick Toates (Book 4)
Heather McLannahan (Book 5)

Authors

Janet Bunker (Books 1, 2 and 3)
Melanie Clements (Book 3)
Basiro Davey (Books 1 and 2)
Brian Goodwin (Book 1)
Linda Jones (Book 1)
Jeanne Katz (Book 5)
Heather McLannahan (Book 5)
Hilary MacQueen (Books 1 and 4)
Jill Saffrey (Book 3)
Moyra Sidell (Book 5)
Michael Stewart (Book 2)
Margaret Swithenby (Book 1)
Frederick Toates (Books 2, 3 and 4)

Editors

Andrew Bury
Sheila Dunleavy
Sue Glover
Gillian Riley
Margaret Swithenby

Design Group

Mandy Anton (Designer)
Martin Brazier (Designer)
Sarah Hofton (Designer)
Steve Best (Graphic Artist)
Andrew Whitehead (Graphic Artist)

BBC

Sandra Budin
Rissa de la Paz
Phil Gauron
Paul Manners
Ian Thomas
Nick Watson

OU Course Consultant

Chris Inman

External Course Consultant

Bill Tuxworth (University of Birmingham)

External Course Assessor

Professor Jennifer Boore (University of Ulster)

First Published 1997, Reprinted 2001

Copyright © 1997 The Open University.

Edited, designed and typeset in the United Kingdom by the Open University.

Printed and bound in Singapore under the Supervision of MRM Graphic Ltd. Winslow

ISBN 0 7492 81545

This text forms part of an Open University Second Level Course. If you would like a copy of *Studying with The Open University*, please write to the Course Reservations and Sales Centre, PO Box 724, The Open University, Walton Hall, Milton Keynes, MK7 6ZS. If you have not enrolled on the Course and would like to buy this or other Open University material, please write to Open University Educational Enterprises Ltd, 12 Cofferidge Close, Stony Stratford, Milton Keynes, MK11 1BY, United Kingdom.

1.2

CONTENTS

CHAPTER 1
INTRODUCTION

At the beginning of this course, we stressed that in order to take an holistic view of human biology it is necessary to look at different levels, both within the body and also outside it – at the interactions between individuals and their social and physical environments. In Book 1, you saw how an individual is formed and develops, and how these events both affect and are affected by other individuals – in particular, the mother of the developing individual. In Book 2, you learnt something of how humans grow, and how different parts of the body are constantly communicating with each other at many levels: via interactions between molecules, between cells, right through to the level of the organ systems of the body. You also saw how individuals move and how they interact with components of their environment, both those distance from the body (e.g. through vision) and those in closer contact; these could be macroscopic objects that cause, or threaten to cause, tissue damage or potentially damaging microbes which can enter the body and may cause disease. All the multitude of such functions require that the body *maintains* itself. This maintenance requires the intake of oxygen from the air and the ingestion and assimilation of food and water obtained from the outside environment. Once in the body, the oxygen and absorbed nutrients must be distributed, via the bloodstream, to satisfy the requirements of all the cells. The metabolic reactions in which oxygen and nutrients are used generate potentially harmful waste products; the elimination of these wastes is also a vital part of maintaining the body.

In this book we will look at the processes involved in the maintenance of the body. The well-being of the individual depends on the balance both of the body's molecular constituents and of the various processes going on inside the body. The maintenence of a stable internal environment is known as *homeostasis*, a term introduced in Book 2. The concept of homeostasis is an essential biological principle. We should emphasize, however, that the internal environment is not completely stable, in the sense of being perfectly constant, static and fixed, but rather it is dynamic and continually varying within a regulated range of conditions. Moreover, this range of conditions within which the body is maintained may be different at different times in the lifespan.

The principle of homeostasis has two important and related aspects. The first is that life is only possible provided that certain of the key variables of the body are maintained within limits. The second is that deviations from these optimum conditions in the body tend to cause responses that return the system to the optimum. For example, when our body temperature falls we start to shiver. The heat generated by the muscle movements involved in shivering will tend to return body temperature to normal. This negative feedback aspect, which you have already met in Book 2, is an important feature of homeostasis. Although negative feedback is crucial in re-establishing normal conditions when deviations occur, it is not the only homeostatic mechanism involved in the maintenance of the internal environment.

❑   Think about your own experiences and try to recall some examples of where homeostasis is maintained by your behaviour even though no deviations from normal have yet happened.

■   In winter you might start to put on warm clothes even before leaving your centrally heated home. You might begin to consume cool drinks on a hot summer's day even before losing significant body water or feeling uncomfortably hot. Visitors to the tropics will often take in extra salt before they travel. These are all examples of anticipatory, pre-emptive action.

Such a process is termed feedforward, to distinguish it from feedback control where the response is to a disturbance that has already occurred.

The above examples of feedforward are forms of behaviour that we perform in full consciousness of their effects and with this purpose in mind. In fact there are other, involuntary, feedforward mechanisms which also play an important role in homeostasis. You will learn more about these, particularly in Chapters 2 and 3 of this book.

The important variables critical for life that are held within limits are said to be *regulated*. The processes that serve such regulation are said to be *controlled*. Thus shivering is controlled in the interests of body temperature regulation. Shivering can be at a high or low level or not occur at all, all in the regulation of temperature.

❑   Describe drinking, urination and body fluids in the terms of regulation and control.

■   Body fluid levels are regulated by means of the control exerted over urination and drinking, both of which can vary enormously in the service of the constancy of the regulated variable.

❑   What are the similarities and what are the differences betwen regulation and control?

■   *Similarities*   Both are crucial aspects of maintaining the integrity of the body. Each depends upon the other.

Differences   There is a biological imperative that regulated variables are held nearly constant irrespective of circumstances. By contrast, controlled variables need to vary considerably, according to circumstances.

Athough the distinction between regulated and controlled variables is an extremely useful concept to aid our understanding of how the internal environment of the body is maintained, it is not always clear-cut. For example, heart rate (a controlled variable) can only vary *within restricted limits* to subserve the maintenance of oxygen levels in the blood (a regulated variable).

In our description of the maintenance of the body, and homeostasis, we will again need to look at different levels; not simply at which body systems are involved, and how molecules are actually used in the body, but also at other factors which influence breathing, feeding and drinking. Oxygen, food and water are all essential for life, and the availability and quality of air, foodstuffs and water has fundamental implications for health. We have little control over the air we breathe, but feeding and drinking are not just a simple matter of passive ingestion. For most of us, eating and drinking are pleasurable experiences, and mealtimes are important times of social interaction. For many of us, the food we eat may have other significance; our religious beliefs, for example, may preclude us from eating certain foods, or direct us to specific foodstuffs at particular times. Cultural influences are inseparable from the consideration of diet, even in these days of global communication and worldwide fast-food chains.

In this book we will examine the biology of the circulation, breathing, eating and drinking at a number of levels. As with some other parts of the course, we have considered different aspects in different sections or chapters. However, the aim is for the book as a whole to present an integrative picture.

You may wish to refer back to Chapter 3 of Book 2, to consolidate your understanding of communication (via nerves and hormones) and also to Boxes 3.2–3.4 in Book 1, Chapter 3 on the passage of molecules and ions across cell membranes. These topics are all relevant to the subjects covered in this book. You will notice that Chapter 4 (Part I) on cell metabolism contains quite a lot of chemistry, which you may find rather daunting. However, we must stress that it is the principles that matter and that you are *not* expected to recall the details of the metabolic reactions described there. We recommend that before you begin reading Chapter 4, you briefly revise the material in the Part I of Book 1, Chapter 3, which provides a valuable background to your study of cell metabolism.

CHAPTER 2
CIRCULATION AND RESPIRATION

The TV Programme 2, *The art of breathing*, is associated with this chapter. We suggest that you view this after you have studied the chapter.

2.1 Introduction

In this chapter we discuss the **circulatory system** and the **respiratory system**. You have already learnt something of these systems earlier in the course. Book 1, Chapter 6, described the development of the heart and lungs and the changes that they undergo at the time of birth. In Book 2 you learned about the innervation of the heart and blood vessels (Chapter 3) and about the involvement of the circulatory system as a defence against infection (Chapter 5). Here we will describe these two systems and their control in greater detail, and show how both systems can adapt to changes in the internal and external environment. Before beginning this chapter, it may be worthwhile to recap what you have already learnt about these systems; in particular it would be useful to refresh your knowledge of the neural control of the heart as described in Book 2. In later chapters in this book you will learn how the circulatory and respiratory systems support the body's metabolism.

2.2 Why do we need a circulatory and a respiratory system?

From your studies so far, you should already be able to provide some answers to this question. Every cell in the human body requires a continuous supply of oxygen (O_2) to fuel its metabolic processes and a means of removing the metabolic waste products that would be toxic if they were allowed to accumulate. Oxygen combines with the carbon and hydrogen supplied by food material (usually from glucose) and this oxidation process provides energy for heat and work as well as the waste products, carbon dioxide (CO_2) and water. The combined respiratory and circulatory systems ensure the efficient transfer of gases in and out of the body. Oxygen enters the body via the respiratory system and is taken up by the cardiovascular system for delivery to the tissues; CO_2 passes from the tissues into the cardiovascular system and is transported to the external environment via the respiratory system. The exchange of gases between the blood and the external environment takes place in the lungs and is termed *external respiration*. The exchange of gases between the tissue cells and their fluid environment is termed *internal respiration*. The circulatory system links these two and provides an internal transport system, transporting not only respiratory gases but all the cells' metabolic needs and waste products. The circulatory system can be divided into two parts, the **cardiovascular system** and the **lymphatic system**, which you are familiar with from Book 2. These two parts work in unison, providing a continuous movement of fluid around the body which penetrates to every cell. This allows the circulatory system to carry substances produced in one part of the body to another part. For example, it provides a means of transporting nutrients from the gut to the rest of the body, and hormones from endocrine glands to the target tissues. Even temperature regulation is achieved, at least in part, by the circulatory system; heat is transported from regions of production, such as exercising muscles, to regions of lower temperature, such as the skin, where it can be lost to the external environment.

❏   Can you think of any other important uses of an internal transport system?

■   One of the critical functions of the circulatory system is to transport the substances produced by the body in defence against invading organisms, in particular macrophages and antibodies (Book 2, Chapter 5).

From this brief introduction, you can see that the circulatory and respiratory systems are essential to the proper functioning of the body. Clearly any disruption of the normal functioning of either system will have drastic effects on homeostasis. In order for these two systems to function at their optimum they have to be very carefully controlled and this control is critical for the healthy body. At the end of this chapter, we will discuss the coordinated control of the circulatory and respiratory systems, but first we will describe in detail the structure and function of the cardiovascular, lymphatic and respiratory systems separately.

2.3 The cardiovascular system

The cardiovascular system is a completely closed system consisting of three parts: a fluid, blood, which contains red and white blood cells in a yellowish, watery **plasma** (the components of plasma are shown in Table 2.1); a pumping device, the heart, and a system of blood vessels and spaces through which the heart pumps the blood. In humans, blood accounts for approximately 8% of the body weight, so for a person weighing 70 kg, some 5.6 litres of blood is circulating around the body. The heart maintains the flow of blood around the body and can be described as a large pumping muscular bag that is capable of increasing in efficiency when a greater blood supply is required. The blood is pumped around the body through a network of blood vessels of which there are three main types in the human circulatory system: **arteries**, **veins** and **capillaries**. Arteries carry blood away from the heart, veins carry blood towards the heart, and the capillaries link the arterial and venous systems, delivering blood to and from the tissues. These vessels and the mechanism of blood flow will be discussed in more detail later, but first we will look at the main organ of the circulatory system, the heart.

Table 2.1   The components of plasma.

Substance	Description
water	90% of plasma is water which maintains the normal hydration of the body and provides a medium for both intra- and extracellular reactions as well as acting as a solvent for many essential ions.
plasma proteins	*Albumins* constitute about 60% of all plasma proteins and they create the colloidal (see Section 2.6.1) osmotic pressure which regulates passage of water and diffusable solids through the capillary walls. *Fibrinogen* constitutes about 4% of all plasma proteins and is essential for blood clotting. *Globulins* constitute about 36% of plasma proteins. They are divided into alpha, beta and gamma-globulins: alpha and beta globulins transport lipids and fat-soluble vitamins in the blood; gamma globulins are antibodies.
plasma ions	Sodium, chloride, potassium, calcium, phosphate, iodide, and magnesium.
nutrients	*Glucose* – the body's main source of energy; *amino acids* – required for protein synthesis; *lipids* (transported with proteins, see Chapter 4) – components of the cell membranes and can be used as a fuel.
hormones	steroid (e.g. sex hormones); peptide (e.g. insulin and ADH) and amines (e.g. adrenaline).
waste products	Metabolic waste products including lactic acid and nitrogenous waste from protein metabolism.
gases	The main gases dissolved in plasma are O_2, N_2 and CO_2: O_2 is transported mainly by red blood cells, with small amounts dissolved in the plasma; N_2 is carried exclusively in the plasma; CO_2 is carried by red blood cells and plasma, both in solution and as bicarbonate ions.

2.3.1   The pumping heart

In order to understand how the heart functions, we have first to remind ourselves of the primary function of the cardiovascular system, i.e. the delivery of O_2, nutrients and other metabolic requirements to the cells and the removal of CO_2 and other waste products from them. Oxygen enters the body from the external environment via the respiratory system when we breathe in (inspire). The main organ of the respiratory system is the lungs which can be described as two large bags which expand and fill up with air when we inspire (approximately 21% of the air we breathe is O_2). In order to collect this inspired O_2 and release waste carbon dioxide, the blood has to be pumped around the lungs by the heart. **Oxygenated blood** from the lungs returns to the heart to be pumped around the body. Blood returning from the body to the heart contains the by-products of cellular respiration, i.e. CO_2. This blood is termed **deoxygenated blood** and is pumped through the lungs to release CO_2 and to collect more O_2. The design of the heart, and the blood vessels which lead into and away from the heart, make this sequence possible and ensure that blood going to the lungs is kept separate from that going around the body.

❑   Why is it important that blood returning from the body to the heart is
        kept separate from that which is pumped around the lungs and then
        around the body?

■   Carbon dioxide is removed from the blood passing through the lungs
        in exchange for O_2. The oxygenated blood returns to the heart and is
        then pumped around the body. It is essential that deoxygenated and
        oxygenated blood are kept separate, to maintain an adequate supply
        of O_2 to the tissues.

How does the design of the heart maintain this separation between the flow
of blood through the lungs and that around the body? The circulatory
system actually consists of two separate circuits, the *pulmonary circulation*
(heart → lungs → heart) and the *systemic circulation* (heart → body → heart)
arranged in parallel; by virtue of its unique chambered design, the heart is
able to serve both circuits at once, simultaneously pumping blood from one
circuit through one half of its structure and blood from the other circuit
through its other half. Figure 2.1 shows a diagrammatic representation of
the adult heart. It may be worthwhile to look back and compare this with the
fetal heart in Figure 6.8 of Book 1.

The heart is basically a four-chambered, muscular bag. The left and right
sides of the heart are separated by a muscular wall, the *septum*, and each side
is divided into a small chamber, the **atrium** (pl. atria), and a larger chamber,
the **ventricle**, connected through a channel with a valve to ensure one-way
flow. Deoxygenated blood returns from the body through two main veins,
the **inferior** and **superior vena cavae**. These veins drain into the right
atrium, a thin-walled chamber, which expands with little resistance as the
blood enters. Blood from the right atrium flows into the right ventricle which
is separated from the atrium by a valve, the atrioventricular valve, also
known as the *tricuspid valve* (shown in greater detail in Figure 2.2). The
three-cusped valve receives support from strong tendinous cords or *chordae
tendinae* ('heart-strings') which pass from papillary muscles at the base of
the ventricles to the ventricular surface of the valve flaps. The cords act like
guy ropes, preventing the valves from being inverted into the atria by the
pressure within the ventricles. Thus the valve acts like a swing door which
will only open in one direction. When blood enters the right atrium, the
valve is open and blood flows into the right ventricle. When the ventricles
contract, the pressure of the blood forces the valves to close. Contraction of
the papillary muscles holds the cords in place to prevent backflow into the
atria.

Figure 2.1   The structure of the heart. (a) Cross-section through the heart showing
the atria, ventricles and vessels; (b) movement of blood through the heart and into
the arteries: (i) ventricular filling; (ii) beginning of ventricular contraction;
(iii) arteries filling due to ventricular contraction; (iv) movement of blood away from
the heart; (v) atrial filling.

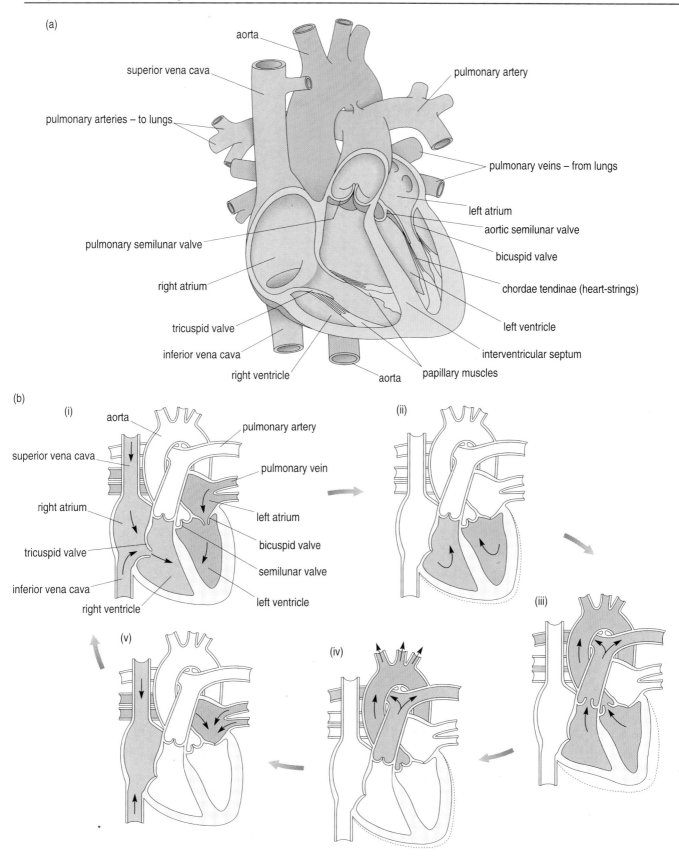

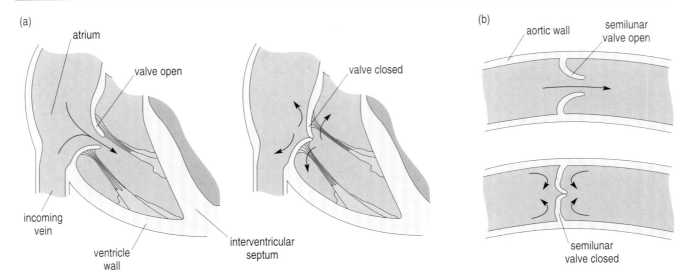

Figure 2.2 Diagrammatic representation of valve mechanisms for (a) the tricuspid and bicuspid valves and (b) the semilunar valves.

❏ Why is it important that the blood is prevented from flowing back into the atrium by the tricuspid valve?

■ Without a tricuspid valve, contraction of the heart would force the blood back into the atrium and into the main vein. The blood would be mixed with blood returning to the heart and this would prevent a one-way flow of blood out of the heart and into the lungs and reduce the pumping efficiency of the heart.

All blood leaving the heart is pumped into arteries; the blood leaving the right ventricle is pumped into the **pulmonary artery** which is the only artery in the body to carry deoxygenated blood. This vessel branches into two, one branch leading to each lung. Blood is prevented from draining back into the ventricles by a valve in the pulmonary artery. The cusps of the valve are half-moon-shaped and so the valve is known as a *semilunar valve* (Figure 2.2b). There is also a semilunar valve in the other main artery leaving the heart, the **aorta**. When the heart contracts, blood is forced out of the right ventricle into the pulmonary artery and the *pulmonary valve* is forced open. At the end of the contraction phase, the ventricle relaxes and the pressure in it temporarily falls below that in the pulmonary artery, causing a momentary reverse flow of blood. The valve closes and prevents blood draining back into the ventricle. Blood from the pulmonary artery passes around the lungs where it collects O_2 and releases CO_2 and some water vapour. The oxygenated blood from the lungs passes back through the heart before it is pumped around the rest of the body. Blood from the lungs returns to the left side of the heart through the four large **pulmonary veins** (two from each lung) and enters the left atrium.

❏ What is the difference between the contents of the pulmonary veins and all other veins?

■ The *pulmonary veins* are the only veins that carry *oxygenated* blood. All other veins carry deoxygenated blood.

From the left atrium, blood flows into the left ventricle through the *bicuspid valve* (or mitral valve). When the heart contracts, the blood from the ventricle is forced into the main artery, the aorta, and leaves the heart. This blood is oxygenated and it is this blood which then flows around the rest of the body via the systemic circulation. Again, back flow of blood into the atrium is prevented by the bicuspid valve, and back flow of blood from the aorta to the ventricle is prevented by another semilunar valve, the aortic valve. Both the ventricles have much thicker walls than those of the atria, particularly the left ventricle. Contraction of the ventricular muscles is responsible for the main pumping action of the heart and the delivery of blood to the pulmonary and systemic circulations.

2.3.2   How does the heart work?

The heart is basically a four-chambered pumping bag, but how does it pump? You may have seen in horror films a heart which has been cut out of a body beating on its own. This is not pure fantasy, because a heart will continue to beat for several hours if it is removed carefully from the body and kept in a solution containing nutrients and O_2. This is possible because the muscular activity of the heart, which generates the heartbeats, begins within the heart muscle itself and can continue without a nerve supply, i.e. it has an innate or intrinsic rhythm. So what generates this activity? The muscle fibres which make up the heart muscle (**cardiac muscle**) are very similar, though not identical, to skeletal muscle fibres (Book 2, Chapters 2 and 4). They are striated and each muscle cell is in close association with the next cell, which ensures a rapid and uniform spread of contraction throughout the wall of the heart.

What initiates the contraction? There is a small mass of specialized cardiac muscle cells embedded in the wall of the right atrium close to where the superior vena cava enters it. This is called the **sino-atrial node (SAN)** and experiments have shown that this small mass of muscle cells functions as the heart's **pacemaker** (Figure 2.3 overleaf). If the SAN is cut from the surrounding tissue it will contract at about 80 beats per minute. Other pieces of excised atrial tissue will also beat on their own but at a slightly slower rate, and tissue from the walls of the ventricles will contract even more slowly at about one third of the rate of the SAN. Although the different parts of the heart can contract at their own intrinsic rhythm, the contraction of the heart follows the activity of the SAN, which sets the rate for the whole organ.

Contraction of the heart is thus initiated by electrical activity in the SAN. This wave of electrical excitation is transmitted through the right and then the left atrium leading to contraction of the atrial muscle fibres. When the wave reaches the junction between the atria and ventricles, it excites another group of specialized muscle fibres, the **atrio-ventricular node** or **AVN** (Figure 2.3). Here the speed of electrical conduction slows so that transmission is delayed briefly to allow the atria to complete their contraction before the ventricles contract. The AVN is continuous with a bundle of modified cardiac muscle fibres known as *Purkinje fibres.* These larger fibres

Figure 2.3 Transmission of the electrical activity (shown by the black arrows) through the heart .

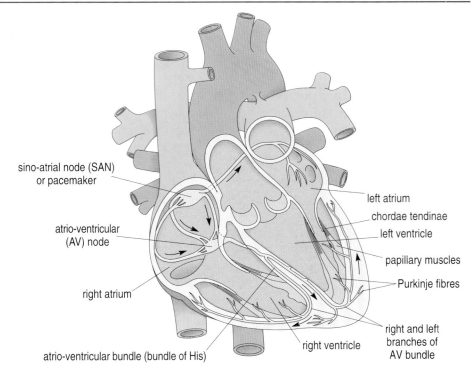

sino-atrial node (SAN) or pacemaker

atrio-ventricular (AV) node

right atrium

atrio-ventricular bundle (bundle of His)

left atrium

chordae tendinae

left ventricle

papillary muscles

Purkinje fibres

right and left branches of AV bundle

right ventricle

form a bundle, the *atrioventricular bundle*, also known as the *bundle of His*, which runs down the septum between the ventricles; the speed of electrical conduction increases here and the impulse reaches the Purkinje fibres which divide and fan out in a network over both ventricles at the base of the heart. When an electrical impulse reaches the ends of the Purkinje fibres it spreads through the ordinary cardiac muscle fibres and leads to contraction of the ventricles. The impulse first stimulates the cardiac muscle at the base of the heart, which contracts from the bottom of the ventricle upwards, forcing the blood upwards out of the heart. Thus, the pacemaker of the heart, the SAN, sends out rhythmical waves of electrical excitation which are transmitted through the atria and then via the AVN and Purkinje fibres, to the ventricles (Figure 2.3). One complete heartbeat takes about 0.8 seconds and is known as a **cardiac cycle**. It consists of a period of contraction, known as **systole** (sis-tol-eh), and a period of relaxation, **diastole** (die-as-stol-eh). You may already have come across systole and diastole since anyone who has had their blood pressure taken has it defined as a ratio such as 120/70. This refers to measurements relating to systolic pressure during contraction (120) and diastolic pressure during relaxation (70) and will be discussed in greater detail later in this chapter (see Section 2.4.2).

2.3.3   Heart sounds and the ECG

The condition of the heart can be monitored by listening to the **heart sounds** or by studying the **electrocardiogram (ECG)**. The heart sounds give information about the condition of the valves which normally prevent backflow of blood. The ECG gives information about the transmission of the electrical activity through the heart.

If you listen to your heartbeat through a stethoscope you can hear two main heart sounds known as 'lubb-dupp', which repeat rhythmically. The first sound, 'lubb', is a low-pitched sound which is not very loud and lasts for a fairly long time. The sound corresponds to the closing of the two atrioventricular valves – the mitral and the tricuspid valve.

❑   What are contracting during the 'lubb' heart sound?

▩   The ventricles.

The noise of the ventricles contracting and blood turbulence cause the prolongation of the first heart sound compared with the second. The second heart sound, 'dupp', is higher pitched, louder, sharper and shorter than 'lubb' and corresponds to the closing of the semilunar valves in the arteries.

❑   What information do you think an abnormal heart sound would provide a doctor with?

▩   The heart sounds provide information about the state of the valves and whether they are closing properly. (For example, if the semilunar valves are damaged in any way the 'dupp' sound is replaced by a hissing sound ('lubb-shhh') which indicates that blood is draining back into the ventricles during diastole when the heart is relaxing.)

The muscular contraction of the heart is preceded by a wave of electrical activity similar to a nerve impulse (see Book 2, Chapter 3). Since body fluids are good conductors of electricity, this electrical pattern or wave of *depolarization* (a reduction in the size of the membrane potential) spreads through the tissues and can be detected if electrodes are placed on the skin on opposite sides of the heart. The electrical activity can be amplified and recorded to give an ECG trace. A typical trace of an ECG is shown in Figure 2.4 overleaf. The normal ECG is composed of a P wave, a 'QRS complex', and a T wave. In some people there is also a smaller U wave, but this is not always seen.

Each section of the ECG trace corresponds to a particular phase during the cardiac cycle, i.e. the sequence of events taking place in one cycle of the heart's action. The P wave is produced by depolarization of the atria, prior to atrial contraction. This is followed by the 'QRS complex' which indicates depolarization of the ventricles before ventricular contraction, and finally the T wave which indicates repolarization of the ventricles, i.e. the ventricular muscle cells returning to a relaxed state. In those cases where the U wave can be observed, it is suggested that this corresponds to the slow repolarization of the papillary muscles which attach the heart-strings to the ventricle wall. By altering the position of the electrodes in relationship to the heart, it is possible to monitor the electrical activity of each individual part of the heart, and abnormalities in heart muscle function or transmission through the heart can be detected.

Figure 2.4 A typical electrocardiogram (ECG) trace.

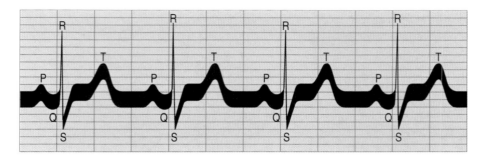

2.3.4 Cardiac output

The **cardiac output** is a measure of the volume of blood pumped out of the ventricles per minute and so, in effect, it is a measure of the total blood flow through the lungs and around the body. The calculation of cardiac output depends on the volume of blood pumped out of the heart during one beat, the **stroke volume**, and the number of times the heart beats per minute, i.e. the heart rate.

cardiac output = stroke volume × heart rate

Heart rate is determined simply by measuring the pulse, but the volume of blood pumped out of the heart with each beat is not measured so easily. Thus, the cardiac output is measured directly and, by simple calculation, the stroke volume is determined. There are established techniques available to measure the cardiac output but the details of these are beyond the scope of this chapter.

❏ If the average heart rate is 70 beats per minute and cardiac output is 5 litres per min, what is the average stroke volume?

■ cardiac output = stroke volume × heart rate

Therefore stroke volume = cardiac output/heart rate

= (5 litres per min)/(70 beats per min)

= 5 000 ml/70 beats

≈ 71 ml per beat

2.3.5 Alterations in cardiac output

The cardiac output is not a fixed volume but can be altered if the body needs a greater supply of blood.

❏ Can you think of any situations where there may be a need for an increased supply of circulating blood?

■ You may have thought of a number of different situations but one of the most common is during exercise. Exercising muscles need a greater supply of blood than do resting muscles.

The effects of a variety of different conditions on cardiac output are summarized in Table 2.2.

Table 2.2   Effect of various conditions on cardiac output. Approximate percentage changes are shown in brackets.

Condition or factor	Effect
sleep	no change
moderate changes in environmental temperature	no change
anxiety and excitement	increase (50–100%)
eating	increase (30%)
exercise	increase (up to 70%)
high environmental temperature	increase
pregnancy (late)	increase
sitting or standing from lying position	decrease (20–30%)
rapid arrhythmia (heart beating irregularly)	decrease
heart disease	decrease

What brings about a change in cardiac output? From the equation defining cardiac output (Section 2.3.4) it can be seen that a change in the stroke volume and/or heart rate will alter cardiac output.

2.3.6   Control of stroke volume

The stroke volume, the amount of blood pumped out with each contraction, depends on the amount of blood that returns to the heart from the veins, or the **venous return**. If a large volume of blood returns to the heart, a large volume of blood will be pumped out of the heart. This is because the strength of contraction of the heart depends on the initial length of the muscle fibres in the atria. If the venous return is large, a large volume of blood will enter the right atrium during diastole when the heart is relaxed. The muscle fibres in the atrium stretch to accommodate the greater volume of blood, the systolic contraction is greater, and stroke volume is increased. This is **Starling's law**, named after the man who discovered it. Since the two sides of the heart work in parallel, it follows that the same amount of blood will be pumped out of each ventricle.

❑   Can you think of any situations where the blood volume returning to the heart would be increased?

■   During exercise the skeletal muscles are contracting and squeezing the blood vessels running through them. This increases the blood pressure and the volume of blood returning to the heart. (This illustrates how the whole body is involved in the pumping activity and not just the heart itself.)

Athletes who train hard can actually increase the length of the heart muscle fibres and the heart becomes enlarged, sometimes by as much as 50%. The atrial muscle fibres can stretch further than those of untrained people and consequently venous return can be increased. The volume of blood pumped out by a trained athlete's heart is greater than that of an untrained person; an increase in stroke volume therefore relies on an increase in the volume of blood returning to the heart.

2.3.7   Control of heart rate

> It may be helpful at this point to revise details of the autonomic nervous system covered in Book 2, Chapter 3.

Although the heart rate is intrinsically set by the heart's internal pacemaker, the SAN, it is also carefully regulated by the nervous system. The SAN is innervated by both parasympathetic and sympathetic nerves. Signals originate in the two cardiac centres of the brain that are responsible for regulating heart rate; the parasympathetic nerves originate in the **cardio-inhibitory centre** in the medulla of the brain and descend to the heart via the vagus nerve. The sympathetic nerve signals originate in the **vasomotor centre**, also in the medulla of the brain, but reach the heart via the spinal cord and sympathetic ganglion as shown in Figure 2.5. The SAN is under **tonic inhibition** from the parasympathetic, cholinergic vagus nerve. This means that the activity of the SAN is continuously held in check by the vagal input. In other words, if the vagus nerve to the heart was cut the heart rate would increase. If there is increased activity in the vagus nerve fibres, the heart rate is slowed further (**bradycardia**); shock or fear can cause reflex bradycardia as a result of increased vagal activity – this is the classic 'heart stopping' scenario. The heart rate can also be increased (**tachycardia**) by sympathetic (noradrenergic or noradrenalin-releasing) nerves which increase the activity of the SAN.

The heart rate is also altered in response to changes in blood pressure. Receptors that detect alterations in blood pressure are called **baroreceptors**. Baroreceptors are found in a small protrusion from each carotid artery (the main arteries which deliver blood to the brain) called the *carotid sinus*, and also in the walls of the aorta. These receptors detect small changes in the pressure of the blood in the carotid artery and aorta. If a larger volume of blood has been pumped out of the heart due to an increase in the venous return, the blood pressure in these arteries will increase. The baroreceptors detect this increase and send the information to the cardio–inhibitory and vasomotor centres in the medulla of the brain. In the cardiac centres, the information is processed by interneurons and returned to the SAN via the sympathetic and parasympathetic nerves. If the blood pressure increases, the cardiac centres reflexly stimulate activity in the vagus nerve to instigate bradycardia which results in a reduced cardiac output and decreased blood pressure. Circulating hormones such as adrenalin and noradrenalin will increase the heart rate by their stimulatory activity on the SAN. This is the reason our heart rate increases during times of stress since these are the so-called 'fight or flight' hormones.

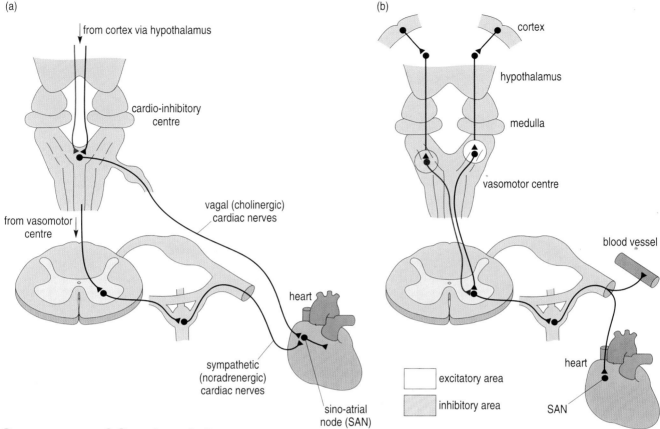

Summary of Section 2.3

1   The heart is a four-chambered, muscular pumping bag. The right-hand side of the heart receives deoxygenated blood from the body through the superior and inferior vena cavae, and pumps it via the pulmonary artery to the lungs where it is oxygenated and returned to the left side of the heart through the pulmonary veins (pulmonary circulation). The oxygenated blood is pumped out via the aorta to the rest of the body (systemic circulation).

2   The contraction of the heart is initiated by electrical activity in the SAN, the heart's pacemaker. This activity is distributed around the heart by modified muscle fibres, producing atrial contraction followed by ventricular contraction. The period of contraction (systole) when blood is pumped out of the heart is followed by a period of relaxation (diastole) when the heart again fills with blood.

3   The condition of the heart can be monitored by listening to the heart sounds which give information about the condition of the valves of the heart or by studying the electrocardiogram (ECG) which gives information about the transmission of the electrical activity through the heart.

4   Cardiac output is a measure of the volume of blood pumped out of the heart in one minute and depends on the stroke volume and the heart rate. Cardiac output can be increased when required, by an increase in either the heart rate or the stroke volume, or both.

Figure 2.5   Schematic diagram showing the innervation of the sino-atrial node by nerves from the cardio-inhibitory centre (a) and the vasomotor centre (b) in the brain.

5   Stroke volume is increased by an increase in venous return.

6   The heart rate is increased by an increase in the activity at the SAN. This can result from a reduction in tonic inhibition, i.e. a reduced rate of firing of the vagus (parasympathetic) nerve, an increase in sympathetic stimulation or stimulation by circulating hormones (adrenalin and noradrenalin).

7   Changes in blood pressure are monitored by baroreceptors situated in the sinus carotid and the aorta; information is sent from these sensors to the cardiac centres in the medulla which instigate either an increased or decreased heart rate as appropriate.

2.4 The blood vessels

The vessels of the cardiovascular system are a branching network of tubes which become progressively smaller and more branched the further they are from the heart. They are composed of three main tissue types: smooth muscle, connective tissue and a specialized type of epithelial tissue known as **endothelium**. (Endothelial cells are very thin and form a delicate inner lining to the blood vessels.) The relative proportions of these vessel wall components are shown in Figure 2.6. The smooth muscle is innervated by sympathetic and parasympathetic nerves and can contract, causing **vasoconstriction** (a narrowing of the vessel) or relax, causing **vasodilation** (a widening of the vessel). The first set of vessels, the arteries, carry blood away from the heart and this blood is oxygenated blood.

❑   Which is the only artery that carries deoxygenated blood?

■   The pulmonary artery, which carries deoxygenated blood from the heart to the lungs.

The major artery leaving the heart and delivering blood to the systemic circulation is the aorta. The walls of the aorta and other arteries contain a large amount of elastic tissue (elastin). When blood is pumped into the aorta, the elasticity of the artery walls allows the aorta to stretch or distend. When the heart relaxes, the stretched portion of the artery recoils, just like an elastic band, and forces the blood to move along the vessel. In this manner a wave of distension and constriction is created in the arteries which is known as the **pulse wave** (Figure 2.7; this will be explained in greater detail in Section 2.4.1).

The walls of the aorta are approximately 2 mm thick and they form a tube which is about 2.5 cm in diameter. The aorta feeds into the smaller arteries, which have thinner walls (approximately 1 mm thick) and are about 0.4 cm in diameter. The arteries branch and divide into progressively smaller vessels. When the walls of the arteries are only some 30 μm thick (1 μm =

one millionth of a metre) and the lumen diameter is about 20 μm the vessels are called **arterioles**. The walls of the arterioles consist mainly of smooth muscle; they can contract and relax in response to innervation. Stimulation by noradrenergic nerve fibres (sympathetic nerves) leads to contraction of the smooth muscle, whilst cholinergic nerve stimulation (parasympathetic nerves) causes the smooth muscle to relax.

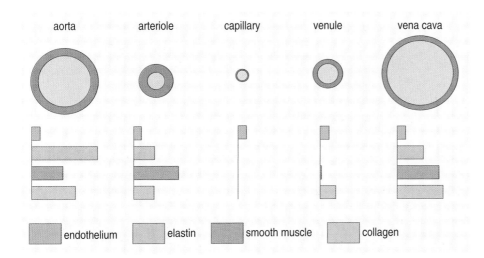

Figure 2.6   Composition of the walls of the main types of blood vessels, showing relative lumen sizes. The proportion of the different tissue components varies with the size of the vessels. For example, the amount of smooth muscle in venules increases with their diameter; the smallest venules have no smooth muscle. The main connective tissue components of blood vessel walls are elastin and collagen (Book 1, Chapter 3).

❑   What do you think would be the consequence of contraction of the smooth muscle lining the arterioles?

◼   Contraction of the smooth muscle causes constriction of the arterioles. This reduces the amount of blood that can flow through the arterioles and therefore increases the overall blood pressure.

Because they are so narrow, and the network so extensive, and because they can be stimulated to constrict or dilate, the arterioles provide the major resistance to blood flow through the body. Any small change in the diameter of their lumen causes a large change in **peripheral resistance**, i.e. the resistance of the systemic circulation to blood flow. (This will be discussed in greater detail in Sections 2.4.1 and 2.4.3.)

The arterioles divide into smaller vessels with muscular walls, which in turn feed into the smallest vessels in the circulatory system, the capillaries. The diameter of the capillaries is only about 5 μm and their walls are formed by a single layer of endothelial cells approximately 1 μm thick. In fact, the capillaries are so small that even the blood cells have to squeeze through these vessels in 'single file'. Although they are so small, the overall total area of the capillary walls in the body exceeds 6 300 square metres, and on average the capillaries contain 5% of the total blood volume.

❑   What function is served by the thinness of the capillary walls and their very small diameter?

■ The capillaries are the site at which exchange of materials between the blood and the tissues occurs. The capillaries need to be small with thin walls to enable this exchange, most of which occurs by diffusion. Also, because the capillaries are so abundant they provide a large surface area over which exchange can occur.

The capillaries form a network of capillary beds which supply all parts of the body with the nutrients they require and remove the waste products of metabolism. Blood passes along the capillaries and then enters the vessels of the venous system. At this point, O_2 has passed from the blood to the tissues by diffusion (and CO_2 has diffused from the tissues into the blood) so the venous system carries deoxygenated blood loaded with CO_2. The venous system receives blood from the tissues and returns it to the heart. The **venules** are the smallest vessels of the venous system and collect blood from the capillary beds. Venules drain into the veins and eventually into the vena cavae and back to the heart. The walls of the venules and veins are much thinner and contain less smooth muscle and elastic tissue than the corresponding arterial walls. However, they have a larger internal diameter and are very distendible (so much so that during a complete blood transfusion the venous system can accommodate 90% of the transfused blood) and the venous system plays an important role in maintaining blood flow back to the heart. Blood flow through the veins depends largely on muscular movement (the 'milking' action described in Book 2, Chapter 2). Contraction of the muscles compresses the veins and forces blood back towards the heart. There are valves along the length of the veins, that function in the same way as the semilunar valves in the arteries leaving the heart, and prevent blood flowing backwards down the veins. Because there is some smooth muscle in the walls of the veins and venules, they can, like arteries, be stimulated to relax and contract by the action of acetylcholine and noradrenalin respectively. Contraction of the smooth muscle in the venous system causes constriction of the vessels, i.e. vasoconstriction. This reduces the movement of blood through the veins and reduces the venous volume. In contrast, relaxation of the smooth muscle causes dilation of the vessels, i.e. vasodilation, and this increases the blood volume. Hence, the venous system can adjust the total capacity of the circulation to meet the requirements of the body and regulate the blood volume returning to the heart, thus influencing the stroke volume.

2.4.1   Pulse and blood pressure

You will, no doubt, have measured your pulse rate at some time or another, either by placing a finger over the radial artery in your wrist or over the carotid artery in your neck. The pulse that you feel is a measure of the pulse wave, and relates to the alternate expansion and recoil of the artery walls. Systolic contraction forces blood into the aorta, the walls expand to accommodate the blood and during diastole the elastic recoil of the walls moves the blood down the aorta in a wave (Figure 2.7). Every time that the heart contracts, a pulse wave begins; it is these pulsations that you can feel in your arteries and which are counted to indicate your heart rate. The pulse wave can be compared to a shock wave that is transmitted through the arteries ahead of the blood. The velocity of the pulse wave is about 4–5 metres per second whereas the velocity of blood flow is less than 0.5 metres per second.

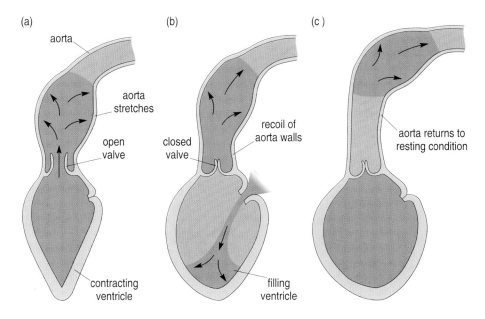

(a) aorta / aorta stretches / open valve / contracting ventricle

(b) closed valve / recoil of aorta walls / filling ventricle

(c) aorta returns to resting condition

Figure 2.7   Development of the pulse wave. (a) Systolic contraction forces blood into the first section of the aorta which distends under the pressure. (b) The aortic valve closes as the aortic walls recoil and blood is forced further up the aorta, distending the walls there. The ventricle is filling with blood again. (c) The first section of the aorta returns to its 'resting' state and the next section is beginning to recoil and force blood further along the vessel with expansion of the vessel walls. The ventricle has filled again and is about to contract and initiate the next pulse wave.

Blood pressure is the pressure that is exerted by the blood on the inner walls of the blood vessels. The blood pressure is determined by the blood flow rate, and the resistance to blood flow. Blood flow in turn is directly dependent on the pumping activity of the heart and therefore on cardiac output. When cardiac output increases, blood flow increases and blood pressure increases. When cardiac output decreases, blood flow decreases and blood pressure decreases.

❏   With your knowledge of the factors that affect cardiac output, can you suggest what might increase blood pressure?

■   Exercise, which can increase cardiac output up to 70%, will increase blood pressure. Reduced elasticity of the artery walls (hardening of the arteries) will also increase blood pressure.

Blood pressure also depends on the volume of blood flowing through the system. If the blood volume falls, e.g. during bleeding, the blood pressure will fall. If the blood volume increases, the blood pressure will increase. Some people who have a high salt intake in their diet can experience problems with high blood pressure since excess salt in the diet causes retention of water in the blood which in turn increases blood volume and thus blood pressure (You will learn more about this in Chapter 5 of this book.)

The flow of blood, like that of any other liquid, is affected by the resistance of the system through which it is flowing. If the resistance increases then the blood pressure increases. Peripheral resistance, the resistance to blood flow through the systemic circulation, is caused by the thickness, or viscosity, of the blood and the friction between the blood and the vessel walls.

In a healthy individual and under normal circumstances, the viscosity of the blood remains fairly constant and has little bearing on blood pressure. Far more important in determining blood pressure is the friction between the blood and the vessel walls through which it flows. Friction depends on the surface area of the vessel, which depends on the length and diameter of the blood vessel. The length of blood vessels does not change, but the diameter of the blood vessels decreases as the route progresses from the aorta to the arteries and arterioles.

❑   What causes a change in the peripheral resistance?

■   A change in the diameter of the lumen of arterioles.

Thus, if the walls of the arterioles contract, the size of the lumen will decrease, increasing the friction and increasing peripheral resistance. There is a simple equation which allows the calculation of blood pressure:

blood pressure = cardiac output × peripheral resistance

2.4.2   Measurement of blood pressure

Blood pressure is a measure of the maximum pressure during the period of ventricular contraction, i.e. the **systolic blood pressure,** and the minimum pressure during ventricular relaxation, i.e. the **diastolic blood pressure**. The systolic blood pressure is normally between 100 and 140 mmHg and the diastolic blood pressure is normally between 50 and 90 mmHg. You can see that there is a large difference in the normal values indicating that each individual will have their own 'normal' blood pressure which may be very different from another individual's. The difference between the systolic and diastolic blood pressure is the *pulse pressure*.

The systolic and diastolic blood pressure can be measured using a **sphygmomanometer** (sf íg-mo-man-óm-e-ter; Figure 2.8). This is a glass column containing mercury (a mercury manometer) attached to an inflatable rubber cuff which is wrapped around the upper arm at the level of the heart. The manometer measures the pressure in the cuff and this pressure is altered by pumping air into the cuff and releasing it through a valve. A stethoscope is placed over the main artery of the arm at the inner elbow. When the pressure in the cuff is increased above that of the systolic blood pressure (say, for example, 120 mmHg) the artery is forced to close and no sound is heard through the stethoscope since no blood is flowing through the artery. As the pressure in the cuff is reduced to the systolic pressure and just below, a small amount of blood squirts through the artery. This produces a tapping sound which is heard through the stethoscope and which corresponds to the contraction of the heart. As the pressure in the cuff is reduced still further, the tapping becomes louder as more blood squirts through the artery. These tapping sounds are known as *Korotkoff sounds*. As the pressure in the cuff approaches the diastolic blood pressure, the Korotkoff sounds become more muffled and eventually disappear. The pressure at which the sounds become muffled gives a value for the diastolic blood pressure, at which point there is no resistance to blood flow through the artery due to constriction by the cuff.

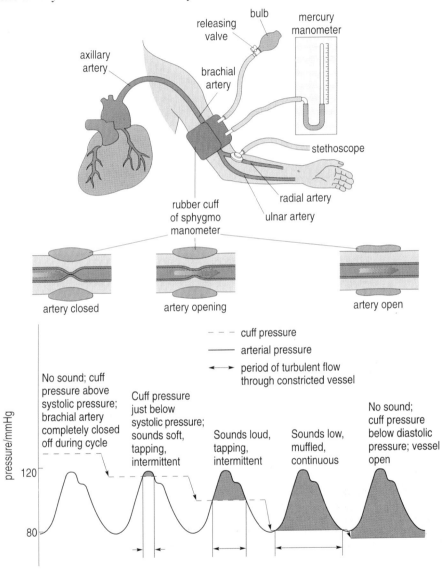

Figure 2.8   The measurement of blood pressure using a sphygmomanometer showing the apparatus set-up and the associated changes in arterial aperture, pressure and Korotkoff sounds.

If the systolic reading exceeds 160 mmHg, or the diastolic pressure is consistently above 95 mmHg, then the measurement is considered to be high and the person may be suffering from high blood pressure or **hypertension**. However, these values depend on age, obesity, inherited tendency to heart disease and other important factors such as lifestyle: diet, smoking, exercise, stress, etc. Moreover, the blood pressure may vary considerably throughout 24 hours, and apprehension or sudden stress can raise it temporarily (even attendance at doctors' surgeries can elevate blood pressure in some people – the so-called 'white coat hypertension'). Hypertension is often associated with an increase in peripheral resistance which may be due to a reduction in elasticity of the arteries or arterioles and results in the heart having to work harder to overcome the increase in resistance. The left ventricle increases in size to maintain cardiac output and the muscle cells may begin to deteriorate.

❑   Pregnancy may also be associated with increased blood pressure. Can you think why this may be?

■   Cardiac output increases during pregnancy due to the added volume of the placental circulation for the fetus. This in turn increases blood flow and consequently blood pressure. (In fact, total blood volume increases by up to one-third in pregnancy and cardiac output can increase up to a maximum of about 40%.)

2.4.3   The control of blood flow

The control of blood flow is achieved by alteration of the peripheral resistance. As mentioned earlier, the diameter of the blood vessels is influenced by the activity of sympathetic and parasympathetic nerves innervating the smooth muscle in the walls of the vessels. Vasoconstriction is stimulated by noradrenalin (sympathetic innervation); this reduces blood flow and increases peripheral resistance. Vasodilation is stimulated by acetylcholine (parasympathetic innervation); this increases blood flow and reduces peripheral resistance. The blood vessels are also affected by a number of circulating substances. These include adrenalin and noradrenalin, produced by the adrenal glands, and angiotensin and ADH which all cause vasoconstriction. Control of blood flow by circulating factors is known as humoral control. Localized changes in blood flow can be affected by substances such as bradykinin and histamine which are released during an allergic response or tissue damage; they cause vasodilation and thus produce a local increase in blood flow through injured/damaged areas of the body (Book 2, Section 5.5.4).

The blood flow to all organs increases when they are metabolically active, thereby maintaining a continuous supply of O_2 and nutrients. The decreased O_2 concentrations and increased CO_2 concentrations that result from the initial raised metabolic rate, act as local vasodilators and increase the blood flow in proportion to the increase in metabolism. This local action due to a change in the metabolism of a particular organ or tissue is known as **metabolic autoregulation**.

Summary of Section 2.4

1   Blood is transported around the body in blood vessels. Vessels transporting blood away from the heart are known as arteries; vessels returning blood to the heart are called veins.

2   Arteries branch many times to give rise to arterioles and these branch again to form capillaries which are the smallest vessels of the circulation. The capillaries link the arterioles to venules which then drain into veins.

3   The arterioles provide the major resistance to blood passing through them and this peripheral resistance can be altered by the degree of contraction of the smooth muscle in their walls.

4   Blood pressure is the pressure exerted by the blood on the walls of the vessels and is measured using a sphygmomanometer.

5   The autonomic nervous system, locally-released factors, humoral control and metabolic autoregulation also influence the diameter of arterioles, thus modifying the peripheral resistance.

2.5 The systemic circulation

The systemic circulation is the circulation of blood around the body. The flow of blood through the systemic circulation is driven mainly by the pumping activity of the heart but it is helped by contraction of skeletal muscles, particularly during exercise, by the elasticity of the arteries, and by the fall in pressure in the chest cavity when we breathe in, which reduces the resistance of the blood vessels. As we have already seen, all blood passes through the lungs before it returns to the heart and is pumped around the body. Unlike the direct movement of blood through the pulmonary circulation, blood flowing round the body does so through a series of parallel circuits. This allows for wide variations of blood flow to different regions of the body, where and when it is required, without disturbance to overall blood flow. Some of the main branches of the systemic circulation are shown in Figure 2.9 overleaf, and in the next few sections we will discuss the systemic circulation of selected organs and tissues.

Figure 2.9   A summary
diagram of the systemic
circulation to show the location
of the heart and major vessels,
and their relationship with some
of the major body organs.

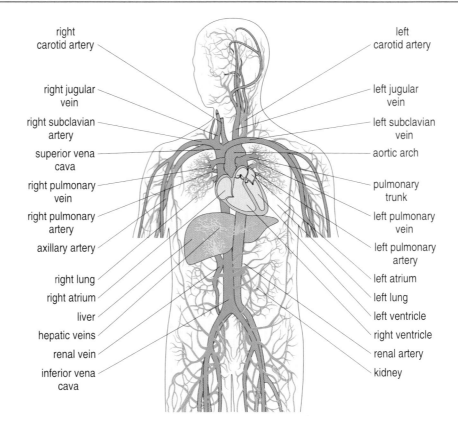

right
carotid artery

right jugular
vein

right subclavian
artery

superior vena
cava

right pulmonary
vein

right pulmonary
artery

axillary artery

right lung

right atrium

liver

hepatic veins

renal vein

inferior vena
cava

left
carotid artery

left jugular
vein

left subclavian
vein

aortic arch

pulmonary
trunk

left pulmonary
vein

left pulmonary
artery

left atrium

left lung

left ventricle

right ventricle

renal artery

kidney

2.5.1   Coronary circulation (circulation of the heart)

Although all the body's blood passes through the heart, the walls of the heart
are so thick that the heart muscle requires its own circulation. The cardiac
muscle is supplied by the two coronary arteries which branch off from the
aorta as it leaves the heart. This supply accounts for about 4–5% of the
output of the left ventricle. The coronary arteries branch within the walls of
the heart, eventually forming a capillary bed through which O_2 and nutrients
diffuse into the cardiac muscle cells. The coronary capillaries drain into the
coronary veins and ultimately into the coronary sinus which drains directly
into the right atrium.

❑   What would be the effect of a blockage in a coronary artery?

■   A blockage in one of the coronary arteries would deprive one area of
        the heart muscle of O_2 and nutrients. If the blockage completely
        impairs delivery of blood, then that area of the heart muscle will die
        through lack of oxygen.

Coronary heart disease (CHD) is one of the most common causes of death in
the UK, the USA and most other industrialized societies. *Atherosclerosis* is
the leading cause of CHD. Atherosclerosis is characterized by deposits of
lipid, cellular debris and calcium salts on the inside of arterial walls. As these
deposits build up, they narrow the artery and reduce the elasticity of the

artery walls, eventually reducing the blood flow through the vessel. Although the underlying cause of atherosclerosis is not known, the condition appears to begin with damage to the endothelial cells lining the arteries. Once the damage has begun, the endothelial cells proliferate and lipids (e.g. cholesterol), cell debris and calcium salts are deposited to form the basis of the blockage. Several factors may increase the progress of atherosclerosis, for example cigarette smoking and an excess of saturated fat in the diet (Chapters 4 and 7). Other factors which may have an adverse effect are hypertension, diabetes, age, stress, heredity and gender.

There are three ways that atherosclerosis can cause a heart attack.

- It can clog a coronary artery.

- It can provide a rough surface where a blood clot (thrombus) can form which closes off the artery, causing a *coronary thrombosis*.

- It can *partially* block the supply of blood to the cardiac muscle or to the SAN, AVN or the Purkinje fibres resulting in the heart beating irregularly. Such irregular heartbeat is called **arrhythmia**.

The typical consequence of CHD caused by atherosclerosis is a reduced supply of O_2 and nutrients to the heart muscle due to decreased blood flow through the narrowed coronary arteries. This is termed myocardial **ischaemia** (ih-skée-mee-uh; defined as lack of blood flow, from the Greek *iskho*, to keep back and *haima*, blood), or local ischaemia if it relates to an isolated area of heart muscle. If the ischaemia is mild, then the amounts of O_2 and nutrients that are delivered to the heart tissue are usually enough to sustain normal activity. However, if the heart rate is increased, e.g. during exercise or stress, then the O_2 supply becomes insufficient, leading to the pain known as angina.

In more severe cases of ischaemia of the heart following a very sudden decrease in coronary blood supply, myocardial infarction (a heart attack) may occur. In these cases, the O_2 supply is severely reduced and the region of the heart muscle deprived of O_2 dies within a few minutes. Although the symptoms of a heart attack are well known, there is still debate over what causes the sudden decrease in coronary blood supply.

2.5.2 Cerebral circulation and the blood–brain barrier

The brain receives approximately 15% of the total cardiac output. Oxygen consumption of the brain is high (18.4% of the body total), exceeded only by the liver and equivalent to that of active skeletal muscle. A continuous supply of O_2 and nutrients is essential for the brain because brain cells are particularly susceptible to damage if shortages of these occur. In situations of high demand in other regions of the body there is no reduction in cerebral circulation to compensate. Blood is delivered to the brain by four arteries: two internal *carotid arteries* (the carotid artery branches to form the internal and external or inner and outer branches), and two *vertebral arteries* (which join to form the basilar artery). The basilar artery branches and joins with the branches of the carotid artery to form a circle of arterial vessels, the *circle of Willis* (Figure 2.10). Arteries branching from this circle supply blood to the cerebellum, brainstem, cerebrum and opthalmic region. Therefore all the blood entering the cerebrum must first pass through the circle of Willis.

❑　　What advantage does the circle of Willis provide for the cerebral blood supply?

◼　　If one of the arteries serving the brain becomes blocked, flow of blood around the circle of Willis will ensure that this blockage can be compensated for by blood from another artery. In this way the circle of Willis provides a system of blood vessels which ensures delivery of blood to all the brain cells.

Figure 2.10　The circle of Willis. (a) The position of the arterial circle within the brain structure. (b) The isolated arterial circle. RIC = right inferior carotid; LIC = left inferior carotid.

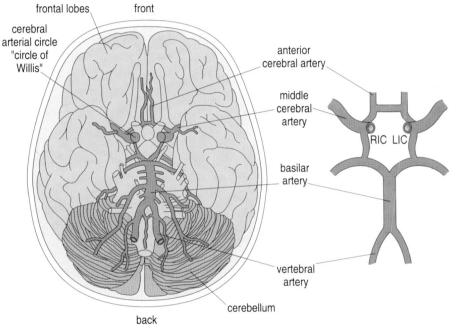

Blood from the brain drains into the jugular veins and returns to the heart via the superior vena cava. Control of cerebral blood flow is highly developed compared with that of other organs. Neural control is mainly via noradrenergic neurons in the cerebral cortex, activity leading to vasoconstriction. The cholinergic input, which has a vasodilatory action, is derived from the cranial nerves which supply the face. Much of the local vasodilation is due to metabolic autoregulation as a result of the O_2 demand of particular areas of the brain.

The arteries of the brain and neck are very prone to atherosclerosis. Narrowing of the carotid arteries by a build-up of deposits in the arteries leads to brain ischaemia and cerebrovascular accident or 'stroke'. The severity of the stroke and the ability to recover completely depends on the duration of the ischaemia and on the particular brain area affected.

Because the brain is so susceptible to small changes in chemical imbalances the need for homeostasis is greater in the brain than in any other organ. Homeostasis in the brain is unique and depends on the capillary network which supplies blood to the brain. The brain is able to absorb some substances (e.g. O_2 and steroid hormones), but not others, because the capillaries are especially adapted to create the **blood–brain barrier**. This restricts the entry of potentially harmful substances to the brain whilst allowing the entry of nutrients and O_2. The brain capillaries have walls composed of endothelial cells (see Section 2.4) joined by tight junctions (Book 1, Chapter 3) which prevent certain substances passing through (Figure 2.11). The capillaries are also surrounded by many so-called 'foot processes' of astrocytes, a type of glial cell. These foot processes store metabolic products and transfer them from the capillaries to the neurons. Once fluid has entered the brain it is known as **cerebrospinal fluid** and it flows through the brain and into the spinal column (the fluid-filled channel at the centre of the spinal cord). This fluid is not the same as blood; it is a clear, colourless fluid, high in protein content and has an almost constant pH which is not influenced by fluctuations in plasma pH. The astrocytes also pick up excess potassium ions and neurotransmitters which would harm the brain if allowed to accumulate, and deliver these, via the foot processes, to the capillaries from where they are removed. The endothelial cells of the capillaries also contain large numbers of mitochondria.

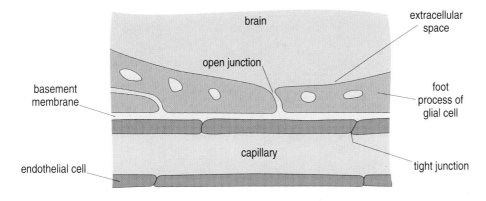

Figure 2.11   Cells of the blood–brain barrier.

❏   What do the large numbers of mitochondria indicate?

◼   That these endothelial cells are metabolically very active.

Because the blood–brain barrier is so well developed, many substances that are essential for the brain, but which the brain cannot synthesize, e.g. glucose and amino acids, have to be transported across the barrier by active transport (see Book 1, Chapter 3). The mitochondria generate the energy (ATP) required for active transport. The only substances that pass easily across the blood–brain barrier are lipid-soluble ones, such as nicotine, caffeine, alcohol and heroin.

❏   Can you suggest why only lipid-soluble substances can passively cross the blood–brain barrier?

■ Like all cell membranes, the membranes of the endothelial capillary cells are composed primarily of lipids. Thus lipid-soluble substances will pass through easily.

Water-soluble substances (such as sodium, potassium and chloride ions) are only able to cross the blood–brain barrier by active transport. Thus the blood–brain barrier tightly controls what enters the brain and contributes directly to its homeostasis.

2.5.3   Circulation within the skin

The circulation of blood through the skin accounts for about 8% of the total cardiac output, but circulation to the skin can be increased dramatically, and rapidly, by up to 150-fold.

❑ Why is it important to be able to increase the circulation through the skin so dramatically?

■ To increase heat loss via the skin.

The circulation within fingers, toes, palms and ear lobes has special channels or 'shunts' which connect arterioles directly with venules, bypassing the capillaries. The shunts are situated close to the skin surface so that the blood may lose heat easily and they have thick muscular walls which are richly supplied by nerves. When body temperature is increased, sympathetic activity to the skin decreases, causing vasodilation, particularly in the shunts. Overall, there is a decrease in peripheral resistance leading to increased cardiac output and an increase in blood flow to the skin regions. Heat loss is increased as blood flow through the skin increases (see Chapter 4).

❑ Where have you met shunts before?

■ In the fetal heart where blood does not need to pass through the lungs but is shunted from the right atrium to the left atrium via the foramen ovale. When the fetal heart contracts, some blood from the right ventricle will pass through the lungs but, since they are collapsed, the resistance is high and most of the blood is shunted directly into the aorta via the ductus arteriosus (see Figure 6.8, Book 1).

2.5.4   Skeletal muscle circulation

Under resting conditions, skeletal muscle receives about 15% of the total cardiac output. However, during exercise this can increase to 90% and O_2 consumption of exercising muscle can increase from 20% at rest to 90%. (During extreme, sustained exercise blood supply to the brain may be slightly reduced.) The increase in blood flow to the skeletal muscles (which is needed to sustain exercise) is brought about by vasodilation in the skeletal muscle capillary beds. A decrease in peripheral resistance and an increase in venous return will in turn increase cardiac output.

Summary of Section 2.5

1   The systemic circulation is the flow of blood around the body.

2   The coronary arteries provide the circulation for the heart muscle. Any disturbance in blood flow to the heart muscle can result in ischaemia and heart attack.

3   Blood flow to the brain is controlled to ensure that there is always sufficient O_2 and nutrients available. The blood–brain barrier provides a protection against the entry of unwanted substances to the brain.

4   Circulation within the skin can be modified by shunting and this mechanism plays an important role in the control of body temperature.

5   Circulation to skeletal muscles can be increased greatly during exercise by the effects of vasodilation in the muscle capillary beds.

2.6 The lymphatic system

The lymphatic system is shown in Figure 2.12 overleaf. It is the second part of the circulatory system and has three important functions:

1   To collect and return **interstitial fluid** (the fluid between the cells) to the blood.

2   To defend the body against invading organisms by means of the immune system.

3   To absorb lipids from the digestive tract.

In this chapter we will concentrate only on the first role of the lymphatic system. Its role in immunity was discussed in Book 2, Chapter 5, and you will learn more about its role in the absorption of lipids from the gut in Chapter 3 of this book.

The lymphatic system consists of a network of lymphatic vessels which carry *lymph* (a clear watery fluid formed from interstitial fluid), and *lymph tissue* which is organized into small *lymph nodes* and *nodules*.

The lymphatic vessels are similar to veins of the cardiovascular system; the vessels have an endothelial lining supported by fibrous tissue and the larger vessels have muscle fibres in their walls. Interstitial fluid in the tissues passes through the walls of the blind-ending lymph capillaries which are present in almost all capillary beds (Figure 2.13). The lymph capillaries join together to form the lymph veins or *lymphatics*. The lymph is propelled along the lymphatics by skeletal muscle activity and respiratory movements, as well as by inherent pulsating activity of the walls of the lymphatics. Valves prevent back-flow of lymph in a similar manner to the valves in the venous system. At intervals, the lymphatics empty into lymph nodes where the lymph is filtered and bacteria and other invading organisms are trapped and inactivated by cells of the immune system (Book 2, Chapter 5). The lymph leaves the nodes and returns to the cardiovascular system via ducts at the base of the neck which empty into the main veins draining the arms below the collar bone (the subclavian veins, see Figures 2.9 and 2.12).

(a)

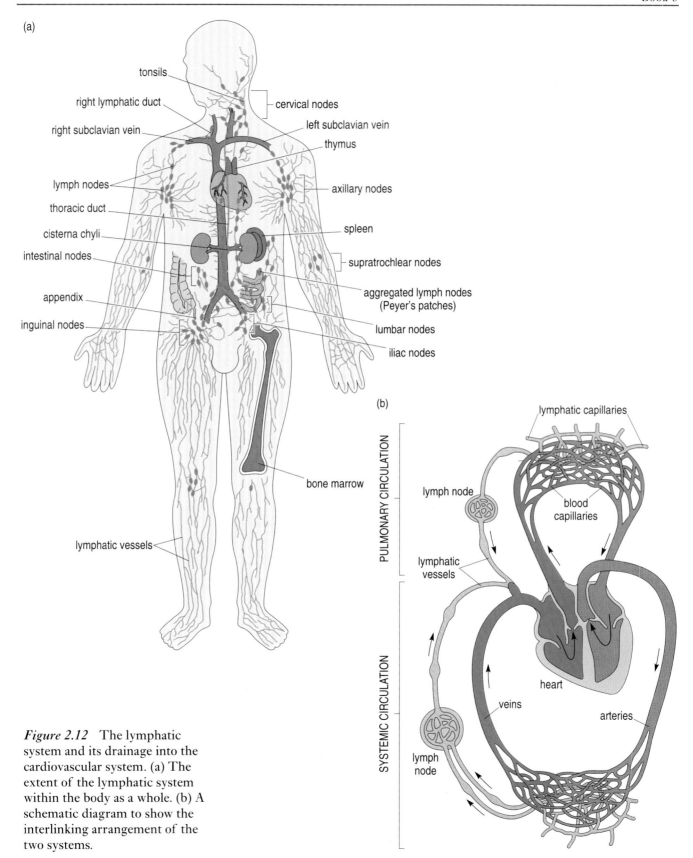

Figure 2.12 The lymphatic system and its drainage into the cardiovascular system. (a) The extent of the lymphatic system within the body as a whole. (b) A schematic diagram to show the interlinking arrangement of the two systems.

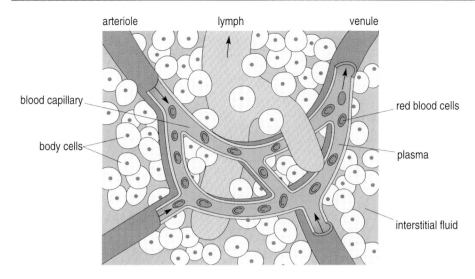

Figure 2.13   Association of a lymph capillary with a blood capillary.

2.6.1   Formation of interstitial fluid and lymph

Interstitial fluid is formed as a result of a net loss of fluid from the
capillaries as blood passes through the capillary beds. The capillary walls
are only one cell thick and so water and small molecules will diffuse easily
across them and into the surrounding tissue. In addition to passive
diffusion, the blood pressure within the capillaries forces fluid out through
the wall. However, sizeable molecules such as large proteins cannot pass
through the capillary wall and are retained within the capillary in the form
of colloid solutions. Their presence creates a difference in osmotic pressure
(see Book 1, Chapter 3, Box 3.4) between the inside and the outside of the
capillary and this is termed the **colloidal osmotic pressure**. If the
proteins were able to pass through the capillary wall, they would do so until
the concentration of proteins on either side of the capillary wall was the
same and an equilibrium was reached. However, since the capillary wall acts
as a barrier to the proteins, they are trapped and there is a concentration
difference between the inside and the outside of the capillary wall. This is
shown diagramatically in Figure 2.14a overleaf. Water is drawn into the
capillary to balance this concentration difference and the force drawing the
water in is the colloidal osmotic pressure which is equivalent to about
25 mmHg. So there are two forces acting in opposite directions on the fluid
in the capillary: the colloidal osmotic pressure tending to draw fluid in, and
the hydrostatic pressure, created by the blood pressure, tending to force
fluid out. If the hydrostatic pressure exceeds the colloidal osmotic pressure
there is a net efflux of fluid from the capillary to the tissues. On the other
hand, if the colloidal osmotic pressure exceeds the hydrostatic pressure
there is a net influx of fluid into the capillary. The colloidal osmotic
pressure remains constant along the length of the capillary, but the
hydrostatic pressure varies, being high (40 mmHg) at the arterial end where
blood pressure is high, and low (15 mmHg) at the venous end where blood

pressure is lower due to the reduced resistance in the venous system. As a result, fluid is filtered out at the arterial end, and re-enters at the venous end of the capillary. This is shown diagrammatically in Figure 2.14b.

(a)

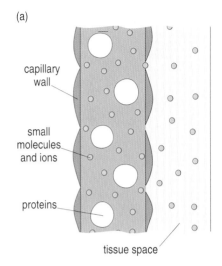

(b)

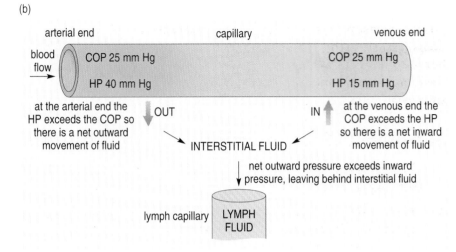

Figure 2.14 (a) A diagrammatic representation of the capillary wall which allows the passage of small molecules and ions (small blue circles) but not the passage of larger proteins (large yellow circles). The presence of the proteins on one side of the capillary wall creates the colloidal osmotic pressure.
(b) Diagrammatic representation of the hydrostatic (HP) and colloidal osmotic pressures (COP) involved in the formation of interstitial and lymph fluid.

❑ From Figure 2.14b, calculate the net pressure on the fluid in the capillaries at each end of the capillary.

◼ At the arterial end there is a net outward pressure of 40 – 25 = 15 mmHg. At the venous end there is a net inward pressure of 25 – 15 = 10 mmHg.

From these calculations it can be deduced that net outflow of fluid from the capillary exceeds the net re-entry of fluid into the capillary. The fluid that remains in the interstitial space is the interstitial fluid. In composition it is similar to the blood plasma (the fluid inside the capillaries) but without any red blood cells or any large proteins, and a smaller number of white cells. A number of small proteins leak out of the capillaries and are not returned to the venous system but remain in the interstitial fluid.

❑ What would be the effect of a build-up of interstitial fluid in the tissue?

◼ The fluid balance in the body would be seriously disrupted, too much fluid would be present in the tissue and not enough in the circulating blood and the body would swell up like a sponge. If the situation were to continue, death would occur within about 24 hours.

The lymphatic system acts as a drainage system for about 10% of the interstitial fluid and any proteins that have leaked out from the capillaries. Once the interstitial fluid enters the lymphatic system it is called lymph. The walls of the lymph capillaries are made up of endothelial cells which overlap each other. As the volume of interstitial fluid increases in the tissue, it pushes against these endothelial cells which separate like one-way swing doors (similar to the semilunar valves in the heart) allowing the fluid to enter, but preventing it from leaking out again. The lymph is then transported via the lymph vessels to be returned to the cardiovascular system via the subclavian veins.

Summary of Section 2.6

1   The lymphatic system is part of the circulatory system and consists of a network of vessels, lymph nodes and nodules and lymph.

2   The lymphatic system returns excess fluid to the blood, transports lipids from the gut, and filters and destroys microbes and other foreign particles which enter the body.

3   Excess interstitial fluid which has passed out of the capillaries and is not absorbed by the tissues is collected by the lymphatic capillaries and returned to the blood.

2.7 The respiratory system

Respiration is the exchange of gases between the external environment and the body. More precisely, respiration should be divided into two processes: **external** and **internal respiration** which is gas exchange, and **cellular respiration** which is the utilization of O_2 by cells (usually in the oxidation of glucose) to provide energy, with the concomitant production of CO_2 and water as waste products according to the equation:

$$6O_2 + C_6H_{12}O_6 \longrightarrow 6CO_2 + 6H_2O + ATP$$

Since cells require a continuous source of O_2 for metabolism, there needs to be a continuous exchange of gas with the environment. Breathing (or ventilation) is the mechanical activity of moving air into and out of the lungs; it has two phases, inspiration and expiration.

2.7.1   Structure of the respiratory system

The respiratory system consists of the lungs (the gas-exchange organ), the system of airways which deliver the air to the blood vessels, and the musculo–skeletal system which ventilates the lungs. Figure 2.15 overleaf shows the main structures of the respiratory system.

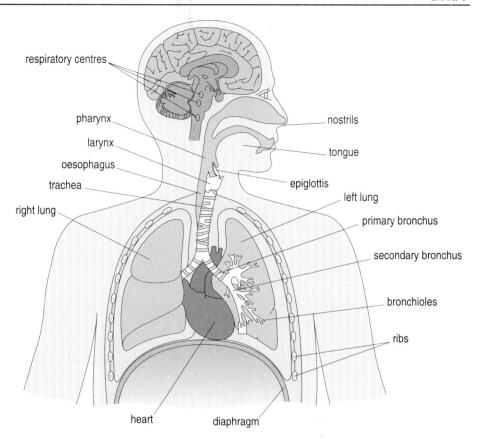

Figure 2.15 The components of the respiratory system.

Air enters the body through the nostrils and passes into the nasal cavity. The lining of the nasal cavity is formed from epithelial cells which are covered with cilia (hair-like processes) and mucus-producing cells. The mucus is sticky and so traps dirt and other particles which are inhaled with the air; the cilia form a continuously beating 'conveyor belt' which moves the mucus to the throat where it is swallowed with saliva and passes into the digestive system. This protects the rest of the respiratory system from invading particles. The air which passes through the nasal cavities is warmed to body temperature and is moistened by the mucus. From the nasal cavities, the air passes to the pharynx at the back of the mouth where it is joined by air that has entered the system through the mouth.

❑   What is the advantage of breathing through the nose rather than the mouth?

◼   Air that enters through the nose is filtered by the cilia and mucus. The air entering the mouth is not filtered, so any particles in the air entering the body by this route will pass into the respiratory system.

At the base of the pharynx are two openings; one leads to the larynx (or 'voice-box'), and the rest of the respiratory system, and the other is the entrance of the oesophagus, near the beginning of the digestive tract. Obviously it is essential that these two openings are kept separate otherwise

when we eat or drink food particles or fluids would enter the respiratory
system and cause choking. To prevent this there is a small flap of tissue, the
epiglottis, which closes the larynx during swallowing, preventing food or
water from passing into the respiratory system. If this 'diversion system' fails
and foreign particles enter the larynx then a cough reflex is initiated,
expelling the unwanted particles.

❑   What happens if the cough reflex fails and the respiratory blockage is
     not removed?

■   If the cough reflex does not remove the blockage then choking will
     follow and eventually death by asphyxiation will occur. If the object is
     small, e.g. a peanut, it may be sucked further into one of the branches
     of the respiratory system and obstruct the area of lung tissue beyond
     that point.

The larynx is also called the 'Adam's apple' and contains the vocal cords.
These are epithelial folds which vibrate and produce sound as air passes over
them. From the larynx, air passes into the **trachea** or windpipe, a hollow
tube kept permanently open by rings of cartilage. The trachea divides into
two branches called **bronchi** (singular, bronchus). These separate to serve
the left and right lung. Like the trachea, the walls of the bronchi contain
cartilage to prevent collapse. The respiratory tract, like the circulatory
system network from main vessel to capillary, progressively divides into
increasingly smaller pathways. Each main bronchus divides into two smaller
tubes a further 15 times, forming increasingly smaller bronchi, then
bronchioles, and then terminal bronchioles. The bronchi, bronchioles and
terminal bronchioles conduct gas to and from the exterior and thus form the
conducting zone; the epithelium in these regions also contains ciliated and
mucus producing cells. The terminal bronchioles each divide a further seven
times into respiratory bronchioles, alveolar ducts and alveolar sacs (alveoli).
Gas exchange occurs in the respiratory bronchioles, alveolar ducts and the
alveoli, which thus form the **respiratory zones**.

The alveoli are surrounded by pulmonary capillaries. Oxygen from within
the alveolus diffuses into the pulmonary capillary while CO_2 diffuses from
the blood into the alveolus. Since the walls of the alveolus and the pulmonary
capillary are each only one cell thick, the gases have only to diffuse through a
two–cell-thick layer (Figure 2.16 overleaf) and this facilitates rapid diffusion
and very efficient gas exchange. The total surface area for gas exchange is
about 70 square metres, roughly equivalent to the size of a tennis court.

The walls of the alveoli are composed of two different types of epithelial cell.
The first are similar to the endothelial cells of the capillaries and the second
produce *surfactant*, a detergent–like fluid which lines the walls of the alveoli
(Book 1, Chapter 6). Surfactant prevents collapse of the alveoli and is
particularly important in allowing the lungs to inflate when babies are born
and take their first breaths. Premature babies born before their surfactant
production system is fully functional suffer from respiratory distress
syndrome (Book 1, Chapter 6). Surface tension in the lungs of these babies is

Figure 2.16 Schematic diagram of alveoli in contact with pulmonary capillaries.

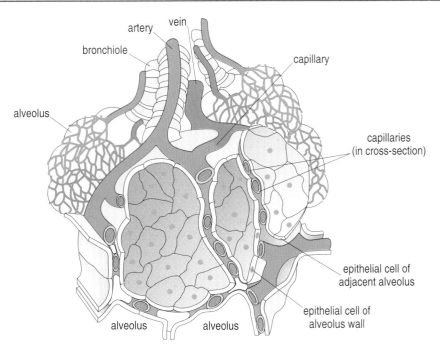

high and there are many areas where the alveoli have not expanded. Smoking also reduces surfactant production, increasing the likelihood of breathing difficulties in smokers compared to non-smokers.

There are no cilia or mucus-producing cells lining the walls of the respiratory zone, so any particles which may have escaped the filtering system higher up in the lungs will be deposited in the alveoli. This occurs in individuals routinely inhaling small particulate matter, e.g. smokers, people exposed to asbestos and miners exposed to coal dust. All these particles are so small that they are not trapped in the mucus of the upper respiratory tract. Some of these particles may be phagocytosed (engulfed) by macrophages in the lungs and transported to the lymph nodes of the lungs where they form black deposits. Those particles that remain in the respiratory zone continue to cause irritation to the lungs and eventually cause disease.

2.7.2   The mechanics of inspiration and expiration

The lungs are located within the thoracic (chest) cavity, which is formed by the chest wall consisting of the ribcage and sternum (breastbone), and the muscular *diaphragm*, which separates the thoracic cavity from the abdominal cavity. Both the lungs and the chest wall are elastic structures which slide against one another on expansion and deflation. This is made possible by the **pleura**, thin membranes which cover the lungs and the inside of the chest wall. There is a thin layer of fluid between the lung pleura and the chest wall pleura (this space is called the *pleural cavity*) which allows the lungs to move easily within the thoracic cavity and prevents collapse of the lungs by maintaining the surface tension which holds the lungs to the chest wall.

Inspiration is an active process which involves the diaphragm and the external and internal muscles between the ribs, the **intercostal muscles**. In its resting state, the diaphragm is dome-shaped, arching upwards into the thoracic cavity. On contraction, the diaphragm flattens out and moves downwards, increasing the air intake capacity by up to 75% (see Figure 2.17). The distance moved by the diaphragm is between 1.5 cm during shallow breathing to as much as 7 cm during deep inspiration. The majority of the rib movement during breathing is achieved by the external intercostal muscles. On inspiration, the ribs, which are attached to the backbone and the sternum, are moved upwards and outwards by contraction of the external intercostal muscles. Contraction of the diaphragm and the external intercostal muscles increases the volume within the rib cage so there is a large area for the lungs to expand into. The movement of the diaphragm and ribcage are shown diagramatically in Figure 2.17. Because the pleural membranes covering the lungs are so tightly stuck to the chest wall by the film of fluid (due to surface tension), expansion of the chest wall will cause expansion of the lungs. Therefore, as the chest expands, the air pressure within the lungs decreases, air flows in through the trachea and thus forces the alveoli to expand and fill with air.

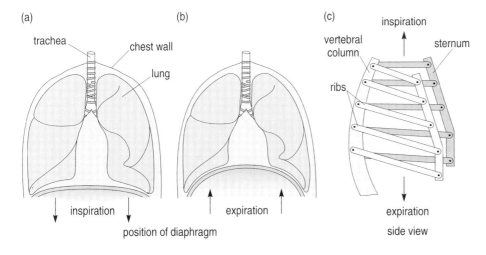

Figure 2.17   The mechanics of inspiration and expiration. (a) The diaphragm flattens and moves downwards to increase the thoracic capacity as air fills the lungs. (b) During expiration, the diaphragm curves upwards and the thoracic capacity is reduced. (c) A mechanical model to illustrate the movement of the ribs and sternum. During inspiration, the ribs and sternum move upwards and outwards; during expiration, the ribs and sternum move downwards and inwards.

❏   What do you think would happen if this film of fluid was disrupted, say, if the lung was punctured allowing an air bubble to form between the lung and the chest wall?

■   If there was an air bubble between the lung and the chest wall, it would break the surface tension holding the lung to the chest wall and make inflation, and therefore inspiration, difficult.

Expiration is generally a passive event brought about by relaxation of the diaphragm and external intercostal muscles. The ribcage and diaphragm return to their original positions and the retraction of the chest wall forces air out of the lungs. The internal intercostal muscles are also involved but are primarily expiratory muscles which pull the ribcage downwards when they contract; they are only used to any significant extent when there is a forced expiration, e.g. when trying to blow up a balloon.

Place your hands over your ribcage and see if you can feel the difference between the muscles contracting when you breathe normally and those that contract as you force out a breath.

The volume of air breathed in and out at every breath is known as the **tidal volume**. It is normally around 0.5 litres. If you take a deep breath in, i.e. inspire as hard as you can, the extra volume of air inspired is the *inspiratory reserve volume*. Likewise, if you breathe out as hard as you can after a normal breath, the extra volume breathed out is the *expiratory reserve volume*. There is always a small amount of air left in the lungs in addition to the expiratory reserve volume and this is known as the *residual volume*. Average values of lung volumes for men and women are given in Table 2.3.

Table 2.3   Average values of lung volumes in litres. Note the large differences between the inspiratory reserve volume and total lung capacity values for men and women. Tidal volume is the same in men and women but lung capacity is much greater in men due to their generally larger chest size.

	men	women
tidal volume	0.5	0.5
inspiratory reserve volume	3.3	1.9
expiratory reserve volume	1.0	0.7
residual volume	1.2	1.1
total lung capacity	6.0	4.2

2.7.3   Gas exchange in the lungs and tissues

Oxygen from inspired air which has reached the alveoli diffuses into the blood of the capillaries which surround the alveoli. Carbon dioxide in the bloodstream diffuses into the alveoli and is removed on expiration (Figure 2.18). The concentration of a particular gas in a mixture of gases is expressed as the partial pressure of that gas. The atmospheric pressure, i.e. the pressure exerted by the Earth's atmosphere, is 760 mmHg. Oxygen accounts for about 21% of the Earth's atmosphere so the partial pressure of O_2 (P_{O_2}) in the atmosphere is $0.21 \times 760 = 160$ mmHg. Although the P_{O_2} of the inspired air is 160 mmHg, the P_{O_2} in the alveoli is lower (100 mmHg).

❑   What does the lower partial pressure of O_2 in the alveoli mean?

■   It means that there is a lower percentage of O_2 in the alveolar air.

❑   Can you suggest why the P_{O_2} in the alveoli is less than the P_{O_2} of the inspired air?

■ Not all of the inspired air reaches the alveoli because of the volume of air which makes up the residual volume. The inspired air mixes with the residual air and reduces the P_{O_2} of the air in the alveoli, thus ensuring that the P_{O_2} in the alveoli is always less than that of the air entering the lungs.

The P_{O_2} in venous blood is much lower than in the alveoli, because O_2 has been removed from the blood by the tissues. The P_{O_2} in blood entering the lungs is 40 mmHg, thus a partial pressure (i.e. concentration) gradient exists between alveolar gas and the blood, so O_2 diffuses into the blood, giving a P_{O_2} for the blood leaving the lungs of 95 mmHg. There is also a small partial pressure gradient for CO_2 between the blood and the alveolar gas. The P_{CO_2} of venous blood is 46 mmHg, whereas that of the alveolar gas is 40 mmHg. The P_{CO_2} of the blood leaving the lungs is 40 mmHg, indicating that equilibrium is reached between the blood and alveolar gas, and demonstrating the ease with which CO_2 moves across membranes.

❑ Is equilibrium reached between the amount of O_2 in the alveoli and that in the blood?

■ No. The P_{O_2} in the alveoli is 100 mmHg whereas in the blood leaving the lungs it is 95 mmHg. This suggests that O_2 is not as soluble in the blood as CO_2.

The inability of O_2 to reach equilibrium is due to its method of transport in the blood, which is described in the next section.

(a)

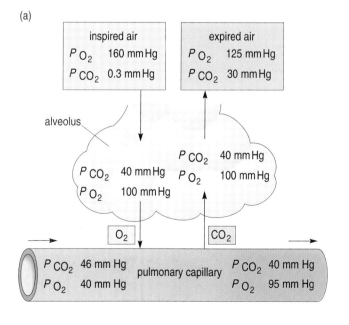

(b)

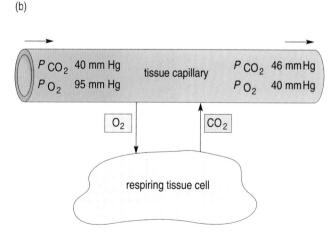

Figure 2.18   Gas exchange at (a) the lungs and (b) the tissues, showing the partial pressure of the gases, P_{O_2} and P_{CO_2}.

2.7.4 Oxygen transport in the blood

Although O_2 diffuses into the blood, it is not very soluble in plasma, so how does the blood accommodate such a high concentration of O_2 without it coming out of solution and forming bubbles? The ability of blood to carry O_2 is due to the presence of a respiratory pigment, **haemoglobin,** present in red blood cells. Haemoglobin (Hb for short) is a protein formed from four polypeptide chains, called *globins* (2 alpha chains and 2 beta chains). Attached to the centre of each globin is a small non–protein structure known as a *haem group*. The haem group has at its centre an iron atom which will pick up one O_2 molecule. Since there are four globin chains and four haem groups each with one iron atom (Figure 2.19), one haemoglobin molecule can carry four O_2 molecules.

Figure 2.19 Schematic diagram showing the structure of the haemoglobin molecule.

When O_2 is bound to haemoglobin the haemoglobin is said to be oxygenated and the complex formed is called **oxyhaemoglobin**. The binding of O_2 to the haemoglobin molecule can be written in terms of a simple equation:

$$\text{Hb} \quad + \quad 4\,O_2 \quad \rightleftharpoons \quad \text{Hb}(O_2)_4$$
$$\text{haemoglobin} \quad \text{oxygen} \qquad\qquad \text{oxyhaemoglobin}$$

The two–way arrow indicates that this reaction is a reversible one, i.e. the reaction can proceed in both directions. So in a situation where there is a plentiful supply of O_2, e.g. in the capillaries surrounding the alveoli of the lungs, the reaction will proceed to the right and oxyhaemoglobin will be formed. However, if the amount of O_2 available is low, e.g. in the capillaries within the tissues, then the reaction will proceed in a leftward direction and O_2 will be released from the oxyhaemoglobin.

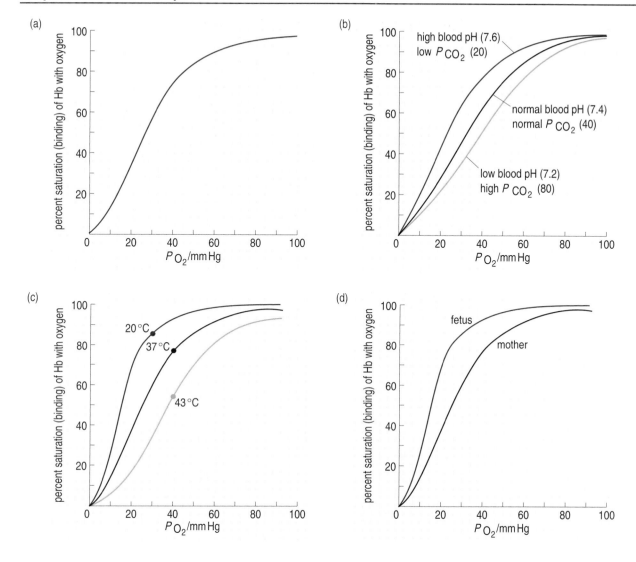

Figure 2.20   Oxygen–haemoglobin dissociation curves: (a) normal curve; (b) the effect of pH; (c) the effect of temperature; (d) the curves for adult and fetal haemoglobin.

This may seem quite straightforward, i.e. where there is abundant O_2 it is picked up by haemoglobin and where there is little O_2 it is released from haemoglobin. However, as with many other biological phenomena, it is more complicated than this. Figure 2.20 demonstrates graphically the interaction of O_2 and haemoglobin which is known as the **oxygen–haemoglobin dissociation curve**. Each vertical axis indicates the amount of oxyhaemoglobin present in the blood as a percentage of the total haemoglobin. So in simple terms, if the value was 50% then half of the haemoglobin molecules would be bound with O_2 (oxyhaemoglobin) and the other half would have no O_2 (haemoglobin). The horizontal axis indicates the P_{O_2} values so if the P_{O_2} is given as 100 mmHg then the amount of O_2 present is high, equivalent to the amount present in the alveoli (see Section 2.5.3). If the relationship between the amount of O_2 and the amount of haemoglobin was a direct one, then the line on the graph would be straight. For example, if the percentage of oxyhaemoglobin was 100% at a P_{O_2} of 100 mmHg then you would predict that at 50% oxyhaemoglobin the P_{O_2}

would be 50 mmHg. If you look at the graph you can see that this is not the case because the graph is not a straight line, but a sigmoid curve. The curve can be explained by one of the properties of haemoglobin. That is, when one O_2 molecule binds to haemoglobin it makes it much easier for a second O_2 molecule to bind. That is to say that it greatly increases the *affinity* of haemoglobin for oxygen, so a second O_2 molecule binds much more easily. Likewise, when two O_2 molecules are bound the affinity is again increased and a third O_2 binds much more easily than either the first or second, and increases the affinity to facilitate binding of the fourth O_2 molecule. (This is another example of ligand binding at one site on a molecule influencing the binding behaviour at another site further away; recall the description of allostery in Chapter 3, Book 1.) So, where the concentration of O_2 present is very high, i.e. in the capillaries of the lungs as a result of diffusion of O_2 from the alveoli, haemoglobin is rapidly converted to oxyhaemoglobin and it is in this form that O_2 is carried in the blood. In the tissues, the O_2 concentration is low and it dissociates from the haemoglobin and diffuses into the tissues.

The association of O_2 and haemoglobin is affected by three conditions: the pH (see Figure 2.20b), the temperature (see Figure 2.20c) and the concentration of *2,3-diphosphoglycerate* (*2,3-DPG*), a substance produced from an intermediate of the glycolytic pathway (Chapter 4). A decrease in the pH (i.e. an increase in acidity) of the blood will move the oxygen–haemoglobin dissociation curve to the right. This means that O_2 will dissociate from the oxyhaemoglobin complex at a higher partial pressure of oxygen. What is the significance of this? In exercising muscles, which have a high O_2 demand, there tends to be a decrease in the pH because of production of lactic acid. (You will learn more about this in Chapter 4.) Production of lactic acid reduces the pH of the blood and so moves the dissociation curve to the right. Figure 2.20b shows the effect of pH on the O_2 haemoglobin dissociation curve. If a line is drawn from the point at which 50% of the haemoglobin is present as oxyhaemoglobin on the vertical axis, across to the curve, and then down to the horizontal axis as shown, we can estimate the partial pressure of O_2 at which 50% of the haemoglobin is in the oxyhaemoglobin form (approximately 27 mmHg). If you look at the same point but use the pH 7.2 curve, you can see that the partial pressure of O_2 at which 50% of the haemoglobin is in the oxyhaemoglobin form is increased (approximately 42 mmHg). Thus, at the lower pH, the Hb releases O_2 at a much higher partial pressure of the gas. This means that in exercising muscles where O_2 demand is high, the pH is lower, and O_2 is released *earlier* from the oxyhaemoglobin than under conditions where the pH is not reduced. This decrease in affinity of haemoglobin for O_2 with a decrease in the pH of the blood is called the **Bohr shift**. The pH of the blood also falls with an increase in P_{CO_2} (associated with a high rate of respiration and hence high O_2 requirement). In the tissues, where CO_2 concentrations are high, the Bohr shift accounts for an extra 1–2% increase in release of O_2 from oxyhaemoglobin.

❑   Look at the oxygen–haemoglobin dissociation curve in Figure 2.20c. What is the effect of increased temperature on the oxygen–haemoglobin dissociation curve and what could be the significance of this effect?

▉   An increase in temperature shifts the dissociation curve to the right, causing O_2 release to occur at a higher P_{O_2}. Since a high rate of respiratory activity (such as that of exercising muscle) is associated with an increase in temperature, this will serve to increase the rate of O_2 supply.

The concentration of 2,3-DPG is very high in red blood cells and has a similar effect on the O_2 dissociation curve as pH and temperature. The reason for this is that 2,3-DPG binds to the globin (polypeptide) chains of deoxygenated haemoglobin, but not to oxyhaemoglobin. Thus an increase in 2,3-DPG concentration will encourage oxygen release from oxyhaemoglobin. Exercise increases the rate of glycolysis and hence the concentration of 2,3-DPG, as do thyroid hormones, growth hormone and sex hormones. An interesting and important effect is that of altitude on the concentration of 2,3-DPG in red blood cells. 2,3-DPG synthesis is stimulated by **hypoxia** (shortage of oxygen) and the increased levels achieved in such conditions are important in facilitating the unloading of O_2 in the tissue capillaries: at high altitude, atmospheric pressure is lower, the P_{O_2} in the atmosphere is lower and therefore the P_{O_2} in inspired air decreases. A change to high altitude increases 2,3-DPG levels in the red blood cells and so the oxygen–haemoglobin dissociation curve shifts to the right allowing tissues to obtain O_2 more easily and counteracting the effect of reduced atmospheric P_{O_2}.

Figure 2.20d shows the oxygen–haemoglobin dissociation curve for adults (adult haemoglobin) and for the fetus which has a different type of haemoglobin (fetal haemoglobin). The oxygen–haemoglobin dissociation curve for fetal haemoglobin is shifted to the left so fetal haemoglobin has a greater affinity for O_2 than does adult haemoglobin.

❑   What is the advantage to the fetus of having a form of haemoglobin which has a greater O_2 affinity than the mother's haemoglobin?

▉   The fetal haemoglobin will pick up O_2 from the mother's blood more efficiently.

The capacity of the blood to carry O_2 is greatly reduced by carbon monoxide, a gas emitted by car exhausts and faulty gas appliances. Carbon monoxide competes with O_2 for the haemoglobin and in this chemical competition, carbon monoxide always 'wins' because it binds much more strongly than O_2. Inhaling carbon monoxide will therefore progressively reduce the amount of haemoglobin available to bind O_2. Carbon monoxide poisoning results, and eventually death will occur if the source of carbon monoxide is not removed, because no O_2 is available to the cells for respiration and they die from asphyxiation.

2.7.5 Carbon dioxide transport in the blood

Carbon dioxide is carried in the blood in a number of forms. About 7% of the CO_2 is carried dissolved in the plasma as carbonic acid (H_2CO_3) and bicarbonate, or hydrogen carbonate (HCO_3^-) according to the equation:

$$CO_2 \ + \ H_2O \ \rightleftharpoons \ H_2CO_3 \ \rightleftharpoons \ HCO_3^- \ + \ H^+$$

carbon dioxide   water   carbonic acid   bicarbonate   hydrogen
                                                    ion   ion

❑ What effect will increased CO_2 levels have on the pH of the blood?

◼ The blood pH will be reduced because the H^+ ions produced by the dissociation of carbonic acid make the blood more acidic.

The reaction between CO_2 and water is normally very slow; however, in the red blood cell there is an enzyme, **carbonic anhydrase**, which greatly speeds up this reaction. The concentration of CO_2 in the tissues is much higher than the concentration in the red blood cells so a partial pressure gradient exists between the tissue and the red blood cell. Figure 2.21 shows the reactions which take place in a red blood cell when it reaches the tissue. CO_2 diffuses into the cell and, due to the presence of carbonic anhydrase, reacts immediately with water to produce carbonic acid. This conversion reduces CO_2 concentrations, thereby maintaining the partial pressure gradient for CO_2. As a result, 70% of the CO_2 in the circulation enters the red blood cells. Blood spends on average 0.75 seconds in the capillary and so the time available to pick up a full load of CO_2 from the tissues is very short. The presence of carbonic anhydrase allows the rapid uptake of CO_2 into the blood.

❑ Can you suggest another reason why it is necessary to retain CO_2 in the red blood cells, rather than in the plasma?

◼ CO_2 is then readily accessible in the red blood cells for removal in the lungs. Also, if CO_2 was allowed to accumulate in the plasma and react with water it would decrease the pH of the blood and it is important that blood pH values are maintained within strict limits.

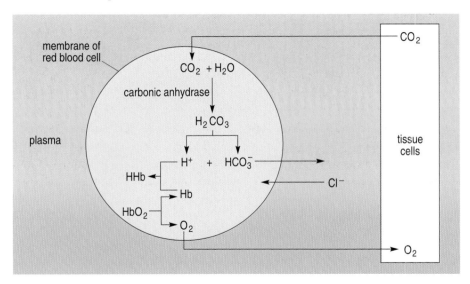

Figure 2.21 Carbon dioxide transport between the tissues and red blood cells.

Within the red cells, the carbonic acid dissociates into bicarbonate (HCO_3^-) and a hydrogen ion (H^+). If the H^+ ions were to accumulate in the red blood cell they would eventually kill it, but the ions are buffered (neutralized) by haemoglobin. The presence of H^+ ions encourages the displacement of O_2 from the oxyhaemoglobin. The O_2 then diffuses out of the red blood cell and into the tissue.

CO_2 enters the red blood cell and its reaction with water produces HCO_3^-. The red blood cell membrane is permeable to these negatively charged ions which diffuse out into the plasma. This outward movement of negative charge results in an excess of positive charge inside the cell. The red cell membrane is not permeable to positively charged ions, so positive charge cannot leave the cell to maintain neutrality. Instead, there is an inward movement of chloride (Cl^-) ions, known as the chloride shift, which compensates for the loss of HCO_3^- ions.

In addition to the carbonic acid/carbonate forms, a small amount of CO_2 is carried in the red blood cell bound to haemoglobin in the form of carbamino–haemoglobin. This accounts for approximately 10% of the total CO_2 present in the blood and is very important physiologically, accounting for approximately 23% of all CO_2 exchanged.

2.7.6 The control of respiration

The control of respiration is brought about by innervation of the inspiratory muscles. Generally, respiration is an involuntary, automatic event. We are not aware of it happening unless we try to hold our breath, or breathe out deeply, when control becomes voluntary. Two separate areas of the brain are responsible for the involuntary and voluntary control over respiration. An area in the pons and medulla at the base of the brain is the site of automatic control and an area responsible for voluntary control is found in the cerebral cortex. Each of these centres receives information about the respiratory status of the body – from muscles and tissues via nerves, and from the blood by chemical stimuli – and sends out impulses to the respiratory muscles to increase or decrease the rate of breathing accordingly.

The diaphragm is innervated by the phrenic nerve, and the intercostal muscles receive inputs from the thoracic nerves. Information from the medulla produces a regular cycle of activity in these nerves, controlling the rate of ventilation. It can be said that the respiratory centres act as the respiratory pacemaker. There are two types of neurons in the respiratory centres which send impulses to the phrenic and thoracic nerves. The first set are activated or *fire* during inspiration (*the inspiratory neurons*) and the second set of neurons fire during expiration (*the expiratory neurons*). The inspiratory neurons inhibit the firing of the expiratory neurons and vice versa.

When we breathe in, the inspiratory centre in the medulla is active and the inspiratory neurons are firing to stimulate contraction of the diaphragm and the intercostal muscles. Inspiration is terminated by two things: (a) activity in the respiratory centre which stops us breathing and (b) information from **stretch receptors** (see Book 2, Chapter 3) in the intercostal muscles which tell the brain when the lungs have expanded to full capacity. The inspiratory neurons stop firing and this relieves the block on the expiratory neurons and leads to relaxation of the inspiratory muscles. The respiratory centre therefore acts as a 'pattern generator' for respiration. The pattern generator can be modified in response to changes in the metabolic requirements of the body which are monitored by **chemoreceptors**, receptors which respond to the chemical environment. There are two sorts of chemoreceptors involved in respiration – central and peripheral chemoreceptors. Central chemoreceptors in the medulla are a group of modified nerve cells which respond to the concentration of H^+ ions in the cerebrospinal fluid. If the concentration of H^+ ions increases, these cells become more active, increasing the activity of the respiratory centre and increasing ventilation.

❑   Under what circumstances would the hydrogen ion concentration of the extracellular fluid increase?

◼   If there is an increase in the partial pressure of CO_2, the gas will pass into the plasma where it will react with water, resulting in the formation of HCO_3^- ions and H^+ ions.

Peripheral chemoreceptors are specialized groups of cells found in small extensions of the aorta and the external carotid arteries known as the aortic and carotid sinuses respectively. These sensory cells respond to decreases in O_2 concentration of the blood and send information to the respiratory centres to stimulate ventilation. Their activity will be discussed in greater detail in the next section. Figure 2.22 is a schematic diagram illustrating the control of ventilation.

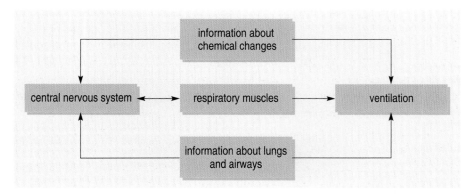

Figure 2.22   The physiological interactions controlling ventilation.

2.7.7   The effect of pollution on the respiratory system

We take, on average, about 20 000 breaths a day, inspiring approximately 16 kg or 10 000 litres of air. Any pollutants present in the air (such as nitrogen oxides, carbon monoxide, sulphur oxides) will also be inhaled. As mentioned earlier, the respiratory system works hard to remove any noxious particles by means of the cilia and mucus produced by the cells lining the large airways. If particles continue to be inhaled the system responds by producing more mucus, the ciliated cells become damaged and eventually the respiratory system cannot remove all the trapped particles. The coughing reflex is an attempt to expel these pollutants, but continued coughing leads to damage of the airways, leaving them susceptible to infection.

The airways respond to continual inhalation of polluted air by narrowing to reduce the volume of air entering the lungs, thus increasing the likelihood of trapping inhaled particles. If the bronchioles are affected, the condition is known as *chronic bronchitis*, where the bronchioles are narrowed, and secrete excess mucus so reducing the amount of air passing to the alveoli. Often chronic bronchitis leads to *emphysema*, where the lungs have to work extra hard to obtain sufficient O_2 for the body; the walls of the alveoli stick together, greatly reducing the gas exchange potential of the lungs. In order to compensate, cardiac output is increased to increase the volume of blood passing through the lungs and the right ventricle becomes enlarged. This enlargement, or hypertrophy, of muscle fibres increases the intercapillary distance and reduces the chances of the cardiac muscle being adequately supplied with O_2. The end result may be attacks of myocardial ischaemia, left ventricular failure, and ultimately, heart attack. One of the big problems associated with chronic bronchitis is that most people suffering from this disease find it very difficult to work. This is particularly so if their normal work involves physical exercise.

One of the fastest growing health problems throughout the world is a respiratory disease, **asthma**, which affects about three million people in Britain; the number of people affected globally has doubled over the last 20 years. Asthma is associated with a narrowing of the airways, swelling of the airway linings, an over-production of mucus and difficulties in expiration. The causes of asthma are hard to pinpoint. It is now estimated that there are over 200 factors which trigger asthma. These include pollen, house dust mite, pollutants, dairy produce, chest infections, exercise, and emotional stress. It appears that the increase in the incidence of asthma is not only restricted to industrial nations. For example, in the 1970s, in the highlands of New Guinea, there were no cases of asthma reported; but in the 1980s, 7.5% of the population of the New Guinea highlands tribes were found to have asthma. The trigger for this condition in these people is likely to be house dust mites contained in cotton blankets imported from the Western world.

Summary of Section 2.7

1   The respiratory system allows the passage of O_2 from the external environment to the internal environment. It also allows the release into the external environment of CO_2, a potentially toxic by-product of respiration.

2   The respiratory system consists of the lungs, a branching series of tubular airways, and the ribcage, intercostal muscles and diaphragm whose movements allow the filling and emptying of the lungs.

3   Oxygen diffuses from inspired air into the capillaries where it is carried in the blood bound to the respiratory pigment haemoglobin. The oxygen–haemoglobin dissociation curve predicts the uptake and release of O_2 and is altered by pH, temperature and concentrations of the glycolytic intermediate 2,3-diphosphoglycerate.

4   Carbon dioxide diffuses from the tissues into the capillaries. In the red blood cell, CO_2 reacts rapidly with water due to the presence of the enzyme carbonic anhydrase. The CO_2 and water form carbonic acid and then bicarbonate and the majority of the CO_2 in the blood is carried in this converted form.

5   Respiration is controlled by the respiratory centre in the brain which modulates the activity of inspiratory and expiratory neurons that effect inspiration and expiration respectively.

6   The respiratory centres receive information from stretch receptors in the lungs which inform the brain when the lungs are fully expanded, and from peripheral and central chemoreceptors which monitor the pH and O_2 content of the blood.

2.8 Control of the cardiovascular and respiratory systems

Although we have mentioned some of the control mechanisms of both the circulatory and respiratory systems individually, it should be apparent that the workings of each are closely interlinked. A change in the O_2 requirements of the tissues, e.g. during exercise, will lead to an increase in heart rate and a simultaneous increase in ventilation rate. Many of the sensors that monitor these changes, like the baroreceptors and chemoreceptors, lead to an adjustment of the activity of both systems at the same time. In this section we will look in greater detail at the control of both the respiratory and cardiovascular systems and consider them as one integrated system. Figure 2.23 shows some of the interactions between the two systems.

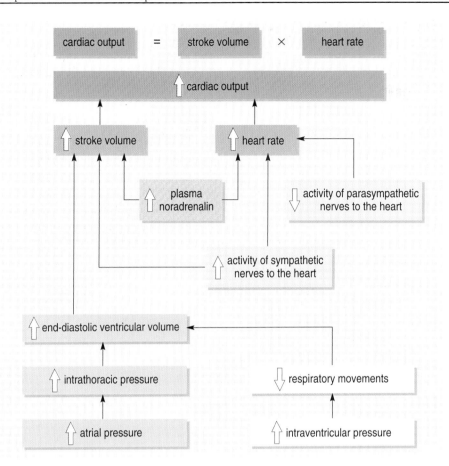

Figure 2.23 An illustration of
the interactions between the
cardiovascular and respiratory
systems leading to alterations in
cardiac output.

2.8.1   Control centres in the brain

Although the heart rate and rate of breathing can be quickly modified by
changes in the internal or external environment, the overall control of both
systems is driven by neural activity from the brain. The next section is an
overview of what you should already have learnt about the control centres of
the cardiovasular and respiratory systems. The centres are located in the
pons and the medulla and form part of the brainstem. If there was no centre
controlling the heart rate, the heart would contract at the rate of activity of
the SAN, i.e. at about 80–90 beats per minute. The SAN receives
parasympathetic inputs from the vagus nerve. Activity in the vagal nerve to
the SAN reduces the heart rate. This tonic inhibition of the SAN from the
parasympathetic vagus nerve reduces the intrinsic heart rate to, on average,
70 beats per minute. The tonic inhibition is initiated in the cardio-inhibitory
centre in the medulla.

❑   Why is it necessary to have tonic inhibition to reduce the heart rate
        below that of the SAN?

■   If the heart was beating continually at the full potential of the SAN it
        would not be possible to increase the heart rate when required. A
        reduction in tonic inhibition from the cardio-inhibitory centre will
        increase heart rate.

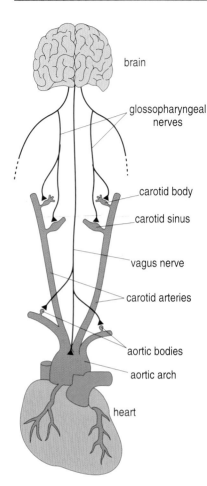

Figure 2.24   The location of the aortic arch, carotid sinuses, carotid bodies and the efferent (motor) nerves.

The control centre for breathing is also found in the medulla. The inspiratory centre drives the inspiratory nerves, stimulating the activity of the inspiratory muscles and at the same time inhibiting the expiratory centre. The respiratory centre responds to the activity of stretch receptors in the lungs by inhibiting activity of the inspiratory nerves to terminate inspiration and by releasing the block on the expiratory nerves. Activation of the latter causes relaxation of the inspiratory muscles.

2.8.2   Sinus arrhythmia

In a healthy individual breathing normally, the heart rate goes up slightly on inspiration and goes down slightly on expiration. This variation is known as **sinus arrhythmia**. As we breathe in, the stretch receptors in the lungs respond to the expansion of the lungs. This information is relayed to the medulla via nerve fibres in the vagus nerve and serves to inhibit the inspiratory nerves and prevent excessive inspiration. This inhibition is also relayed to the cardiac centre and the tonic vagal activity (which slows the heart rate under normal conditions) is reduced, leading to an increase in activity of the SAN and an increase in heart rate. During expiration, the reverse is true and the heart rate decreases. Sinus arrhythmia demonstrates the close association between the respiratory and circulatory systems.

2.8.3   The baroreceptors and chemoreceptors

The location of the baroreceptors and chemoreceptors is shown in Figure 2.24. Baroreceptors respond to changes in the degree to which the walls of the arteries are stretched. The most important baroreceptors are found in the carotid sinus (Section 2.3.7) of each of the internal carotid arteries which supply the brain. A second set of baroreceptors are found in the walls of the aorta at the point where the aorta curves away from the heart, an area known as the *aortic arch*. Also in this area are a number of stretch receptors which respond to the distension of the aorta that results from an increase in blood pressure. The chemoreceptors are found in small extensions of the aorta and in the external carotid arteries and are known as aortic and carotid bodies respectively. Information from all these receptors is delivered to the medulla of the brain by specific nerves some of which are in the vagus nerve, others of which are known as the glossopharyngeal nerves. The activity in these nerve fibres is tonic, i.e. they fire at a slow rate under 'normal' conditions, but if the conditions change they can increase or decrease their rate of firing accordingly.

❑   What else receives information from the vagus nerve?

◼   Electrical impulses from the vagus nerve slow down the heart rate by reducing the activity of the sino-atrial node.

Thus, there are 'loops' of neural activity from the baroreceptors and chemoreceptors, the medulla of the brain (the area where the respiratory and cardiac centres are found), and the effectors (the sino-atrial node of the heart and the inspiratory muscles). These are examples of reflex feedback mechanisms (see Book 2, Chapter 3).

What happens if blood pressure changes? If arterial blood pressure increases, the reflex feedback will bring into effect changes to reduce it to normal values. The increase in blood pressure causes the walls of the arteries to be stretched and the change is sensed by the baroreceptors and stretch receptors. This increases the rate of firing of the nerve fibres from the carotid sinus and aortic arch. The information is relayed to the cardiac centre which increases the vagal (parasympathetic) activity to the heart, so reducing the heart rate. There is also a reduction in the activity of the sympathetic nerves. This reduces the stroke volume and causes the smooth muscle in the arterioles to relax, leading to vasodilation. Overall, the reduction in heart rate and stroke volume reduces cardiac output, and vasodilation reduces the peripheral resistance. All these changes together reduce the arterial blood pressure. An increase in the activity of the baroreceptor nerves leads to a small reduction in inspiration, although this has very little physiological benefit. Figure 2.25 shows schematically the reflex feedback in response to an increase in arterial blood pressure.

Figure 2.25 A schematic diagram to show how the cardiac and respiratory centres interact to accommodate an increase in arterial blood pressure.

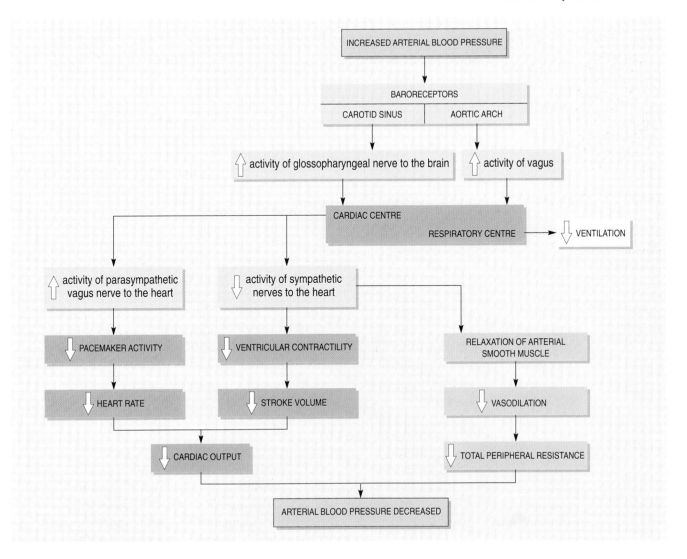

❏   From Figure 2.25, describe what will happen if the baroreceptors detect a decrease in blood pressure.

■   A reflex increase in blood pressure would occur. This would result from a reduction in the firing rate of the nerves from the baroreceptors to the cardiac and respiratory centres, causing a decrease in parasympathetic activity of the vagus nerve to the heart, and hence an increase in heart rate. Stroke volume would be increased and vasoconstriction would occur due to an increase in the firing rate of sympathetic nerves. Cardiac output and total peripheral resistance would increase, thus increasing arterial blood pressure.

What happens if there is a change in the partial pressure of O_2 in the arterial blood? The chemoreceptors in the carotid and aortic bodies are the only chemoreceptors that respond to changes in PO_2. Other chemoreceptors, like those in the respiratory centre of the brain (see Section 2.7.6), respond to changes in H^+ ion concentration as a result of changes in PCO_2. If the PO_2 is reduced due to an increase in the rate of utilization of O_2 by the tissues or due to a decrease in the blood flow through the carotid and aortic bodies, a reflex feedback will be initiated to return the PO_2 value to normal. The activity in the nerve fibres from the chemoreceptors in the carotid and aortic bodies increases with a fall in the arterial $PO_2.$ This information is relayed to the respiratory
and cardiac centres in the medulla and a reflex increase in the rate and depth of breathing is initiated by stimulation of the inspiratory neurons. This serves to increase the PO_2 in the alveoli. At the same time, the heart rate, stroke volume and total peripheral resistance are increased, which in turn raises the arterial blood pressure and increases the flow of blood through the carotid and aortic bodies. These chemoreceptors respond in a similar manner to an increase in arterial PCO_2 or H^+ ion concentration.

2.8.4   What happens when things go wrong?

The maintenance of a fully functional, integrated cardiovascular and respiratory system is dependent on the continual accurate monitoring of the circulating blood by chemoreceptors and baroreceptors. If either of these sensor systems fails, the reflex feedback mechanisms will not maintain the homeostatic control of heart and lung function.

When we are asleep, the control of respiration is not as rigorous as when we are awake. Consequently there are times during sleep when we stop breathing briefly. These periods are known as **apnoea** (ap-nee-ah) and are due to a decrease in the sensitivity of the chemoreceptors to alterations in PCO_2. For some individuals, these spells of apnoea become a serious problem; they wake up with headaches, fatigued, and in the most serious cases show all the clinical symptoms of respiratory failure although they have perfectly healthy lungs. This is known as *sleep–apnoea syndrome* and one of the causes is believed to be a failure, during sleep, of contraction of the muscles which normally hold the tongue in place. The tongue drops back, blocking the airway and preventing air entering the lungs. If the chemoreceptors fail to detect the resulting rise in P_{CO_2} there will be no reflex increase in ventilation and so this syndrome can have disastrous effects. Some instances of *sudden infant death syndrome* (SIDS), more commonly known as cot death, may be caused by a form of sleep apnoea, due to malfunctioning of the chemoreceptors, although there is still much debate about the cause of this phenomenon. (A short review by Blackwell *et al.* (1995) gives more detailed information on the immunological basis of SIDS, for those of you who are interested.)

All the changes that have been described in this section are reflex changes which are initiated subconsciously. In the next section, we will discuss a few situations where the cardiovascular and respiratory systems respond to changes in the environment, and the responses in some cases are voluntary.

Summary of Section 2.8

1   The circulatory and respiratory systems work in unison to maintain blood flow and respiration.

2   The close interaction between the cardiovascular and respiratory systems is shown by the phenomenon of sinus arrhythmia where the heart rate increases as we breathe in and decreases as we breathe out.

3   The baroreceptors and chemoreceptors are central to the integrated control of both systems and initiate reflex, subconscious changes in blood pressure and respiration rate.

4   If the baroreceptors or the chemoreceptors fail to initiate these reflex changes, then problems of respiration and blood flow result.

2.9 Adjustment of the cardiovascular and respiratory systems in response to altered conditions

In the previous section, the reflex neural control of the cardiovascular and respiratory systems was described. In this section, we will look at a number of conditions requiring rather more drastic alterations in cardiovascular and respiratory physiology. It should be noted that although these modifications may appear to us to be more of a conscious alteration in the functioning of the two systems, they are still stimulated, in the main, by the involuntary reflexes described above.

2.9.1   Adjustments during exercise

The cardiovascular and respiratory adjustments which take place to sustain us through exercise actually begin before exercise commences, i.e. there are anticipatory changes preparing the body for the increased demands to be made on its resources. The first anticipatory event is activation of the sympathetic nervous system and the release of adrenalin from the adrenal glands into the bloodstream. This leads to an increase in the strength of contraction of the ventricles. Simultaneously, vasoconstriction of the arterioles increases the arterial blood pressure and vasoconstriction of the venous system increases venous return, which increases stroke volume and cardiac output. The onset of exercise is accompanied by vasodilation of the muscle blood vessels, which increases the blood flow through the muscles. As the muscles continue to exercise, the metabolic demands increase, i.e. the cells of the active muscles need an increased supply of glucose and O_2 for respiration. This increase in metabolic rate is the most significant factor in the local control of blood flow through the exercising tissues. Carbon dioxide is produced in greater quantities than normal and acts as a local vasodilator, increasing the blood flow though the tissues. The increase in temperature and the fall in pH (due to the increase in CO_2) causes the Bohr shift in the oxygen–haemoglobin dissociation curve, and so O_2 is released from oxyhaemoglobin at higher P_{O_2}.

In anticipation of exercise, the ventilation rate is also increased in response to raised levels of adrenalin and noradrenalin activating the inspiratory muscles. The increased rate of ventilation is maintained during exercise due to the high demands for O_2.

❑   By what mechanism is the increased demand for O_2 in the body detected?

■   The decrease in P_{O_2} and the increase in P_{CO_2} in the blood following the increased use of O_2 by exercising muscles is detected by both central and peripheral chemoreceptors.

❑   What effect does this have on the rate of ventilation?

■   The rate of ventilation is increased. The chemoreceptors effect an increase in the efferent (motor) activity of the inspiratory nerves, which stimulates inspiration.

Stretch receptors in the muscles are also activated during exercise and they inform the respiratory centres of the need for increased respiration. As exercise continues, the increased demands for O_2 and glucose cannot always be met by increased ventilation and increased blood flow through the tissues. The muscle cells begin to respire anaerobically, i.e. without consuming O_2, and mobilize energy sources such as glycogen, a storage carbohydrate. Although anaerobic respiration can provide energy for the muscles, one of the by-products of respiration in the absence of O_2 is lactic acid or **lactate**. The details of the biochemical pathways that lead to the production of lactate are covered in Chapter 4 and need not concern us here. The important thing to remember is that lactate builds up in the muscles and can only be removed when sufficient O_2 is again delivered to the muscles.

❑   How does a build-up of lactate lead to an increase in O_2 delivery?

■   An increase in acid concentrations in the muscles will shift the oxygen–haemoglobin dissociation curve to the right and this will increase the release of O_2 from oxyhaemoglobin.

Most of the lactate produced during exercise is transported in the bloodstream to the liver where it is metabolized to replenish glucose stores. This process, however, requires oxygen and, although the muscles are no longer exercising, the rate of O_2 supply must remain elevated until all the lactate is broken down. The O_2 needed after exercise to break down lactate is known as the **oxygen debt**. The build-up of lactate is often experienced as a type of cramp in the muscles. This can be painful and is only relieved when the lactate is removed. When exercise is finished, the O_2 debt is repaid by a continued increase in ventilation which provides the necessary O_2. The heart rate remains elevated as long as the ventilation rate is increased and this maintains the flow of blood through the muscles, which removes the lacate and delivers the necessary oxygen. During sustained exercise, the initial peak O_2 debt can be at least partially repaid while the muscles are still working if an equilibrium is established between the supply and demand for O_2 once the exercise rate has been established at the so-called *steady state*. The period following this establishment of equilibrium is known as the 'second wind'. However, its onset depends on the type and level of exercise and the fitness of the individual; even top-class endurance athletes cannot perform beyond their maximum lactate tolerance.

The increases in ventilation and cardiac output which allow the muscles to exercise are brought about by a combination of neural activity and responses to local changes in the chemical composition of the blood. The anticipatory changes in cardiac output and the rate of ventilation set the background which permits sustained exercise.

2.9.2   Adjustment to high altitude

The partial pressure of O_2 in the atmosphere decreases with increased altitude. The ability to adjust to the decrease in P_{O_2} depends on the degree of altitude and how quickly the person ascends. For example, if a pilot flies an aircraft straight up to 4 000 m without the use of an oxygen mask, symptoms of hypoxia will develop, including headaches, drowsiness, impaired judgement, loss of pain sensations, excitement, disorientation and loss of sense of time. If the pilot carries on flying to 8 000 m then eventually unconsciousness will occur. If, however, the ascent to these heights is slow, and O_2 supply is supplemented using an oxygen mask, these symptoms will not occur.

Similarly, if a mountaineer gradually ascends a mountain over a period of weeks, he/she will eventually become accustomed to the change in atmosphere and will adapt to the low levels of O_2 in the air. However, at 4 000 m some mountaineers do experience *mountain sickness*, a form of hypoxia, where they suffer headaches and feel nauseous. As they remain at that level for a few weeks, the symptoms wear off and they become acclimatized.

So what adjustments occur to allow this acclimatization? There are five main compensatory events which permit acclimatization:

(a)   increased pulmonary ventilation in response to low P_{O_2} and high P_{CO_2} detected by the peripheral and central chemoreceptors;

(b)   an increase in the carrying capacity of the blood for O_2 due to an increase in the number of red blood cells plus an increase in haemoglobin production;

(c)   an increase in blood volume which increases cardiac output and the amount of blood flowing in the capillaries of the lungs thus allowing more O_2 to diffuse from the alveoli to the blood;

(d)   an increase in blood supply to the tissues because there is an increase in the number of blood vessels in the tissues, i.e. the vascularization of the tissues is increased;

(e)   an increase in the ability of the tissues to utilize O_2 at higher P_{O_2} because of an increase in 2,3-DPG concentrations in the red blood cells (Section 2.7.4).

❑   Can you suggest why athletes choose to train at high altitude to improve their cardiovascular fitness and their ventilation?

◼   Training at high altitude means that after a period of time the body adjusts and can function normally at low P_{O_2}. Oxygen carrying capacity is increased and the tissues utilize O_2 more efficiently. Cardiac output is increased, ventilation is maximized, and there is an increase in the number of red blood cells. On return to lower altitude, these compensatory adjustments are retained for a short period and so an athlete can perform at a higher level than he or she did previously at low altitude.

2.9.3   Adjustments during diving

Deep-sea diving poses a further problem for the respiratory and cardiovascular systems. As well as the requirement for increases in ventilation and cardiac output sufficient to sustain exercising muscles, the body has to cope with the problem posed by increased water pressure in the diving environment. As the body goes deeper under water, the pressure of water exerted on the body increases. At some critical point this will cause the lungs to collapse. Deep-sea divers therefore have to breathe in air which is under higher pressure than the water, i.e. compressed air, to prevent the lungs collapsing as they dive. There is, however, a problem when breathing compressed air. As well as oxygen, the nitrogen in compressed air is forced through the alveoli, into the blood and into the tissues, particularly lipid-rich ones. This is not a problem under water, because the supply of O_2 to the tissues is sufficient. When the diver comes back up to the surface however, the water pressure is reduced, but the pressure of the gases inside the body are still equal to those of the compressed gas, i.e. much higher than the surrounding pressure. The gases begin to come out of solution and can form bubbles in the blood and tissues, and since nitrogen comprises nearly 80% of the inspired gases, it is the major cause of problems. Bubbles of nitrogen formed in the body cause *decompression sickness*, commonly known as *the bends*. In the most serious cases of the bends, bubbles of gas coming out of solution can tear through tissues or block blood vessels, and damage nerve pathways in the brain and spinal cord; they cause severe pain and may lead to permanent paralysis, permanent mental disturbance or, in severe cases, death.

The bends can be avoided if the diver is brought to the surface very slowly so that the gases do not come out of solution while still in the tissues and are eliminated from the body through the lungs. For example, if a diver remains at a depth of 65 m below the surface for two hours then the time needed to bring the diver to the surface safely or to decompress the diver in a decompression chamber is at least six hours.

Fortunately, we can survive being under water at low depth for a short period of time. This is particularly apparent in infants and young children who show a diving response very similar to that of aquatic diving mammals such as seals and whales. As the child goes under water, he or she experiences a situation where there is no external O_2 available, i.e. total O_2 deprivation or *anoxia*. In this situation, ventilation is stopped immediately and, within 30 seconds, stimulation of the vagus nerve to the heart initiates bradycardia. The arterioles of all but the vital organs constrict, so blood flow is maintained only to the heart and the brain. Obviously this situation cannot be maintained indefinitely, but some children have been able to survive for up to ten minutes underwater without drowning.

Summary of Section 2.9

1   The heart rate and respiratory rate alter during adjustment to changes in the environment and/or the state of the body.

2   Heart rate, stroke volume and thus cardiac output are increased during exercise to maintain blood flow to the active muscles. Ventilation and respiration are increased so maintaining an increased supply of O_2 and removing the increased levels of CO_2.

3   The body is able to acclimatize gradually to high altitudes, where the amount of O_2 in the air is reduced.

4   Decompression sickness is a problem for deep sea divers when they return to the surface. The decrease in the pressure of water results in the formation of gas bubbles in the blood which can amongst other things block blood vessels and damage nerves to the brain.

Objectives for Chapter 2

After completing this chapter, you should be able to:

2.1   Define and use, or recognize definitions and applications of, each of the terms printed in **bold** in the text.

2.2   Describe the basic anatomical features of the cardiovascular system. (*Question 2.1*)

2.3 Describe the path of electrical stimulation which leads to contraction of the ventricles and its control. (*Question 2.1*)

2.4 Explain what is meant by cardiac output and how it can be modulated. (*Question 2.2*)

2.5 Describe how the heart is regulated by neural activity. (*Question 2.5*)

2.6 Show the differences between the various types of blood vessels and how blood pressure and peripheral resistance can be controlled. (*Question 2.3*)

2.7 Describe the main anatomical features of the respiratory system. (*Question 2.4*)

2.8 Describe how O_2 and CO_2 are carried in the blood. (*Question 2.4*)

2.9 Describe the integrative control of both the respiratory and circulatory systems. (*Question 2.5*)

Questions for Chapter 2

Question 2.1   *(Objectives 2.1, 2.2 and 2.3)*

Describe: (a) the pathway of blood through the heart, naming the chambers and valves that the blood passes through; and (b) how contraction of the heart muscle is initiated by electrical activity.

Question 2.2   *(Objectives 2.4, 2.5 and 2.6)*

(a) If the heart rate is 70 beats per minute and the stroke volume is 70 ml per stroke, what is the cardiac output? (b) What factors affect the cardiac output?

Question 2.3   *(Objective 2.6)*

What is peripheral resistance and how is it altered?

Question 2.4   *(Objectives 2.7 and 2.8)*

Describe: (a) the pathway and mechanism by which air enters the body; and (b) how O_2 and CO_2 are transported in the blood.

Question 2.5   *(Objectives 2.4, 2.5, 2.6, 2.8, and 2.9)*

What changes occur in the cardiovascular and respiratory systems in response to the onset of exercise and how are these changes brought about?

CHAPTER 3
DIGESTION AND ABSORPTION
OF NUTRIENTS

3.1 Introduction

Growth, development and the maintenance of good health rely upon an adequate supply of nutrients, which must be available to all the cells of the body. The foods we eat are, by and large, composed of a complex mix of molecules, many of which are macromolecules. These are insoluble and too large to be taken up by cells, so must be broken down into smaller, soluble subunits, which can be taken up from the gut into the circulation and then delivered to the different parts of the body. These processes involve the action and interactions of several different organs which are collectively known as the *digestive* or *gastrointestinal system*. In this chapter you will learn about the digestive system and about the physiological processes that are concerned with the digestion and absorption of food.

A number of distinct physiological activities are involved in the assimilation of foods. The processes by which the components of food are broken down into simpler forms are collectively known as **digestion**, while the uptake, into the body, of the products of digestion and of small molecules and ions such as water, mineral salts and vitamins is known as **absorption**. Special **secretions** (i.e. substances exported from cells) are needed to digest foods; important constituents of these secretions include catabolic enzymes which break the chemical bonds linking the components (i.e. subunits) of macromolecules together. The mixing of ingested foods with digestive secretions and the propulsion of intestinal contents along the length of the gut are achieved by intestinal movements, which are referred to as **motility**. The elimination of faeces (waste matter together with unabsorbed materials) is known as **excretion**. (Other wastes are excreted in urine; you will learn about this in Chapter 5.)

Not surprisingly, these different activities of the digestive system require considerable coordination. As in other body systems, this coordination is achieved by the actions of nerves and hormones.

There is a final important process which goes on in the gut, and that is one of defence. Along with the foods we eat, we ingest a vast number of potentially pathogenic microbes. The immune system of the gut has some unique features which help defend us against harmful microbes in our food.

3.2 Organization of the digestive system

The gastrointestinal or digestive tract, often simply termed the *gut*, is essentially a long tube, the shape and dimensions of which vary according to the physiological activities that take place in each particular region. The different parts of the gut are given different names, some of which will probably be familiar to you.

3.2.1 The anatomy of the digestive system

The overall structure (anatomy) of the gut is shown in Figure 3.1. The gut is very long; in an average adult it measures about 4.5 metres in length. Associated with the gut are a number of other organs which play an essential role in digestive processes, for example by producing digestive secretions. These organs, such as the liver and pancreas, are also shown in Figure 3.1.

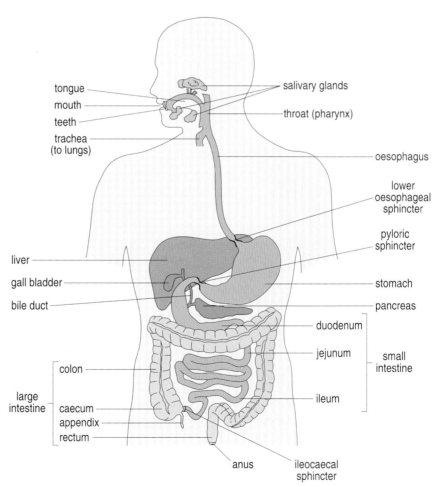

Figure 3.1 Anatomy of the digestive tract (gut) and associated organs.

Foods enter the gut through the mouth, which is involved in the initial processing of food. Chewing and lubrication of each mouthful of food with saliva aids swallowing and eases the passage of the **bolus**, as it is now called, through the throat and, via the **oesophagus**, to the **stomach**. The stomach is a bag-like organ where the first major digestion and mixing processes occur. The partially digested food then passes into the **small intestine** which is the longest part of the gut and is where most digestion and absorption occurs. Some digestive secretions enter the small intestine from the pancreas and the liver, while others are produced by the cells lining the inside of the small intestine itself. The digestion of the dietary macromolecules and the absorption of the products of digestion are largely achieved in the first two parts of the small intestine (called the *duodenum* and *jejunum*); the last part (the *ileum*) provides reserve capacity. Absorption of water and salts, however, continues along the whole length of the gut.

From the small intestine food passes into the **large intestine**, so called because it is wider than the small intestine. The first part of the large intestine is the *caecum*, which is a pouch-like structure from which the very narrow appendix protrudes. The caecum merges with the major region of the large intestine, known as the *colon*. (Sometimes the term 'colon' is used to describe the entire large intestine.) In the caecum and colon, some further absorption of water and salts occurs, concentrating the remains of unabsorbed food and waste products into a semi-solid form called *faeces*. The colon is also the home of many beneficial bacteria; these break down some of the non-digestible plant materials which constitute an important part of the human diet. The last region of the large intestine is the *rectum*, in which faeces remain until they are expelled by passage through the **anus**.

These processes are summarized diagrammatically in Figure 3.2.

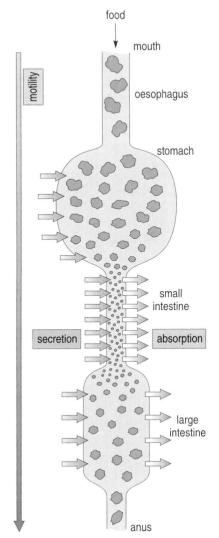

Figure 3.2 Diagram illustrating the processes occurring in the different parts of the gut.

3.2.2 Cell types of the gut wall: a functional view

Although the shape and dimensions of the gut vary along its length, the organization of the different cell types that make up the gut wall is essentially similar throughout and is shown in Figure 3.3a. The three main layers in the gut wall, from the inside outwards, are the *mucosa*, *submucosa* and *muscularis externa*. Each of these layers, in turn, contains several cell types.

Mucosa

Starting from the inside of the gut, or **lumen**, through which the food passes, first there is a layer of epithelium.

❑   You have met this type of tissue before, in Book 1, Chapter 3. Where is it found?

■   It forms the outermost layer of the skin. Epithelium is the type of tissue that lines the external and internal surfaces of the body.

In fact, if you think about it, you will realize that the inside of the gut is continuous with the outside of the body (the two meeting at the mouth and the anus) and, like the skin, it is a major interface between the internal environment and the outside world. The properties of the epithelium of most parts of the gut, however, are rather different from those of the skin. In some areas such as the mouth, oesophagus and anus, where some physical protection is needed, the epithelium is several layers thick and is something like that of the skin. In most parts of the gut, however, the epithelium is only a single cell thick, and the epithelial cells are specialized to perform digestive or absorptive roles. As you will see, digestive functions are carried out both by secretions (including enzymes) from specialized epithelial cells and also by enzymes that are *not* secreted but are an integral part of the epithelial cell membrane. In the stomach and intestines, the epithelium is frequently invaginated (i.e. folded inwards) to form glands, as illustrated in Figure 3.3b. Glands consist of groups of secretory epithelial cells; different types of gland are found in different regions of the gut.

The surface area of the intestinal epithelium available for absorption is greatly increased by the presence of numerous finger-like projections called **villi** (singular, villus, see Figure 3.3c). There are about 20–40 villi per square millimetre (mm) of mucosa, and each villus extends about 0.5–1.5 mm into the lumen. A further increase in surface area is provided by tiny projections from the surface of individual epithelial cells. These structures are called **microvilli** and they form what, for obvious reasons, is called the **brush border** of the cell (Figure 3.3c). The combined increase in the surface area of the epithelium resulting from these specializations is about 600-fold, making the surface area of the human small intestine approximately 300 square metres – about the same area as that of a tennis court.

❑   You have seen how the intestinal epithelial cells have specializations which increase their absorptive ability. Which organelles would you expect to be particularly abundant in a cell which is actively involved in secretion? (Think back to Book 1, Chapter 3.)

■   Rough endoplasmic reticulum, the site of protein synthesis; Golgi apparatus, where molecules are packaged prior to secretion; and mitochondria, since the synthesis and export of secretory products requires energy.

There is an extremely rapid turnover of epithelial cells in the gut. In the small intestine some 17 billion epithelial cells are shed into the lumen and replaced each day, the entire epithelium being renewed every five days. The new epithelial cells are formed by mitosis of a population of undifferentiated cells (called *stem cells*), at the base of the villi. The rapid and continual turnover of the epithelium makes this tissue very sensitive to agents that inhibit cell division, such as radiation and the drugs used in chemotherapy for the treatment of cancer.

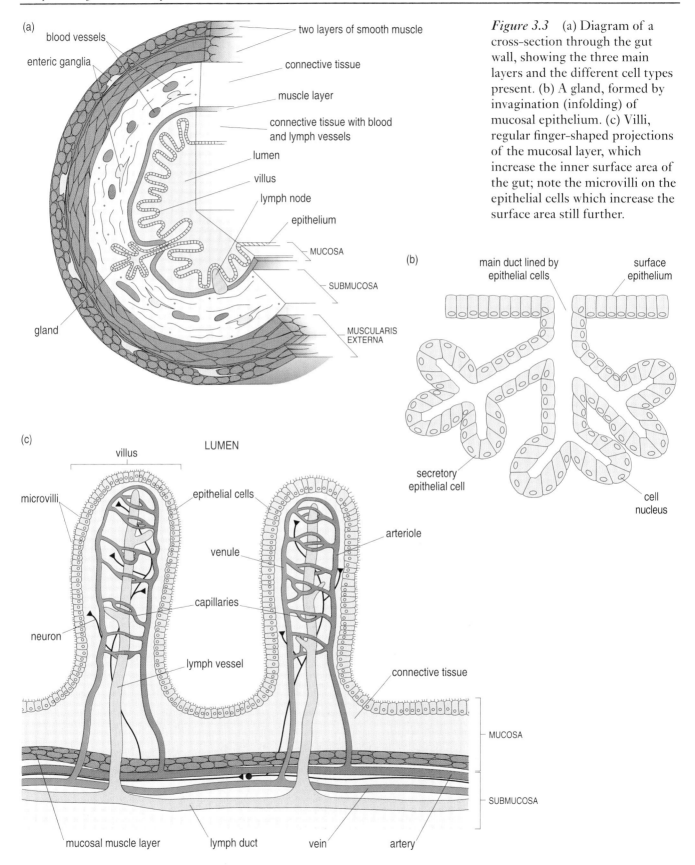

(a)
blood vessels
enteric ganglia
two layers of smooth muscle
connective tissue
muscle layer
connective tissue with blood and lymph vessels
lumen
villus
lymph node
epithelium
MUCOSA
SUBMUCOSA
gland
MUSCULARIS EXTERNA

Figure 3.3   (a) Diagram of a cross-section through the gut wall, showing the three main layers and the different cell types present. (b) A gland, formed by invagination (infolding) of mucosal epithelium. (c) Villi, regular finger-shaped projections of the mucosal layer, which increase the inner surface area of the gut; note the microvilli on the epithelial cells which increase the surface area still further.

(b)
main duct lined by epithelial cells
surface epithelium
secretory epithelial cell
cell nucleus

(c)
villus
LUMEN
microvilli
epithelial cells
venule
arteriole
capillaries
neuron
lymph vessel
connective tissue
MUCOSA
mucosal muscle layer
lymph duct
vein
artery
SUBMUCOSA

If you look again at Figures 3.3a and c, you will see that below the epithelium is a layer of connective tissue, which is richly supplied with blood vessels and also with lymph vessels. It is here that the absorbed nutrients enter the bloodstream or, in the case of fats, the lymphatic system. Blood passes from the intestinal vessels directly to the liver, via a blood vessel known as the **hepatic portal vein**.

Despite the protective nature of epithelium, and the bactericidal (bacteria-killing) action of stomach secretions (about which you will find out shortly), some pathogens do gain entry into the body from the gut lumen. As protection against these pathogens, the connective tissue immediately below the epithelium is well supplied with immune system cells (see Book 2, Chapter 5). Phagocytic cells, mast cells and lymphocytes are all abundant in this part of the gut. Many of these immune system cells are scattered among the other cells of the connective tissue layer; others are grouped into aggregates. These aggregates contain lymphocytes and are particularly abundant in the **tonsils** (at the back of the throat) and the **appendix** (shown in Figure 3.1), but are also plentiful in the ileum where they are known as **Peyer's patches** (not shown in the figure). It is believed that antigens are 'sampled' from the lumen via special epithelial cells that overlie the Peyer's patches; these epithelial cells are thought to take up small amounts of the gut contents by endocytosis (described in Book 1, Chapter 3), and then to convey the endocytosed material by exocytosis to nearby immune system cells. Thus antibodies can be formed against potential pathogens in the gut. This process is particularly important during lactation, when antibody-producing cells from the Peyer's patches migrate to the breast and secrete antibodies into the milk, thus giving the infant some passive immunity against the pathogens to which the mother has been exposed.

The innermost part of the mucosa (i.e. that furthest from the lumen) consists of a thin layer of smooth muscle cells, which cause gentle movement of the mucosal layer (Figure 3.3a and c).

Submucosa

The next major tissue layer is called the submucosa (see Figure 3.3a). This is a loose matrix of connective tissue in which lie blood and lymph vessels, and a large number of neuron cell bodies. These neuron cell bodies are part of the enteric nervous system (Book 2, Chapter 3) and are organized, together with some glial cells, into enteric ganglia. The enteric neurons extend axons to the mucosa (see Figure 3.3c), where they release neurotransmitters which influence both the production of digestive secretions by the epithelial cells and also the state of dilation of the mucosal blood vessels.

Muscularis externa

On the outer side of the submucosa is another layer of smooth muscle cells, called the muscularis externa. This layer of smooth muscle is much thicker than the thin mucosal muscle layer. In fact, it consists, in almost all parts of the gut, of two separate layers, which lie at right angles to each other. These two muscle layers play an essential role in the propulsion of gut contents along the digestive tract, a process known as **peristalsis**.

All gut movements involve the synchronous contraction of groups of smooth muscle cells. This results in a shortening of the cells which, in turn, causes the constriction of a short section of the gut. The two muscle layers work together to effect such movements. Movement of the gut contents towards the anus, i.e. peristalsis, is achieved by waves of contraction which spread from the upper to the lower part of the tract. Coordinated with this contraction is a relaxation of the smooth muscle cells slightly further along the gut. This causes a widening of the lumen just ahead of the bolus and facilitates the passage of food along the gut. Peristalsis is illustrated schematically in Figure 3.4.

Peristalsis is controlled by the action of another group of enteric neurons which lie in ganglia between the outer smooth muscle layers (Figure 3.3a). Many of these enteric neurons have axons that extend to and innervate the smooth muscle, but others have axons that make connections with neurons in other enteric ganglia, and often extend quite long distances. These neurons transmit signals along the gut, to other enteric neurons, and are involved in the control of intestinal reflexes, about which you will learn later in this chapter.

To return to the smooth muscle cells, we have stressed that they are different from skeletal muscle fibres, which you have already learnt about in Book 2. While we cannot go into great detail here, the main differences are that, unlike skeletal muscle cells, smooth muscle cells are small, and have only one nucleus per cell. They contract spontaneously, in a rhythmic fashion, without any input from nerves, although their activity is constantly being modulated by the autonomic nervous system and by hormones (Book 2, Chapter 3). The contractile proteins present and the mechanism of contraction also differ between the two muscle types.

Smooth muscle is found in organs that have the need for involuntary contraction, rather than voluntary contraction, which is performed by skeletal muscle.

❑   Smooth muscle is a major component of other body structures apart from the gut. Can you name two of these?

■   The uterus (Book 1, Chapter 6) and the walls of blood vessels (Chapter 2 of this book).

Although most gut movements (and other gastrointestinal processes) occur involuntarily, there are two parts of the gut where strong, short-lived voluntary control is needed: (a) the throat and upper oesophagus, which are involved in swallowing; and (b) the external anal sphincter, which relaxes during defaecation. (A **sphincter** is a constriction in a

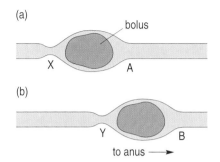

Figure 3.4   Peristalsis. The smooth muscle cells of the muscularis externa contract behind a bolus of food, but relax ahead of it, propelling the bolus along the length of the gut: (a) contraction at X and relaxation at A followed by (b) contraction at Y and relaxation at B results in movement of the bolus in the anal direction.

tubular organ, such as the gut, surrounded by a ring of either smooth or skeletal muscle; relaxation and contraction of this muscle controls the opening and closing of the sphincter.) In both these regions of the digestive tract, skeletal muscle takes the place of smooth muscle.

Returning to our description of the cell types of the gut wall, the final, outermost layer consists of another very thin layer of connective tissue, which in places has a covering of flattened epithelial cells. This layer is known as the *serosa* (not shown in Figure 3.3a).

3.2.3 The gut of the new-born baby

How well developed is the gut of a new-born baby? Essentially all the tissue layers have differentiated by birth, and the enteric nervous system is in place, precursors of the enteric neurons having migrated to the developing gut of the embryo from the developing neural tube (Book 1, Chapter 5). The smooth muscle is certainly well developed at birth. As you have seen in Book 1, Chapter 6, waves of gut contraction can be detected in the fetus while in the uterus. However, it is likely that there is some fine tuning of these processes for some time after birth. Moreover, although the gut epithelium of a new-born baby is in place, it is not fully differentiated. The villi, although present, are not finger-like but leaf-like in shape. In fact, it is not until 10–15 years of age that the villi assume their adult appearance. There are also differences in the digestive enzymes produced by a new-born baby compared with those of an adult. In addition, intact proteins can cross the gut epithelium in a new-born baby, but these cannot be absorbed in the adult. Finally, the gut must – along with the rest of the body – undergo dramatic growth during childhood.

Summary of Section 3.2

1   The digestive system is responsible for the processing and absorption of nutrients from food and the absorption of water.

2   The gut is a tube-like organ which can be divided into regions where different stages in the processing and absorption of foods occur.

3   The main physiological processes performed by the gut are: production of digestive secretions; digestion of food; absorption of the products of digestion (and also of mineral salts, vitamins and water); motility, which allows movement of intestinal contents; excretion of undigested and unabsorbed gut contents; and defence against potential pathogens.

4   The gut wall consists of several different cell types and components: epithelial cells, specialized for secretion or absorption; smooth muscle cells, responsible for motility; neurons, essential for the coordination of gut functions; blood and lymph vessels, allowing transport of absorbed nutrients to the rest of the body; and immune system cells, providing defence against ingested pathogens.

3.3 Passage of food along the gut

Now you have a general picture of the organization of the gut, we can turn to how the digestive system actually processes foods. Perhaps the easiest and most logical way to describe this is to follow what happens when we eat a meal. First, however, we should reconsider the molecular nature of the foods we eat.

3.3.1 Overview of the components of the human diet

A typical human diet is composed of mixtures of different types of molecules. You have learnt something of this in Book 1, Chapter 3, and you will learn more about diet and health in Chapter 7 of the present book.

Most of the foods we consume consist of insoluble macromolecules, which cannot cross cell membranes by diffusion.

❑ What are the main types of macromolecule and their small-molecule components?

▉ Proteins, which are composed of amino acids; polysaccharides (carbohydrate polymers), which are composed of monosaccharides (sugars); the nucleic acids, DNA and RNA, which are composed of nucleotides. You may also have thought of the lipids, such as fats and oils, which are not strictly macromolecules, but which do form large molecular aggregates; these are made up of fatty acids and glycerol.

Carbohydrates, proteins and fats are the major components of our diet, whereas nucleic acids form only a minor part of the foods we eat.

The major task of the gut, then, is to break down these large molecules into their simpler components, which are soluble and which, with the aid of specialized molecules and processes (to be described shortly), can then cross the epithelial cell membranes and so be assimilated into the body.

❑ In addition to the macromolecules, what are the essential small-molecule or ionic components of the human diet?

▉ Examples you may have thought of include vitamins, which are required in only very small amounts, minerals, such as iron and calcium, and also water. All these nutrients have to be absorbed from the gut.

Before it reaches the main part of the digestive system, material that is to be digested must be bitten, chewed, and swallowed. The process of digestion, then, actually begins with ingestion via the mouth.

3.3.2 Ingestion of food and its passage to the stomach

Although human diets are varied, most consist of at least a proportion of very bulky material such as vegetables, and tough material such as meat. For food to be digested it must be in contact with the digestive secretions which act on it, so the bulky food material must first be broken down into small pieces; this process serves to increase the surface area of the food, thereby making it more accessible to the digestive secretions.

The initial processing of the food is performed in the mouth, and involves the actions of the tongue, teeth, jaws and secretions produced by the salivary glands. The arrangement of these structures is shown in Figure 3.1.

Teeth

Humans (and most other mammals) have two sets of teeth in a lifetime. The first set of teeth are known as **milk teeth** and usually erupt (break through the gums) at between seven months and two years of age, although there is considerable variation in this. There are 20 milk teeth, which are lost gradually during childhood (usually between seven and 13 years of age) and are replaced with what are optimistically called **permanent teeth**. The full complement of permanent teeth in the adult varies between 28 and 32, some individuals having wisdom teeth, which are the last permanent teeth to erupt, at the back of the mouth. The incisors (front teeth) cut off pieces of food; canines, premolars, and molars chew and grind the food, mixing it with saliva. (See Figure 3.5.)

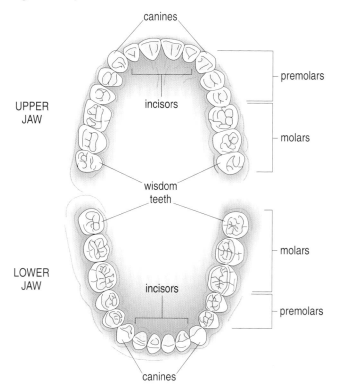

Figure 3.5 Diagram showing a complete set of permanent teeth, including the wisdom teeth.

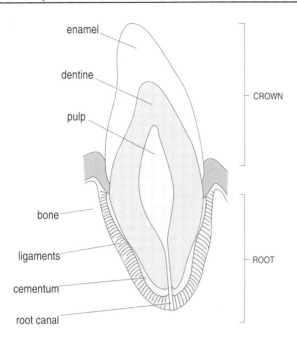

enamel

dentine

pulp

CROWN

bone

ligaments

ROOT

cementum

root canal

Figure 3.6 Diagram of a vertical section through a tooth.

The structure of a tooth is shown in Figure 3.6. The part of the tooth that protrudes into the mouth is known as the **crown**; the part that fits in the jaw is the **root**. The crown is covered by a substance called **enamel**. Enamel is the hardest material in the body and, if well looked after, is very resistant to corrosion by acids and enzymes. It consists of a very strong protein, similar to keratin, in which large, dense crystals of calcium salts (calcium carbonate and calcium phosphate) and other minerals (e.g. sodium, magnesium and potassium salts) are embedded.

Within the enamel is the *dentine*, which forms the main part of the tooth and has a similar composition to bone. The innermost part of the tooth is known as the *pulp*, and is composed of connective tissue and is supplied with blood vessels, nerves and lymph vessels. The tooth is held in place by ligaments, consisting of tightly packed collagen fibres, and by a substance called *cementum*, which is secreted by the cells lining the tooth socket. The layer of cementum becomes thicker both with age and with increased strain, so that the teeth become more firmly seated in the jaws.

Development of the teeth

The development of teeth begins when the embryo is six weeks old, and continues during fetal development and childhood. The formation of teeth, then, is an extremely slow process.

The formation of healthy teeth is dependent upon an adequate supply of minerals, particularly calcium and phosphate, and also vitamin D (which plays an important role in calcium absorption, as you will see later) and parathyroid hormone (which stimulates the formation of the active form of vitamin D). The rate of tooth formation can be stimulated by thyroid hormones and growth hormone (see Book 2, Chapter 2).

Like bone, the teeth are a dynamic part of the body; mineral salts are constantly being absorbed from the teeth into the bloodstream and at the same time, new material is deposited. Evidence suggests that this turnover of minerals occurs mainly in the dentine and cementum, and that little occurs in the enamel. For this reason, the enamel is particularly vulnerable if damaged.

Dental caries

The main damage that occurs to teeth in the Western world is the formation of **caries** (cavities) due to decay. Although this course is about healthy humans, there are probably very few of us who would have included 'perfect teeth' in our list of definitions of health in Book 1, Chapter 2. The problem of caries is almost entirely due to our consumption of the sugary foods to which we have become accustomed in our affluent Western diet. The other major factor is the frequency with which we eat foods, and the habit of 'snacking', particularly on sweet items, between main meals. Carbohydrates present in the mouth serve as an ideal source of nutrients for the bacteria that normally live there, in the moist film of saliva covering the teeth; this is called **plaque**. The plaque bacteria produce lactic acid and **proteolytic** enzymes (enzymes that break down proteins). Over a period of time, the acid gradually dissolves the calcium salts in the enamel, allowing rapid digestion of the enamel protein remaining, by the bacterial proteolytic enzymes (and also by proteolytic enzymes present in saliva). Although the enamel presents an extremely resistant barrier to this process, once decay has penetrated this layer, the underlying dentine is much more vulnerable, because the salts of which it is composed are more easily dissolved.

There is individual variation in the susceptibility of our teeth to the formation of caries and, as in other aspects of our lives, environmental factors are also important. The enamel of children who drink water containing small amounts of fluoride is more resistant to decay than that of children whose drinking water does not contain fluoride. Fluoride acts by displacing some of the mineral components of the enamel, making it less easily dissolved. However, excess fluoride can cause discoloration of the teeth, and high levels can cause increased fragility of the bones; so, in common with many other substances that have a beneficial effect at low levels, higher levels of fluoride intake can be harmful.

As we get older, many of us lose some teeth; this is largely due to the build-up of food deposits that have become calcified (i.e. contain insoluble mineral salts), as well as the accumulation of debris from bacteria, in the space between the crown and the gum. This space then widens, allowing more material to accumulate and the gum to become inflamed as a result of bacterial infection. If untreated, tissue damage will be more extensive and the tooth will become loose.

Chewing and the actions of saliva

Now let us return to what happens to our mouthful of food. The movements of the teeth are controlled by the activity of the jaw muscles. These are skeletal muscles which are controlled by motor nerves (see Book 2, Chapter 3). In fact, taste and smell can result in chewing movements (as you will see in Chapter 6 of this book). Although chewing is largely voluntary, some involuntary, reflex action is also involved in the process. During chewing, the food is broken into smaller pieces and mixed with saliva, produced by a number of glands collectively known as the **salivary glands**.

As we start to eat, sensory nerves in the mouth are activated in response to the stimuli of taste and pressure. These activate neurons in the brain which, in turn, activate the motor neurons innervating the salivary glands, and so stimulate the secretion of saliva. Salivation is also stimulated in response to the sight and smell of food, and even by the thought of food.

It is interesting to note that increased salivation can also occur in response to stimuli originating lower in the gut. An example of this is the increased salivation associated with nausea. It is thought that an additional supply of saliva may help to neutralize the agent in the stomach – usually a toxic or harmful substance – that has provided the nausea-inducing stimulus.

About 1.5 litres of saliva are produced each day; in addition to the increased secretion in response to the presence of food, there is a continual low rate of secretion, of about 0.5 millilitres (i.e. thousandths of a litre) per minute.

Saliva is a solution of salts containing a number of other components. The two main ones are an enzyme called **salivary amylase** which begins the digestion of starch (into shorter-chain polysaccharides) and mucus which is a glycoprotein and acts as a lubricant.

❑   What is a glycoprotein?

■   A molecule composed of both protein and carbohydrate.

Saliva also contains small amounts of other enzymes and also antibodies, and is slightly acidic. It plays an important part in oral hygiene – not only does it wash food particles and bacteria away from the teeth into the gut, but the proteolytic enzymes, antibodies and weak acid attack the bacteria in the mouth.

Swallowing is a complex reflex which, like chewing, is partly involuntary and partly under voluntary control. When food is forced to the back of the mouth by the tongue, pressure receptors in the throat are activated. These relay signals to part of the brainstem called the swallowing centre, which in turn activates nerves supplying the muscles of the throat, larynx, oesophagus, diaphragm and intercostal (breathing) muscles. Swallowing requires the coordinated activity of all these muscle groups, so that breathing is interrupted to allow food to pass into the oesophagus and not into the trachea.

Food passes down the oesophagus to the stomach as a result of a wave of peristalsis.

❑   What types of cells are involved in peristalsis?

■   Peristalsis occurs because of the contraction and relaxation of the outer layers of smooth muscle cells in the gut wall and is controlled by enteric neurons.

This wave of peristalsis passes along the length of the oesophagus in about 8–10 seconds and is triggered by the presence of a bolus of food. The lower oesophageal sphincter (a ring of thickened smooth muscle where the digestive tract passes through the diaphragm – Figure 3.1), which is normally closed to protect the oesophagus from the acidic contents of the stomach, then relaxes, thereby allowing food to enter the stomach. The sphincter and the upper stomach muscles relax, in a process known as *receptive relaxation*, which is controlled by enteric neurons. The discomfort associated with inappropriate opening of the lower oesophageal sphincter and reflux of the stomach contents is known in its mild form as *heartburn*, and is unfortunately likely to have been experienced by a number of you.

3.3.3 The stomach

The stomach is a bag-like organ in which food is partially digested and stored until it is transferred to the small intestine. The stomach undergoes great changes in size, varying in volume from 0.05 litres (one-twentieth of a litre) when empty, to 1.5 litres after a large meal, i.e. by a factor of 30. The processing of food in the stomach is achieved by mixing the contents with digestive secretions produced by specialized epithelial cells of the gastric mucosa. ('Gastric' means relating to the stomach.) The mixing occurs as a result of waves of contraction of the smooth muscle of the stomach wall.

The mucosal epithelium of the stomach contains many tube-shaped glands. Cells in these glands are specialized to produce a number of different gastric secretions: mucus (similar to that of saliva), hydrochloric acid (HCl), *pepsinogen* which is a precursor of the enzyme **pepsin**, the gastrointestinal hormone **gastrin**, and a protein called **intrinsic factor** (discussed in Section 3.3.4). As you will see, these secretions have very different actions and they are not produced uniformly by the gastric mucosa, glands in different parts of the stomach producing different amounts of the different secretory products.

Now we will turn to how the secretions present actually break down the components of a meal.

The food arriving in the stomach is usually still rather bulky and consists mainly of small lumps. Contractions of the smooth muscle of the stomach wall mix the stomach contents with HCl; this dissolves the lumps, forming a thick, soup-like mixture called **chyme**, made up of liquid and small particles of food. As a result, the proteins and polysaccharides present become accessible to digestive enzymes, which would not effectively penetrate lumps of food.

How does HCl break down foods? The answer lies in the fact that HCl is a strong acid. Acids are compounds that release hydrogen ions into solution (see Book 1, Chapter 3). HCl is a strong acid because it is almost completely dissociated in solution into hydrogen (H^+) and chloride (Cl^-) ions:

$$HCl(aq) \rightarrow H^+(aq) + Cl^-(aq)$$

❑   From what you learnt about acid solutions and pH in Book 1, Chapter 3, would you expect a solution of HCl to have a high or a low pH?

◼   It has a low pH. The pH of a solution is *inversely* related to the concentration of H^+ ions it contains. In other words, an acid solution, which has a high concentration of H^+ ions, has a low pH; while an alkaline solution, which has a low concentration of H^+ ions, has a high pH.

You will recall that the value of pH can range from 0 to 14. Pure water has a pH of 7.0; biological systems usually have a pH of between 5 and 9. The extracellular fluids of the body (interstitial fluid, lymph and blood) have a slightly alkaline pH with a normal range of between 7.35 and 7.45, while intracellular fluids have a slightly lower pH of between 7.0 and 7.2. Stomach contents are therefore unusual, in having a pH of between 1.5 and 3.0.

The free H^+ ions which are present at a high concentration in the stomach are able to react with the polar molecules in foods, particularly proteins, denaturing these molecules (i.e. disrupting their three-dimensional form), and hence breaking up the physical structure of most foods. This process releases the proteins and carbohydrates from the particles of food, but does not affect non-polar molecules.

❑   Which major type of molecule in our food will *not* be broken down by acid, and why?

◼   Fats, because they are non-polar. Fats do not mix with watery solutions, but tend to form a separate layer (think of greasy washing-up). However, mixing movements do cause fat to form droplets in the chyme.

The breaking down of bulky foods is a formidable process, as you will appreciate if you consider how long it takes to produce a soup by heating up the ingredients, or how much force is necessary to obtain a similar mixture in a blender. In the stomach, this is achieved largely by the action of HCl.

H$^+$ ions and Cl$^-$ ions do not leave the epithelial cells together, as HCl. The H$^+$ ions are pumped out as a result of the activity of a special membrane protein (an ATPase), situated on the part of the cell membrane facing the gut lumen. The process is driven by energy derived from ATP; the ATPase breaks down the ATP to ADP and P$_i$, a reaction in which energy stored in ATP is made available for the H$^+$ pumping. The Cl$^-$ ions diffuse out of the cell separately, down their electrochemical gradient.

❏ Thinking back to Book 1, Chapter 3, can you recall the name given to this type of ion transport across a membrane?

■ It is an example of active transport (Book 1, Chapter 3, Box 3.3).

The features of the different ways in which dissolved substances (solutes) and water can cross cell membranes are summarized in Figure 3.7.

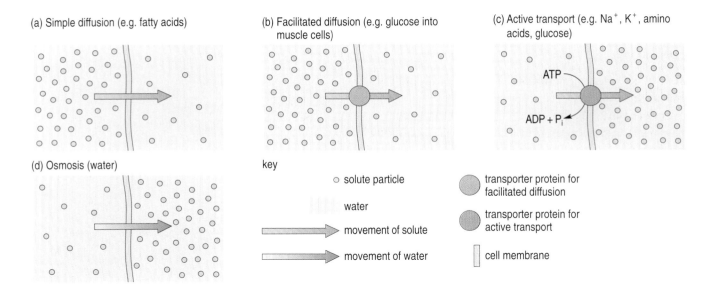

(a) Simple diffusion (e.g. fatty acids)

(b) Facilitated diffusion (e.g. glucose into muscle cells)

(c) Active transport (e.g. Na$^+$, K$^+$, amino acids, glucose)

(d) Osmosis (water)

key
  ○ solute particle
  water
  → movement of solute
  → movement of water
  transporter protein for facilitated diffusion
  transporter protein for active transport
  cell membrane

Figure 3.7 Summary diagrams showing the ways in which solutes (a–c) and water (d) can cross cell membranes. Note that only active transport requires energy, which is obtained either directly or indirectly from ATP.

You have seen how HCl breaks down foods, and that it is produced by specialized epithelial cells. You may be wondering how the other epithelial cells of the stomach are protected from the action of HCl. The answer is that the mucus secreted by another type of gastric epithelial cell forms a protective surface layer immediately overlying the epithelial cells. This provides a less acid *microenvironment* (i.e. local environment), with a pH of between 5 and 6, which is substantially higher (i.e. less acid) than that of the lumen proper.

❏ In addition to its role in the digestion of food, the acid secreted into the stomach also has a beneficial effect. Can you suggest what this might be?

■   The acid destroys many of the harmful microbes that inevitably
enter the digestive tract along with the food consumed. (Not all
microbes are destroyed by acid, however; some microbes have acid-
resistant coats, and survive passage through the stomach, to the
intestines, where they are able to proliferate, and can cause infection,
or 'food poisoning'.)

It has long been thought that the acidic environment in the stomach was
the cause of the common condition of gastric, and also of duodenal,
ulcers. Ulcers are formed by erosion of the gut epithelium which can, in
severe cases, extend to deeper layers of the gut wall. Recently however, it
has been discovered that a large proportion of ulcers are related to infection
by a bacterium, *Helicobacter pylori* (previously known as *Campylobacter
pylori*). This bacterium is found in 67% of patients with gastric ulcer and
90% of patients with duodenal ulcer. It appears that the bacterium resists
destruction by acid in the stomach by adhering to the mucosa, beneath the
protective layer of mucus. It is thought that the bacterium produces
substances that are toxic to epithelial cells. Treatment of patients with
antibacterial therapy has proved to be very effective in the treatment of
these ulcers.

As well as pathogenic microbes, another threat from food is the possible
ingestion of toxic substances. Exposure to such agents is a normal part of
everyday life and reflexes have evolved which eliminate the potentially
hazardous substances as rapidly as possible. The first of these to come into
operation after ingestion is vomiting. Like swallowing, vomiting is a
complex reflex which requires coordinated responses by a variety of
muscles. It is regulated by a centre in the brainstem called the vomiting
centre. The vomiting reflex can be triggered by a number of different
stimuli, the commonest being excessive distension of the stomach and small
intestine and activation of *chemoreceptors* (receptors that respond to stimuli
of a chemical nature) in the gut by harmful chemicals or toxins. Other
stimuli, originating outside the gut, can also activate the vomiting centre.
Examples of such stimuli include increased pressure in the skull (e.g.
concussion), movements of the head that do not match with other sensory
inputs (motion or travel sickness) and chemical stimuli in the brain, e.g. by
intravenous treatment with cytotoxic (cell-poisoning) drugs for cancer
therapy.

In addition to removing the noxious agent from the gut, it is thought that
vomiting may have an additional adaptive benefit, for the nausea that
usually accompanies vomiting can lead to avoidance of further ingestion of
the same substance. (This is an example of *conditioning*, which is dealt with
in Chapter 6.)

To return to the gut in the absence of pathogens and the like, what about
the digestive enzymes present in the stomach? It would seem logical that
these, being proteins, would be denatured by HCl. This is indeed the case
for salivary amylase. Soon after arrival in the stomach, this enzyme is

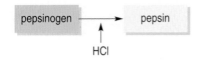

Figure 3.8 Formation of pepsin from the precursor pepsinogen by the action of HCl. Pepsin breaks down polypeptides to peptides.

inactivated, because of denaturation by HCl. The enzymes produced by the stomach itself, however, are rather different to most other enzymes.

Some of the epithelial cells of the gastric mucosa produce a protein called pepsinogen, which on exposure to the acid environment in the stomach is converted into the proteolytic enzyme pepsin; the inactive pepsinogen is thus the *precursor* of the active pepsin (Figure 3.8). Pepsin is unusual, because it is active in highly acid solutions, whereas other enzymes are most active in a neutral or slightly alkaline environment. Pepsin begins the breakdown of polypeptide chains into shorter chains of amino acids (peptides). Between 10 and 20% of total protein digestion occurs in the stomach; pepsin is particularly important in the digestion of collagen in meat (e.g. the gristle).

❑   Can you think of an advantage of producing a proteolytic enzyme via an inactive precursor?

■   The inactive form, stored within the cell, cannot damage intracellular proteins.

There is one other important molecule produced by the gastric mucosa; this is the hormone gastrin. Gastrin is produced by yet another type of specialized epithelial cell type. Instead of being secreted into the gut lumen, it is secreted into the *blood vessels* of the mucosa from which it reaches and acts on other epithelial cells of the gut, including nearby acid-secreting epithelial cells. It plays an essential role in the regulation of both acid secretion in the stomach and the secretion of digestive molecules further along the gastrointestinal tract. We will look at the actions of gastrin in detail towards the end of this chapter.

After being processed in the stomach, chyme enters the small intestine in controlled bursts, not in a continuous flow. At the junction between the stomach and the first part of the small intestine (the duodenum) is an area of thickened smooth muscle, similar to that at the base of the oesophagus. This is the *pyloric sphincter*. Waves of contraction of the stomach muscle reach the sphincter, causing it to close. Between contractions, the smooth muscle relaxes, opening the sphincter. The rate of muscle contraction, then, is important in the regulation of the rate at which chyme passes from the stomach to the small intestine. The time it takes a meal to pass through the stomach is also dependent on the nature of the foods eaten, but is usually between two and six hours. We will return to the control of gastric emptying later in the chapter.

3.3.4 The small intestine and its associated glands

You have seen how, in the stomach, the complex mix of macromolecules which we eat is reduced to a soup-like chyme. By the time the chyme reaches the small intestine, proteins have been denatured and partially broken down into peptide fragments. Polysaccharides have been partially broken down into disaccharides and short chains of glucose molecules by the action of salivary amylase. Lipids, which do not dissolve in water, are in the form of an *emulsion* of lipid droplets, created by the mechanical activity of the lower part of the stomach. The digestive processes of the small intestine are concerned with breaking down these molecules into yet smaller components.

The small intestine is essentially a long tube, with a diameter of about 4 cm and a length of about 3 m. Look again at Figure 3.1 and you will see that there is a duct (a small tube) which is connected to the duodenum almost immediately after the junction of the stomach and small intestine. This duct is the route by which two other digestive secretions enter the gut lumen. These secretions are produced by the liver and the pancreas. Both these organs perform several different functions, and are not just involved in digestion. This is another example of the complex *interdependence* of body systems; they do not operate in isolation. In this chapter, we will be concerned mainly with the digestive functions of these two organs; their other roles will be described in more detail later in this book.

Before we go on with how our meal is further digested in the small intestine, and how the digestion products are absorbed into the circulatory system, we will first digress, briefly, to look at the pancreas and liver.

The pancreas

The pancreas is a long gland which lies adjacent to the duodenum, and stretches upwards, behind the stomach (Figure 3.1). The pancreas produces not only endocrine secretions (i.e. hormones, which are secreted into the bloodstream: Book 2, Chapter 3) but also **exocrine** secretions; these are fluids that are secreted via ducts, on to the surface of an epithelial tissue. (Sweat glands of the skin are an example of exocrine glands.) Most of the pancreas consists of exocrine tissue which is organized as groups of epithelial cells clustered around a central duct. Secretions from the cells pass into the duct, which then joins to other, larger ducts which finally convey the secretions, together with those from the liver, via the sphincter of Oddi (Figure 3.9), into the duodenum.

Lying within this exocrine tissue of the pancreas are groups of endocrine cells known as **islets of Langerhans** (Figure 3.9). The islet cells secrete several hormones into the bloodstream, including two that play an important role in the metabolism of carbohydrates: insulin (which you have already encountered in Book 2, Chapter 3) and glucagon. You will learn more about both these hormones in the next chapter.

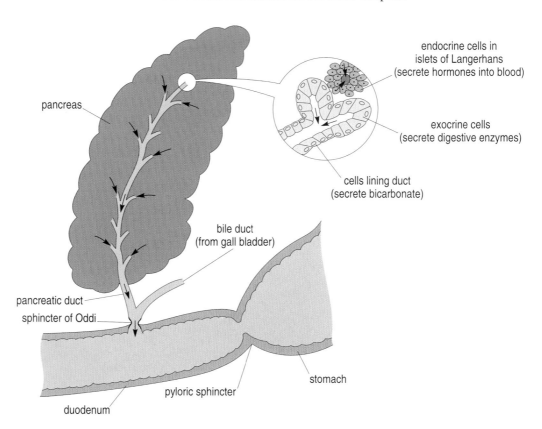

Figure 3.9 Diagram showing the organization of the endocrine and exocrine cells of the pancreas (not to scale). Adapted from Vander, A. J., Sherman, J. H. and Luciano, D. S. (1994) Human Physiology, Sixth International Edition, copyright © 1994, 1990, 1985, 1980, 1975, 1970 by McGraw-Hill, Inc., with permission of the McGraw-Hill Companies.

What, then, is the nature of the pancreatic products involved in digestion? The exocrine glands of the pancreas produce a variety of digestive enzymes, which will be described shortly. In addition, they produce bicarbonate ions (now also known as hydrogen carbonate ions), HCO_3^-.

The chyme entering the duodenum is very acidic. As already stressed, most enzymes are inactivated and denatured by acid solutions, so before digestive enzymes can set to work to further break down the partially digested proteins and carbohydrates present in the chyme, the H^+ ions must be quickly neutralized. This is achieved by the influx of an alkaline solution containing HCO_3^- ions into the duodenum, from both the pancreas and the liver.

The H^+ ions combine with HCO_3^- ions to form carbonic acid (H_2CO_3):

$$H^+ + HCO_3^- \rightarrow H_2CO_3$$

Being a very weak acid, H_2CO_3 has only a very small tendency to dissociate into ions (the reverse of the reaction shown above), so the neutralization of the H^+ ions by reaction with HCO_3^- ions is almost complete. (See Box 3.1 in Book 1, Chapter 3, for further information about acidity and alkalinity.)

Along with HCO_3^- ions, the pancreas produces a number of digestive enzymes. These two types of secretion are produced by different cells in the gland. As in the stomach, the digestive enzymes produced by the pancreas are almost all manufactured as precursor molecules which are converted to their active form in the gut lumen. Pancreatic enzymes are activated by the action of another enzyme, situated in the membrane of the intestinal epithelial cells (unlike the enzymes we have discussed so far, all of which are free in the gut lumen). This enzyme is called *enterokinase* and it acts on *trypsinogen* to produce the proteolytic enzyme **trypsin**, by removing a peptide from the pepsinogen molecule. Trypsin then activates other digestive enzymes in a similar way, i.e. by splitting off peptide fragments from the precursors. This sequence of enzyme activation is illustrated in Figure 3.10.

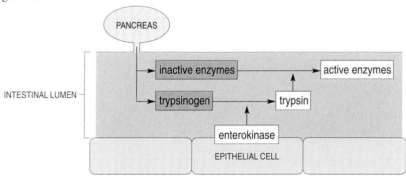

Figure 3.10   The activation of pancreatic enzymes precursors in the small intestine. Adapted from Vander, A. J., Sherman, J. H. and Luciano, D. S. (1994) Human Physiology, Sixth International Edition, copyright © 1994, 1990, 1985, 1980, 1975, 1970 by McGraw-Hill, Inc., with permission of the McGraw-Hill Companies.

Some other pancreatic enzymes are not produced as precursors, but are only fully activated when they reach the gut lumen, where they encounter an appropriate molecular/ionic environment. As shown in Table 3.1, the pancreas produces a rich mix of enzymes. These include: a number of proteolytic enzymes; amylase, which breaks down polysaccharides; lipase, which breaks down fats; and also nucleic acid-digesting enzymes (nucleases).

Table 3.1   The pancreatic enzymes, their substrates and actions.

Enzyme	Substrate	Action
trypsin, chymotrypsin, elastase	proteins	break peptide bonds in proteins to form peptide fragments
carboxypeptidase	proteins and peptides	removes terminal amino acid from carboxyl end of chain
amylase	polysaccharides	splits polysaccharides into disaccharides and short chains of glucose units (dextrins)
lipase	fats	splits two fatty acids from each triacylglycerol molecule, forming free fatty acids and monoacylglycerols
ribonuclease, deoxyribonuclease	nucleic acids (RNA and DNA)	split nucleic acids into nucleotides

The liver

The liver is a large organ, which performs a number of important functions. It lies just beneath and slightly behind the stomach (see Figure 3.1). Like the pancreas, the liver is a complex organ, but its organization is rather different from that of the pancreas; it will be described in more detail in the following chapter. For now, you need to know that, among its products, is an exocrine secretion called **bile**, which is a mixture of substances including HCO_3^- ions, phospholipids, cholesterol and cholesterol-derived molecules known as *bile salts*. Also present in bile are waste products of the various processing reactions of the liver, e.g. bilirubin, an end-product of the breakdown of haemoglobin from red blood cells.

Bile leaves the liver in a duct called the hepatic duct, and between meals is stored in a small bag-like structure, the **gall bladder** (see Figure 3.1). The gall bladder is not an essential organ, however; it can be removed without ill-effect (as long as the hepatic duct is left intact); in fact, it is absent from a number of animal species that produce bile.

The intestinal epithelium

In addition to the digestive secretions from the pancreas and the liver into the duodenum, as mentioned earlier there is a group of digestive enzymes that are located in the cell membrane of intestinal epithelial cells, i.e. in the microvilli making up the brush border (Figure 3.3c). As you will see, the microvilli are the site of several essential enzymes involved in the final stages of protein and carbohydrate digestion.

You now have a general overview of the various secretions and membrane-bound enzymes that are involved in the digestion of foods in the small intestine. Next we go on to see first how macromolecules are actually broken down, and then how the small-molecule breakdown products are absorbed.

Digestion in the small intestine

Proteins

Proteins which enter the duodenum from the stomach are broken down further into peptide fragments by the pancreatic enzymes trypsin and chymotrypsin (Table 3.1). The peptide fragments are then broken down into free amino acids by two enzymes: carboxypeptidase, which is secreted by the pancreas, and aminopeptidase, which is located in the brush border of the intestinal epithelial cells (Table 3.2).

❑   From what you know about protein structure, can you hazard a guess about why these two enzymes are so named?

■   Carboxypeptidase releases amino acids from the carboxyl (–COOH) end of the peptide chain; aminopeptidase releases amino acids from the amino (–NH$_2$) end of the chain (see Book 1, Chapter 3).

The end-products of protein digestion, then, are free amino acids. If food is chewed thoroughly, 98% of ingested protein is broken down to amino acids and absorbed, and only 2% is excreted in the faeces. (How amino acids cross the epithelial cell membrane is discussed later.)

Table 3.2   Enzymes of the intestinal epithelium.

Enzyme	Substrate	Action
aminopeptidase	proteins and peptides	removes terminal amino acid from amino end of chain
dextrinase	dextrins (short chains of glucose units)	splits dextrins into glucose units
lactase	lactose (milk sugar)	splits lactose into glucose and galactose
sucrase	sucrose (table sugar)	splits sucrose into glucose and fructose
maltase	maltose (a disaccharide produced by the action of amylase on starch)	splits maltose into two glucose units

Carbohydrates

You have already seen that digestion of carbohydrates begins in the mouth and continues for a short time in the stomach, until the salivary amylase is inactivated by acid. **Pancreatic amylase** then continues the digestion of carbohydrates in the small intestine. The amylase breaks down polysaccharides either into disaccharides, which are then broken down into monosaccharides by the enzyme *maltase*, present on the brush border, or into short chains of glucose units called dextrins; these are broken down by an enzyme called *dextrinase*, also located on the brush border (see Table 3.2).

In the majority of the world's population, a change in the digestion of sugars occurs during childhood. This involves the enzyme lactase, which splits molecules of the disaccharide lactose, the only sugar present in milk, into one molecule of glucose and one of galactose (see Book 1, Chapter 3). Lactase is an essential enzyme in new-born babies, since their only source of sugars is the lactose in milk. During adolescence, however, many individuals gradually lose lactase from the brush border, until it is completely absent. The absence of lactase is termed *alactasia*. However, this change does not occur in Northern Europeans and their descendants in other parts of the world, who are thus able to digest lactose even as adults.

Since disaccharides are not absorbed, any deficiency in the enzymes that convert disaccharides into monosaccharides will result in an accumulation of that disaccharide in the gut lumen. So, consumption of milk by the many adults who have no lactase in the gut results in accumulation of lactose. This leads to an expansion in the population of gut bacteria which use lactose as a food source, resulting in severe watery diarrhoea and abdominal pain. This extreme reaction is often triggered even by small amounts of milk; it is known as **lactose intolerance**. Milk products in which lactose is converted into other forms, such as the lactic acid in yoghurt, are tolerated by individuals with alactasia.

Lipids

For our purposes in understanding the processes involved in the digestion and absorption of lipids, it is important to remember that most dietary lipids are fats and these are insoluble in aqueous solutions, such as that found in the lumen of the gut. Because fats do not dissolve in water, when mixed with an aqueous solution they separate out and form a layer on top of the liquid, in a similar manner to oil spilt at sea. Perhaps a more relevant example, since we are considering digestion, would be the layer of fat that forms on the top of a stewed meat dish. This property of fats means that the way in which they are digested is very different from the ways in which proteins and carbohydrates are broken down. Fat digestion occurs as a result of the combined action of bile and **pancreatic lipase** (Table 3.1).

Lipase acts on fats (triacylglycerols) by splitting off two of the three fatty acid units from the rest of the triacylglycerol molecule, leaving a *mono*acylglycerol (Table 3.1). However, the chyme entering the small intestine contains fats in the form of large droplets, produced by the mechanical activity of the stomach, and lipase can only act at the surface of these droplets. If lipase were the only agent involved in the digestion of fat, it would be an extremely slow process. The problem is solved by components of bile (i.e. bile salts, cholesterol and phospholipids), which

disperse the large fat droplets into much smaller droplets – a process
known as **emulsification**. This is similar to what happens when washing
up liquid is added to greasy water. Emulsification greatly increases the
surface area of fat droplets accessible to lipase (see Figure 3.11).

How does emulsification occur? The answer lies in a common feature in the
structure of phospholipids, bile salts, and cholesterol. Just like the

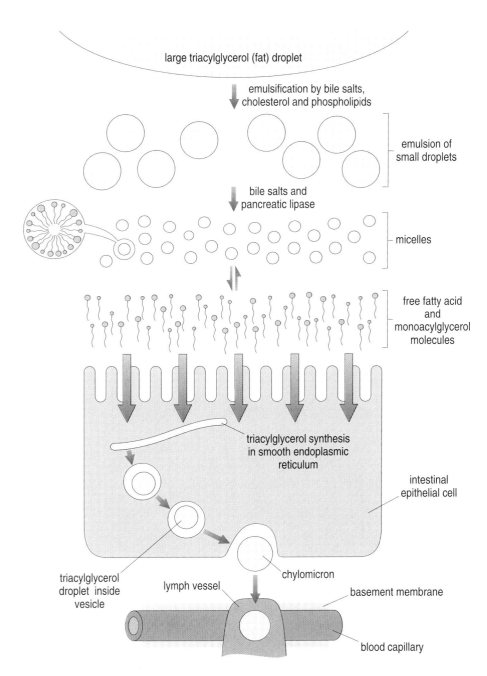

Figure 3.11 Diagram summarizing the emulsification, digestion and absorption of fats. Adapted from Vander, A. J., Sherman, J. H. and Luciano, D. S. (1994) Human Physiology, Sixth International Edition, copyright © 1994, 1990, 1985, 1980, 1975, 1970 by McGraw-Hill, Inc., with permission of the McGraw-Hill Companies.

membrane phospholipids (Book 1, Chapter 3), each of these molecules has a charged or polar end and a non-polar end. The non-polar ends interact with the fat droplets and the charged or polar ends interact with the surrounding aqueous solution. Because the like charges tend to repel each other this keeps the small droplets from reaggregating into large droplets. The triacylglycerols present in small droplets are much more accessible to pancreatic lipase than are those in large droplets, so their digestion, to fatty acids and monoacylglycerols, is speeded up by emulsification.

These products of fat digestion are, like the fat substrate itself, almost insoluble in water, so we would expect their absorption from the aqueous lumen to be very slow. However, this process is accelerated due to the formation of tiny structures (much smaller than the droplets in an emulsion) called **micelles**. These are aggregates of bile salts, phospholipids, fats and the products of lipase action – fatty acids and monoacylglycerol molecules. Like the fat droplets making up an emulsion, in micelles the charged or polar ends of the molecules are at the outside of the droplet and the non-polar ends together on the inside (Figure 3.11). The formation of micelles is a dynamic process, i.e. they are continually breaking down and reforming. This important point means that they provide a reservoir of fatty acids and monoacylglycerols which can move into solution in the lumen; these 'free' molecules are able to diffuse to the brush border of the intestinal epithelium (see below). Fat-soluble vitamins, such as vitamin D, are also transferred to the brush border in the micelles.

Absorption of nutrients in the small intestine

You have seen how the large insoluble molecules which form the major part of the human diet are digested into smaller, soluble molecules. In this section, you will see how these digestion products are actually absorbed into the body, via the intestinal epithelium. This necessitates crossing the epithelial cell membrane.

❑ The cell membrane, as you have seen in earlier chapters, forms an effective barrier between the internal and external environments of the cell. What are the molecular constituents of cell membranes?

■ Animal cell membranes are composed mainly of phospholipids and cholesterol, together with proteins (some with sugars attached).

❑ With this in mind, and from what you have learnt in Book 1, Chapter 3, and above, which type of molecule would be likely to enter the intestinal epithelial cell membrane most easily?

■ Fatty acids and monoacylglycerols, because the cell membrane is composed of a bilayer of phospholipids, the central part of which forms a hydrophobic (non-polar) layer.

Fatty acids

Fatty acids and monoacylglycerols are able to diffuse from the lumen across the cell membrane into the epithelial cells. The only limiting factor to this process would be if the concentration of fatty acids inside the cell was much greater than that outside the cell, in the gut lumen.

Once they enter the epithelial cells, the fatty acids and monoacylglycerols are converted back into triacylglycerols (within the smooth endoplasmic reticulum), and these once again aggregate, together with phospholipids, cholesterol and fat-soluble vitamins, into small droplets known as **chylomicrons**. This sequestration into chylomicrons ensures that the concentration of *free* fatty acids inside the cell is kept low, so that more are able to enter the cell by diffusion (since the concentration in the gut lumen immediately outside the cell, in the microenvironment of the brush border, is greater). The chylomicrons accumulate inside vesicles which bud off from the smooth endoplasmic reticulum and are transported (via the Golgi apparatus) to the other side of the epithelial cell, known as the *basal* side. Here the vesicles fuse with the cell membrane and expel the chylomicrons into the interstitial fluid (i.e. the fluid filling the spaces between cells) by exocytosis. Chylomicrons cannot enter the bloodstream directly, since they cannot pass across the basement membrane (a layer of glycoprotein) which surrounds blood vessels. Instead the chylomicrons enter the lymph vessels, via the large pores in the vessel walls; from here, they are transported into the bloodstream. The process of fat digestion and absorption is summarized in Figure 3.11 (see also Figure 3.3c).

(Another substance that can freely cross cell membranes is alcohol, which explains why it is readily absorbed, even in the stomach – with the result that its effects are felt very rapidly!)

Amino acids and monosaccharides

Amino acids and monosaccharides are polar, hydrophilic molecules, and therefore cannot pass across the cell membrane by simple diffusion, but are transferred by specialized transport proteins in the cell membrane. You learnt something of these transport mechanisms in Book 1, Chapter 3 and also earlier in the present chapter in relation to H^+ transport (Section 3.3.3).

Free amino acids cross the epithelial cell membrane by active transport. The amino acids bind to a protein molecule spanning the width of the membrane, known as a *transporter*. (In fact, five different amino acid transporters have been identified.) Sodium ions also bind to the transporter, and this causes a change in the shape (conformation) of the molecule. This change results in the transfer of an amino acid molecule together with a sodium ion (i.e. *cotransport*) across the membrane, into the cytoplasm of the epithelial cell.

The absorbed amino acids leave the epithelial cells via the opposite (basal) and side (lateral) parts of the cell membrane by several processes, including both facilitated diffusion and other transport systems.

As mentioned earlier, the digestive enzymes of a new-born baby are not fully developed, and the intestinal epithelial cells can absorb intact proteins by endocytosis. Adults retain some capacity for this, but only a very small amount of protein crosses into the mature intestinal epithelium in this way.

Transport proteins are also involved in the absorption of monosaccharides. Glucose and galactose, like amino acids, enter the intestinal epithelial cells by Na^+-coupled active transport (Figure 3.7c and summarized in Figure 3.12); these two monosaccharides compete for the same transport protein. It is important to note, however, that glucose, which is the major fuel for all cells, enters *other* types of cell, such as muscle cells and fat cells, by facilitated diffusion, which involves different membrane molecules and does not require energy. (This process was illustrated in Figure 3.7b.) You will learn more about the control of glucose uptake in the next chapter.

Other sugars, such as ribose and deoxyribose (components of nucleotides, the building blocks of nucleic acids) and also fructose, are much less effective competitors for the monosaccharide active transport protein. It is thought that fructose crosses the epithelial cell membranes by facilitated diffusion.

Facilitated diffusion is an energy-*independent* process which does *not* occur against a concentration gradient. It is limited by the availability of free transport proteins, which are necessary to allow passage of the hydrophilic substances across the hydrophobic parts of the cell membrane. (You will recall that, in contrast to facilitated diffusion, active transport *does* require energy, and involves the movement of molecules *against* a concentration gradient.)

Once absorbed into the epithelial cells, monosaccharides leave via the basal and lateral cell membranes by facilitated diffusion.

Minerals, vitamins and water

Small molecules and ions, including minerals (such as sodium, iron and calcium), vitamins and, of course, water are also essential components of the human diet. How do these cross the intestinal epithelium? We will not describe the absorption of all these substances in detail; we will, however, consider what happens to some of them.

As you know from earlier in the course, sodium is an essential element, present in its ionic form as Na^+ ions. On average, most of us consume some 5–8 g (grams) of sodium each day and an additional 20–30 g are added to the gut in the various secretions that enter it.

❑   You have already learnt of the source of many of the secretions entering the gut. Can you list them?

■   Saliva, gastric secretions, bile and pancreatic secretions.

Between 25 and 35 g of the sodium that enters the gut is absorbed in the small intestine; this represents around one-seventh of the total amount of sodium present in the body. Sodium ions are predominantly absorbed by active transport (together with amino acids and sugars as described above). This is only possible because of the Na^+ concentration gradient across the epithelial cell membrane set up by the Na^+–K^+ ATPase, which, as you learnt in Book 2, Chapter 3, 'pumps' Na^+ ions out of cells. The obvious question then is, if the pump acts to remove Na^+ ions from cells, how is there a net absorption of sodium? The answer to this lies in the organization of the intestinal epithelium. The Na^+–K^+ ATPase is not distributed evenly around the epithelial cell membrane, but is concentrated in the lateral and basal regions. This is illustrated in Figure 3.12. Because of the uneven distribution of the sodium pump, Na^+ ions enter the interstitial (i.e. extracellular) space, not the lumen. This creates a gradient in the concentration of Na^+ ions, so that when the concentration in the lumen is high, transport into the epithelial cells occurs.

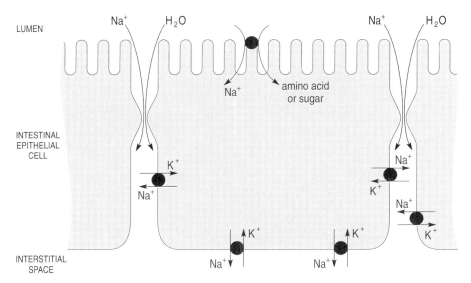

Figure 3.12 Diagram showing the major routes by which the main nutrients are absorbed into the intestinal epithelium. Amino acids and sugars are absorbed by active transport, coupled with sodium ions, through the lumenal surface of the epithelial cells. Note the arrangement of the Na^+–K^+ ATPase (the sodium pump) in the epithelial cell membranes. This arrangement results is the pumping of Na^+ *out* of these cells into the interstitial space, and generates the gradient of Na^+ concentration (i.e. less Na^+ present inside the epithelial cells than is in the lumen), which is required to drive the cotransport of amino acids and sugars. Water is absorbed by osmosis, through the spaces between the epithelial cells, when the osmolarity in the interstitial space is greater than that in the lumen. When levels of Na^+ in the lumen are higher than in the interstitial space, Na^+ is absorbed by diffusion, also through these spaces.

Water, too, enters the body through the digestive tract. In addition to intake in the form of drink, water also forms a significant component of the foods we eat. In fact, a vast amount of fluid enters the digestive tract. Each day, in addition to ingesting up to about two litres of water, the secretions of the digestive system add a further seven litres of water to the lumen of the gut.

There is one further important source of fluid in the digestive system which we have not yet mentioned. This is a large group of epithelial cells in the small intestine, located at the base of the villi. These cells, known as *crypt cells* (not identified in Figure 3.3c), secrete a watery fluid which is almost identical in composition to extracellular fluid, and has a slightly alkaline pH of between 7.5 and 8.0. This liquid provides a suitable environment for the absorption of water-soluble nutrients, and dilutes the ingredients of the chyme, which are highly concentrated when they reach the small intestine. The fluid secreted by the crypt cells is absorbed by epithelial cells further up the villi, so there is essentially a flow of fluid from the base to the tip of the villi.

The sources of the water that enters the digestive tract are shown in Figure 3.13. Almost all this water is absorbed in the small intestine; approximately 80–90% of the remaining half litre is absorbed in the large intestine, leaving only about one-tenth of a litre which passes out in the faeces.

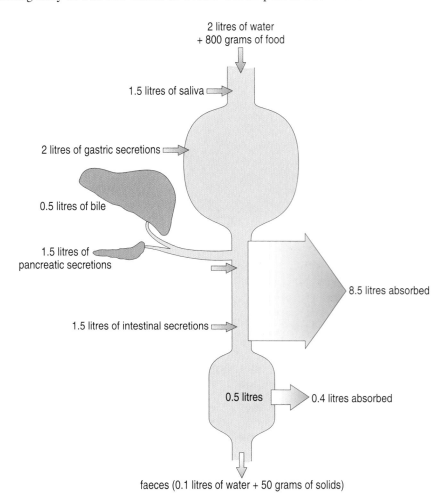

Figure 3.13 Diagram showing the sources of water that enters the digestive tract, and the regions from which water leaves. Adapted from Vander, A. J., Sherman, J. H. and Luciano, D. S. (1994) Human Physiology, Sixth International Edition, copyright © 1994, 1990, 1985, 1980, 1975, 1970 by McGraw-Hill, Inc., with permission of the McGraw-Hill Companies.

How is all this water absorbed? The answer to this is that there are very small pores between the epithelial cells in the small intestine (see Figure 3.12). Water crosses into the interstitial space between the epithelial cells by osmosis (Figure 3.7d). Most of the water is absorbed by this *paracellular* route; as shown in Figure 3.12, some diffusion of ions (e.g. Na^+) occurs here too. However, some water movement occurs by a *transcellular route*, i.e. across the epithelial cell membrane, into the cytosol and then out of the cell into the interstitial space (not shown in Figure 3.12).

The absorption of water, then, is inextricably tied up with that of salts, and is dependent upon the concentration difference between the interstitial space and the gut lumen.

❑   When it first reaches the lumen of the duodenum, the chyme is very concentrated. Will water move into the interstitial space under these circumstances?

■   No, not if the solute concentration in the lumen is greater than that in the interstitial space. In fact, water leaves the interstitial space and enters the lumen, by osmosis, under these circumstances.

As nutrients and ions are absorbed, however, the chyme becomes more dilute, and water is then absorbed. It should be added that absorption is an ever-changing process, the type and extent of absorption of the various nutrients in different gut regions depending on the conditions that prevail there at any particular time.

The absorption of water and salts is of crucial importance to health; normally about 99% of the water and ions that enter the lumen are absorbed. An increase in the amount of water in the faeces is called **diarrhoea**. Diarrhoea can result from disturbance to the processes of both absorption and secretion and causes loss of water and salts from the body. In extreme cases, if untreated this dehydration can be rapid and fatal. Dehydration is a particular risk for new-born babies and young infants; babies have a large body surface area in comparison with their volume, and a rapid breathing rate, so lose fluids rapidly. They also have immature kidneys, so are less able to concentrate urine than are adults. Diarrhoea is usually a result of an infection by pathogenic microbes in the intestines. These organisms may release substances that affect ion transport or, in some cases, damage the mucosa. Secretion from the crypt cells in particular is greatly increased during an episode of diarrhoea; presumably this has the effect of washing the harmful bacteria along the gut. Diarrhoea is usually associated with an increase in gut motility. This also speeds up elimination of the harmful agent. Evidence suggests that both increased secretion and increased motility during diarrhoea can occur by activation of the enteric neurons which control both these processes.

In addition to sodium, other minerals of major importance in the diet include calcium, iron and potassium. Although we cannot describe the details of their absorption here, an important aspect of this from the point of view of health is that the absorption of several of these minerals is dependent not only on the physiological processes involved, but also on the presence of other dietary components. For example, both calcium and iron absorption require the assistance of particular vitamins, as described below.

Calcium is poorly absorbed from the gut, because it is usually ingested in relatively insoluble forms such as calcium phosphate, and because its ions are also poorly absorbed. In fact, about 87% of the daily intake of calcium is not absorbed, but excreted in the faeces. Vitamin D plays an important role in calcium absorption. There is actually a group of similar molecules, known as the vitamin D family; the most important of these molecules is vitamin D_3 (also known as cholecalciferol). Most of this vitamin is formed in the skin, by irradiation of a precursor molecule by ultraviolet light from the Sun. Vitamin D_3 is, in turn, converted to an active form by a stepwise process involving both the liver and kidneys. The active molecule has several effects on intestinal epithelium. Although the precise details of the mechanisms involved in calcium absorption are not fully understood, it seems that the active form of vitamin D_3 causes the formation of a calcium binding protein in the intestinal epithelial cells, and that the rate of calcium absorption is dependent on the amount of this protein present.

This stimulatory effect of vitamin D on calcium uptake has important implications, particularly for those of us from the northern latitudes, who may not be exposed to enough sunlight to promote formation of adequate levels of vitamin D.

The other example of mineral absorption we will look at is that of iron which can be absorbed in several different ways. Iron in the diet occurs in two forms: in the organic molecule haem (present in meat and fish) and in iron salts (from eggs and plants). Whereas haem iron is relatively easily absorbed, only 10–15% of ingested iron salts enter the bloodstream. The first step in the conversion of iron salts into a form that can be absorbed occurs in the gut lumen and is greatly enhanced by vitamin C. However, in contrast to the case of vitamin D and calcium, vitamin C must be present in the gut at the same time as the iron to be effective in this way. Other dietary components, such as calcium, soya protein and some constituents of vegetables, actually inhibit iron absorption.

Most water-soluble vitamins are small molecules and are absorbed either by passive diffusion or by facilitated diffusion. Vitamin B_{12}, however, is a large, charged molecule and so cannot be absorbed directly. It binds to intrinsic factor (a protein produced by a particular type of gastric epithelial cells, see Section 3.3.2) and later, in the ileum (the last part of the small intestine), the resulting complex binds to specific receptors on the surface of epithelial cells. This binding can *only* take place if vitamin B_{12} is complexed with intrinsic factor, the presence of which is thus essential for absorption of the vitamin.

Chyme takes 4–6 hours to pass through the small intestine. It then enters the large intestine, slowly, through the ileocaecal sphincter (see Figure 3.1). This prevents the chyme from passing back into the small intestine when the large intestine is distended.

3.3.5 The large intestine

The large intestine has three parts, called the caecum, colon and rectum. Like the small intestine, it is a tube-like organ, but with a larger diameter – about 6 cm – and is about 1.5 m long.

From the preceding section, it should be clear that most digestion and absorption occur in the small intestine. In fact, a considerable proportion of the small intestine serves as reserve capacity as far as the absorption of amino acids, monosaccharides and fatty acids is concerned; however, absorption of water and salts occurs throughout the small intestine. What then is the function of the large intestine?

Around 1.5 litres of chyme enters the large intestine from the ileum. It moves relatively slowly, taking between 12 and 24 hours, depending on diet, to pass from the ileocaecal sphincter to the rectum. The chyme entering the large intestine contains, for the most part, secretions from the lower part of the small intestine, wastes from the liver and undigested material, the main components of which are plant polysaccharides, often known as *fibre*. Cellulose forms a large proportion of these plant polysaccharides, but other plant polymers, such as pectin, are also present.

The bulk of absorption that occurs in the large intestine is of water and salts, and only about 4% of the digested material is absorbed in this last part of the digestive tract. However, fluid balance and the balance of ions in the body is very tightly regulated; the absorption of water and ions that occurs in the large intestine is an important fine tuning in the maintenance of normal water and salt levels in the body.

The large intestine also plays a role in the absorption of vitamins. This is of importance if dietary intake of vitamins is low. The large intestine is populated by bacteria, which synthesize several vitamins, including vitamin B_{12} (although, as mentioned above, some is ingested in food), vitamin K, thiamine (vitamin B_1) and riboflavin (vitamin B_2). The production and absorption of vitamin K, which plays a role in blood clotting, is of particular importance, since levels of this vitamin in food are usually inadequate. Treatment with antibiotics can affect these intestinal bacteria and can therefore sometimes cause vitamin deficiency in individuals whose vitamin intake is low and who therefore depend on vitamin formation and absorption in the large intestine.

The breakdown of undigested polysaccharides by bacteria in the large intestine also results in the daily production of about 0.4–0.7 litres of gas – predominantly nitrogen and carbon dioxide, but also small amounts of hydrogen, methane and hydrogen sulphide. Some foods, such as beans, contain a large proportion of the types of polysaccharide that cannot be digested by human digestive enzymes, but can be broken down by bacteria in the colon; this is why consumption of certain foods produces a lot of wind!

The absorption of water in the large intestine results in the formation of the faeces, or stools, which are normally composed of about two parts of water and one part of solid material, the latter consisting of bacteria, undigested polysaccharides and small amounts of bile pigments, cholesterol and protein.

The consumption of non-digestible carbohydrates also has other important consequences; the rate of movement of faeces along and out of the large intestine is related to their bulk. Stools containing a lot of solid material are larger, and their passage along the large intestine is accelerated. This is because distension of the gut is one of the important stimuli which result in the activation of the smooth muscle of the gut wall.

In recent years, attention has been focused on the importance of fibre in the diet. There are several reasons for this. Epidemiological studies (see Book 1) have shown that populations with high-fibre diets tend to have lower incidences of certain diseases, in particular cancer of the colon, heart disease and diabetes. What could be the reasons for these observations? There are several possible explanations.

You have already seen that bulky stools move along the colon and are eliminated faster than small stools, and with less straining. As well as avoiding the discomfort of constipation and the associated problems of haemorrhoids (piles), it seems that this has other beneficial consequences. If faeces linger for a long period in the colon, there is an increased chance of a build-up of any toxins that may be present. In particular, the bacteria present in the colon produce wastes that are toxic, and it is thought that prolonged exposure to such agents may contribute to the incidence of colon cancer. Fibre is believed to bind such toxins, so that they are more effectively eliminated from the gut.

Alternative or additional explanations also exist. A high-fibre diet is also likely to contain increased levels of vitamins, which are known to have antioxidant activity. Antioxidants bind to, and hence inactivate, harmful molecules called *free radicals*, which are formed under a number of circumstances, for example, when there is inflammation. Free radicals cause much tissue damage, and have been linked with cancer. Colon cancer has also been linked with diets containing high levels of saturated fatty acids. Since individuals who have a high-fibre diet are also likely to consume smaller amounts of saturated fats, this could be another contributory factor to the lower incidence of colon cancer and heart disease associated with high-fibre diets.

A high-fibre diet can also, in some cases, have deleterious effects. Some vitamins are absorbed by fibre, thus preventing their absorption from the gut. You will learn more about some of the issues of diet and health in Chapter 7 of this book.

There is one other part of the large intestine which we should perhaps mention, and that is the appendix. If you look again at Figure 3.1, you will see that the appendix is situated just after the junction between the small intestine and colon. The role of the appendix is not clear, but it contains abundant lymphoid tissue, particularly in children. This lymphoid tissue is not present at birth, but appears progressively during the first 10 years of life, after which it gradually disappears; the normal adult appendix contains only traces of lymphoid tissue. Although the presence of lymphoid tissue suggests a role for the appendix in defence against pathogens, it is clearly not essential as, like the tonsils, it is commonly removed when inflamed, with no apparent ill-effect.

Summary of Section 3.3

1   The initial processing of food is carried out in the mouth, by the teeth, which break the food into small pieces and mix it with saliva; saliva contains amylase, which begins carbohydrate digestion.

2   A peristaltic wave passes the bolus of food down the oesophagus, through the lower oesophageal sphincter and into the stomach. Here muscular activity mixes the food with hydrochloric acid, which denatures proteins, and with the proteolytic enzyme pepsin, formed from its precursor, pepsinogen. Salivary amylase is destroyed in the acid environment of the stomach.

3   The chyme passes through the pyloric sphincter into the small intestine and is mixed with digestive juices produced by the pancreas and liver. It is in the small intestine that most digestion and absorption occurs.

4   The digestive enzymes produced by the pancreas are released mainly as inactive precursors which are activated in the lumen of the gut. The active forms of these enzymes continue the digestion of proteins and carbohydrates. Proteins are finally broken down into amino acids and carbohydrates are broken down into monosaccharides by enzymes on the brush border of the epithelial cells.

5   Amino acids and monosaccharides are absorbed into epithelial cells by Na^+-coupled active transport using specific transport proteins.

6   The bile salts, produced by the liver, emulsify fats, thereby allowing access by the fat-digesting enzyme, lipase. This results in the production of very small aggregates called micelles, which contain (in addition to bile salts and phospholipids) fatty acids and monoacylglycerols – the products of lipase action. Free fatty acids and monoacylglycerols diffuse from the micelles into the epithelial cells where they recombine to form fat droplets (chylomicrons) which travel across the cell to emerge on the opposite side for release into the lymphatic system and thence into the bloodstream.

7   Most of the absorption of water and salts occurs in the small intestine, by both paracellular and transcellular routes.

8   The large intestine is important as the site of final absorption of water and salts in the gut. Beneficial bacteria also reside in the colon; these synthesize vitamins, including vitamin K, and break down indigestible plant polysaccharides, producing wind. The regular passage of bulky stools, a result of a high-fibre diet combined with adequate water intake, may have a number of beneficial effects on health.

3.4 Control of gastrointestinal functions

You have seen how the breakdown of foods into small molecules which can
be absorbed from the lumen of the gut is dependent upon the combined
actions of the intestinal smooth muscle and the secretions of the mucosal
epithelial cells. But how are these activities coordinated? Clearly, it would
not be useful for intestinal smooth muscle to be very active all the time, or
for high levels of secretions to be produced constantly.

❑   Can you think of any disadvantages this would have?

■   It would waste energy and materials; also, if too much peristalsis
      occurred, ingested nutrients might be eliminated before digestion or
      absorption were completed, and if digestive secretions (enzymes and
      particularly HCl) were produced at too high a rate there would
      would be a greater opportunity for the epithelial cells to become
      damaged.

We will now consider the mechanisms by which gut motility and the
production of digestive secretions are controlled. First, we will describe
some of the cell types and general principles involved; then we will go on to
describe the control of motility and secretion in more detail.

3.4.1 General mechanisms of control in the gut

The activities of the components of the gastrointestinal tract are controlled
by both nerves and hormones. Nervous control is mediated by both enteric
neurons and extrinsic nerves (i.e. those outside the enteric nervous system).

❑   Where are the enteric neurons located?

■   They are grouped into ganglia which are embedded in the gut wall
      (Section 3.2.2).

The extrinsic nerves that regulate intestinal activities are part of the
parasympathetic and sympathetic divisions of the autonomic nervous
system; they transmit messages from the central nervous system (CNS) to
the gut (see Figure 3.14 and also Book 2, Chapter 3).

The intrinsic and extrinsic nerves controlling gut functions are activated by
stimuli within the gut itself. These stimuli are detected by sensory neurons
of the enteric nervous system which activate other enteric neurons, and by
extrinsic sensory fibres which convey information about the state of the gut
to the central nervous system. Both these pathways involve interneurons,
and are illustrated in Figure 3.15.

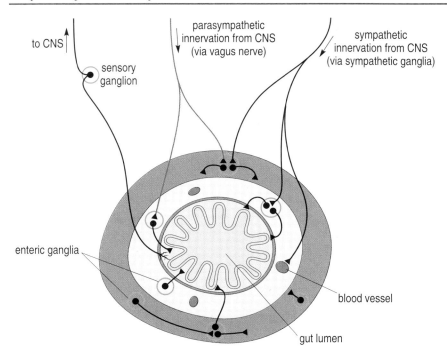

Figure 3.14 Diagram showing, in simplified form, the innervation of the gut.

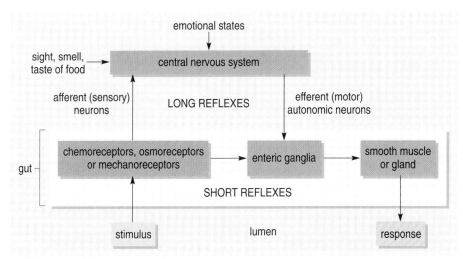

Figure 3.15 Nerve pathways involved in the coordination of gut function. These can be described as long pathways which involve neurons outside the gut, particularly those of the CNS, and short pathways in which the neurons involved are confined to the gut. Stimuli such as the sight, smell or taste of food and emotional states trigger responses in neurons of the CNS. These then transmit signals to enteric neurons which innervate intestinal smooth muscle and glands. Changes in the amount and nature of gut contents are detected by sensory neurons, some of which are located in the enteric ganglia (short pathways), others of which are located in the dorsal root ganglia and transmit information to the CNS. Distension of the gut is detected by neurons known as *mechanoreceptors*, while changes in the osmolarity (related to concentration– see Chapter 5) of gut contents are detected by *osmoreceptors*. Chemoreceptors detect changes in the chemical composition of the gut contents. Adapted from Vander, A. J., Sherman, J. H. and Luciano, D. S. (1994) Human Physiology, Sixth International Edition, copyright © 1994, 1990, 1985, 1980, 1975, 1970 by McGraw-Hill, Inc., with permission of the McGraw-Hill Companies.

In the case of extrinsic nerves, the pathway is, by necessity, long; the message has to pass from the gut to the brain, and back. For this reason, such pathways are often referred to as long reflex pathways. The intrinsic nervous pathways are therefore called short reflex pathways. It turns out that there are a large number of these short pathways in the gut; the circuitry of the enteric nervous system is extremely complex, and we cannot discuss it in detail here. Suffice it to say that the final result of the action of both intrinsic and extrinsic nerves is to control the state of contraction of the smooth muscle, the secretory activity of the epithelium and the dilation of intestinal blood vessels.

❏   Already in this chapter you have met examples of long reflex pathways by which messages are sent from the gut, via the central nervous system and back. What are the processes that depend on activation of such pathways?

■   Long reflex pathways are involved in the regulation of salivation, swallowing, vomiting and defaecation.

The brain also influences the gut in more subtle ways; we are all aware that our 'mental state' can affect our digestive systems. (You will learn more about this in Chapter 6.)

The hormonal control of gastrointestinal activity is mediated to a large extent by endocrine cells which are located in the gut itself.

❏   Thinking back, where are these endocrine cells located?

■   The gut endocrine cells are distributed among the secretory cells in the epithelial layer of the mucosa of the stomach and intestine.

The lumenal surface (i.e. that facing the lumen) of these endocrine cells is exposed to the intestinal contents; the hormones produced by these cells are released on the opposite (basal) side of the cell. The endocrine cells of the gut can therefore detect the state of the lumenal contents, and respond by releasing hormones into the circulation.

❏   Think of stimuli to which the nerves and endocrine cells involved in intestinal regulation might respond.

■   Distension due to a lump (or bolus) of food; levels of salts or particular ions; acidity; levels of specific digestion products (e.g. monosaccharides, fatty acids, amino acids); bacterial toxins, or other noxious agents. In addition, there is another type of stimulus, outside the gut itself, which we have already described, i.e. the smell, taste and even the sight of food.

3.4.2 The three phases of gastrointestinal control: cephalic, gastric and intestinal

Smell, taste and sight, together with a stimulus produced by the chewing of food, constitute one phase of what is often subdivided into three phases of gastrointestinal control. The cells that detect these stimuli are in the head, so this phase is called the **cephalic phase**. This phase can also be initiated by emotional stimuli.

When activated, brain neurons send signals to the intrinsic neurons of the gut, which then act on the intestinal smooth muscle and mucosal epithelial cells, to modify the contractility and secretory processes. As a result of the latter, there is an increase in the secretion of HCl.

Once food reaches the stomach, the **gastric phase** of control comes into play. There are three stimuli involved; distension of the stomach, decreased acidity of the stomach contents and the presence of peptides formed by the breakdown of proteins. The nervous component of this phase involves both long pathways and short pathways. The hormonal component of the gastric phase is mediated by the hormone gastrin, secreted by endocrine cells of the gastric mucosa.

Gastrin release is stimulated by the presence of amino acids and peptides in the stomach lumen, and by the activity of nerves. This hormone stimulates secretion of acid, and also has actions on the ileum, ileocaecal sphincter and large intestine. When acid levels increase, gastrin secretion is inhibited.

❑ This is an example of what type of regulatory process?

■ Negative feedback.

❑ When food *first* reaches the stomach, is gastrin secretion stimulated or inhibited?

■ At first, when food reaches the stomach, acid levels are high, so gastrin secretion is inhibited. When proteins enter the stomach H^+ ions bind to the surface negative charges. As a result, the acid levels in the stomach decrease. This then stimulates gastrin release.

The greater the amount of protein in a meal, the greater the amount of H^+ ions bound. This results in a greater stimulation of gastrin release, which in turn, increases acid secretion. There is another reason for a greater stimulation of acid secretion after ingestion of a high-protein meal. From what you have just learnt, can you say what this is?

If more proteins are ingested, more peptides and amino acids are produced. Both of these, too, stimulate the release of gastrin.

Interestingly, there are some other substances which stimulate acid release when they are present in the stomach. These include calcium and coffee (with or without caffeine). Calcium salts act by binding H^+ ions. The action of coffee, however, is not yet understood.

The third phase of control is called the **intestinal phase**, because it is initiated by stimuli in the intestine. The stimuli involved are similar to those of the gastric phase, i.e. distension, increased acidity, products of digestion, and ion concentrations. Again, this phase of control is mediated by long and short nervous pathways and by gastrointestinal hormones.

The first thing to occur in the intestinal phase is the reflex inhibition of gastric acid secretion as a result of the increased acidity in the duodenum. This reflex ensures that the acidity of the chyme entering the small intestine is reduced if it reaches levels which cannot be rapidly neutralized by the bicarbonate-containing secretions of the pancreas and liver.

In addition to high acidity in the duodenum, there are other duodenal stimuli which inhibit acid secretion in the stomach. These are distension, the presence of amino acids, monosaccharides and fatty acids, and increased concentration of gut contents. In this way, the inhibition of acid secretion is matched to the volume and components of a meal, resulting in a balance between stomach activity and that of the small intestine.

The inhibition of acid secretion in the intestinal phase is again controlled by nerves and by hormones. The hormones involved are released from intestinal endocrine cells and include **cholecystokinin** (**CCK** for short) and **secretin** (see Table 3.3).

It is important to realize that the three phases of control do not actually occur in the strict sequence in which we have described them, but there is overlap between the events occurring in each phase.

3.4.3 Control of release of pancreatic secretions and bile

Rates of release of pancreatic secretions and bile into the duodenum are increased during a meal; these increases are again triggered by changes in the lumenal contents, and involve activation of nerves and release of gut hormones. Bicarbonate secretion is increased mainly as a result of the actions of secretin, which is produced in response to the increased acidity in the duodenum upon arrival of chyme from the stomach. The secretion of pancreatic enzymes is stimulated by CCK which, in turn, is secreted in response to increased levels of amino acids and fatty acids in the duodenum. CCK also has a stimulatory effect on the action of secretin. (These responses are summarized in Table 3.3.)

The bulk (75%) of the control of pancreatic secretion is a result of the actions of these hormones, although nerve-mediated reflexes, initiated by both the taste of food and distension of the stomach, also act to increase pancreatic secretion. CCK is also involved in the control of bile release.

Table 3.3 Summary of the actions of some gastrointestinal hormones. Adapted from Vander, A. J., Sherman, J. H. and Luciano, D. S. (1994) Human Physiology, Sixth International Edition, copyright © 1994, 1990, 1985, 1980, 1975, 1970 by McGraw-Hill, Inc., with permission of the McGraw-Hill Companies.

	Gastrin	Cholecystokinin (CCK)	Secretin
Structure	peptide	peptide	peptide
Location of endocrine cells	stomach	small intestine	small intestine
Stimuli for hormone release	amino acids, peptides in stomach; parasympathetic nerves	amino acids, fatty acids in small intestine	acid in small intestine
Stimulus inhibiting hormone release	acid in stomach		
Effects			
Stomach:			
acid secretion	stimulates		inhibits
Pancreas:			
bicarbonate secretion		potentiates secretin's actions	stimulates
enzyme secretion		stimulates	
Liver:			
bicarbonate secretion		potentiates secretin's action	stimulates
Gall bladder		stimulates	
Sphincter of Oddi		relaxes	
Small intestine	stimulates ileum; inhibits ileocaecal sphincter		
Large intestine	stimulates mass movement (see Section 3.4.4)		

❑   You have already seen that bile, produced by the liver, is released into the duodenum via a storage organ. What is the name of this organ?

■   The gall bladder.

Bile is constantly being produced; it is stored in the gall bladder until required and is released into the duodenum via the sphincter of Oddi (look back at Figure 3.9). Bile is released after a meal by contraction of the gall bladder, and relaxation of the sphincter of Oddi, both of which are stimulated by CCK (Table 3.3).

3.4.4 Control of motility

You have already seen how intestinal contents are moved along the gut by waves of peristalsis involving both contraction and relaxation of the smooth muscle layer and that this process is regulated by enteric neurons. The enteric neurons in fact modulate the underlying spontaneous contractility exhibited by the smooth muscle of the gut.

Gastric emptying

In the stomach, spontaneous slow waves of contraction (at a rhythm of about three per minute) of the muscularis externa occur (Figure 3.3a). The force of the contractions, and hence the rate of gastric emptying, is increased by distension of the stomach (via both long and short nerve pathways) and increased gastrin levels. Chyme is prevented from entering the duodenum too rapidly by stimuli arising in the duodenum; the stimuli are the same as those that inhibit acid secretion, i.e. distension and the presence of fat, acid and high salt levels in the chyme.

The extrinsic autonomic nerves supplying the stomach can be activated or inhibited independently of stimuli arising in the gut itself. Hence our emotional state can affect gastric motility; fear, pain, depression and sadness all tend to inhibit motility, whereas anger and aggression tend to stimulate motility. There is considerable variation in these responses, however, and individuals may not all respond in the same ways.

Motility in the small intestine

Motility in the small intestine, like that in other parts of the gut, is controlled by both nerves and hormones and it changes during the course of the digestion of a meal. We cannot describe these different patterns of motility here but, essentially, the first movements mix the chyme and digestive secretions, while later movements convey the chyme along the intestine.

Defaecation

Slow waves of contraction occur more slowly in the colon than in the small intestine. However, about three or four times a day – usually after a meal – a wave of intense contraction, or **mass movement**, passes along the large intestine. This contraction propels faeces into the rectum, causing it to distend. This distension initiates a defaecation reflex of the internal anal sphincter, which is normally closed. The mass movement usually occurs shortly after food enters the stomach. This is because a reflex pathway (the gastrocolic reflex), involving extrinsic nerves, is activated by stomach distension; this explains the urge to defaecate which often occurs shortly after a meal. The external anal sphincter is under voluntary control, a process which is learnt during childhood.

Summary of Section 3.4

1   Gastrointestinal functions are controlled by nerves and hormones. Nervous control is effected by neurons of the enteric nervous system, located in the gut wall, and neurons located outside the gut, in other parts of the autonomic nervous system. Hormonal control is effected, for the most part, by endocrine cells located in the intestinal epithelium which release their products into mucosal blood vessels.

2   Neurons and endocrine cells respond to stimuli arising in the gut, and also to sensory stimulation prior to, as well as during, eating.

3   There are three phases of gastrointestinal control: cephalic, gastric and intestinal. These names refer to the sites where the neural/endocrine receptors are activated. These controls serve to match intestinal activities such as secretion and motility to the meal that has been ingested.

4   Pancreatic and bile secretion are also controlled by neurons and hormones.

5   The spontaneous activity of intestinal smooth muscle is mainly controlled by the activity of the enteric nervous system. Different types of muscular activity occur during and after absorption of nutrients. Defaecation involves voluntary control of skeletal muscle of the anal sphincter.

Objectives for Chapter 3

After completing this chapter you should be able to:

3.1   Define and use, or recognize definitions and applications of, each of the terms printed in **bold** in the text.

3.2   Describe the different cell types present in the gut, and explain their roles in the processing of foods. (*Questions 3.2, 3.4 and 3.6*)

3.3   List the main functions of the different parts of the gut. (*Questions 3.1 and 3.6*)

3.4   Explain, referring to the digestive molecules involved, how proteins, carbohydrates and fats are digested in the gut. (*Questions 3.1 and 3.3*)

3.5   Describe how nutrients are absorbed from the lumen of the gut into the body. (*Question 3.3*)

3.6   Outline how the different gastrointestinal processes are coordinated. (*Questions 3.4 and 3.5*)

Questions for Chapter 3

Question 3.1   (*Objectives 3.1, 3.3 and 3.4*)

Name each of the gut regions and digestive organs labelled A–J in Figure 3.16 and summarize, in the form of a table, the roles of each region, including the activities of the digestive secretions produced.

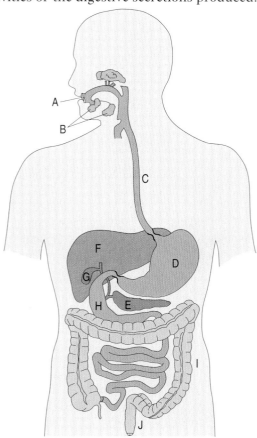

Figure 3.16   For use with Question 3.1.

Question 3.2   (*Objective 3.2*)

What are the structural specializations of the intestinal epithelium that facilitate absorption of nutrients?

Question 3.3   (*Objectives 3.4 and 3.5*)

Outline what happens to carbohydrates as you eat a meal and it passes along the gut.

Question 3.4   (*Objectives 3.2 and 3.6*)

If a drug interfered with the action of enteric neurons, what intestinal processes might be affected?

Question 3.5   (*Objective 3.6*)

Describe the three phases of the control of digestion, referring to the stimuli and secretory responses involved in each phase.

Question 3.6   (*Objectives 3.1, 3.2 and 3.3*)

List some of the ways in which protection against the possible ingestion and absorption of toxic substances and harmful microbes may occur.

CHAPTER 4
METABOLISM AND
THERMOREGULATION

4.1 Introduction

In the previous chapter, you saw how food is digested into simple components, which are absorbed from the gut into the circulation. In this chapter, we will look at some of the ways that these absorbed molecules are used in the body, in chemical reactions which are collectively known as metabolism. In addition to providing building blocks for the numerous molecules that make up our cells, the foods we eat are the source of energy, vital to all cells. The supply of energy-providing molecules to cells is finely regulated, and is an example of homeostasis, described in Chapter 1 of this book. Another example of homeostasis, which is inextricably tied up with metabolism and energy supply, is that of **thermoregulation,** or the maintenance of body temperature. In this chapter, you will learn something of both metabolism and thermoregulation, which are essential to health, and indeed to life itself. Recall, however, that homeostasis does *not* mean maintenance of a specific concentration of a particular molecule in the body, or of temperature at a specific 'set-point'; rather, it is the regulation of naturally fluctuating concentrations and temperatures to levels which are within a typical narrow range of values – the molecular components and physiological activities of the body are in a constant state of change.

This chapter, more than any other in the course, builds on the material covered in Book 1, Chapter 3. You will see that the metabolic processes described in the present chapter involve molecules and ions, so a background in cellular chemistry will help you to understand these processes. Details of some of the chemical reactions that are outlined in the text are given in numbered boxes. You will need to refer to particular boxes at certain points as you study the chapter, but **we do not expect you to memorize the boxed information**. However, you may wish to learn more about the molecular details of reactions that are described only briefly in the main part of the text; or you may have learnt about them elsewhere already and wish to refresh your memory.

PART I   METABOLISM

When studying this part of the chapter, you will probably find it useful to refer back to material in Book 1, Chapter 3, to remind yourself of particular terms and concepts.

In Book 1, Chapter 3, you learnt that the term 'metabolism' refers to the chemical reactions that occur within the cells of the body. You will realize by now that these reactions are both extremely numerous, and often complex. Their study falls into the realm of biochemistry and you may well be relieved to know that we are not going to examine them in great detail. There are, however, some fundamental reactions which occur in all cells, and on which all other reactions and cellular processes depend; these are the reactions involved in the production and supply of energy. Energy production uses oxygen, and energy-producing reactions (collectively referred to as *cell*, or *cellular*, *respiration* – see Chapter 2), are some of the 'core' or 'housekeeping' reactions mentioned first in Book 1, Chapter 3. It is these reactions that we are going to focus on here.

4.2 Energy production

4.2.1 Sources of energy

In the previous chapter you learnt that, apart from water, minerals and vitamins, the main components of the human diet are carbohydrates, proteins and lipids. All these three types of molecule can be used to provide energy, as you will see shortly. However, under ordinary circumstances, most energy is obtained from carbohydrates.

❑   What are the carbohydrate macromolecules, and what are their component subunits which are absorbed from the gut?

■   Carbohydrate macromolecules are *polysaccharides*. These are composed of subunits called *monosaccharides* which are released by digestion of polysaccharides in the gut and absorbed into the bloodstream.

The major dietary monosaccharide is glucose, which has the molecular formula $C_6H_{12}O_6$; the structural formula of glucose is given in Figure 4.1. The two other monosaccharides commonly found in the human diet are fructose and galactose. These are both isomers of glucose; that is, they contain the same number and types of atoms as glucose, but the atoms are joined together or orientated in a different way. The amounts of fructose and galactose absorbed from a typical adult diet are much smaller than the quantities of glucose absorbed. Moreover, since both fructose and galactose are converted to glucose in the liver, and so can enter the same metabolic pathways as glucose, all three monosaccharides essentially can be considered to have the same fate. Thus, the major substance that is used by cells as an energy source is glucose, and the discussion which follows refers just to glucose.

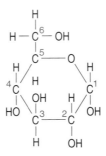

Figure 4.1   The molecular structure of glucose (carbon atom numbers included).

Each glucose molecule is broken down in a stepwise manner, by the action of many different enzymes and via many intermediate molecules. The final products of the breakdown of glucose are carbon dioxide and water. As glucose is broken down, the energy stored in the covalent bonds linking the constituent atoms together in the molecule is released. In almost all cases, each intermediate in the pathway has a slightly lower energy than the one that precedes it. The entire process, for a single glucose molecule, can be summarized by the equation:

$$C_6H_{12}O_6 + 6O_2 \rightarrow 6CO_2 + 6H_2O + \text{energy}$$

glucose   oxygen   carbon   water
dioxide

❑   How many molecules of oxygen are used for each glucose molecule broken down to carbon dioxide and water?

◼   Six molecules of oxygen are used in the breakdown of each glucose molecule. (In addition to the energy released, six molecules each of carbon dioxide and water are produced by the breakdown of each glucose molecule.)

4.2.2   Energy transfer in the cell

Energy released by the series of reactions summarized in the above equation is briefly stored in the form of a vital intermediate molecule, called adenosine triphosphate (abbreviated to ATP). ATP consists of a molecule of the *nucleoside* adenosine (the base *adenine* joined to the sugar *ribose*) linked to three phosphate groups (the *triphosphate* part); its molecular structure is shown in Figure 4.2. (You do not need to memorize these structural details.)

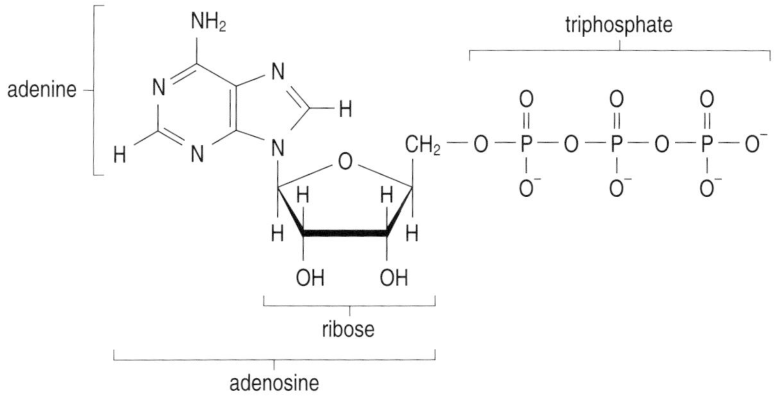

Figure 4.2   The molecular structure of ATP.

ATP is formed by the addition of a phosphate ion (free phosphate ions are called inorganic phosphate, abbreviated to P_i) to adenosine diphosphate (ADP). The energy needed to form ATP comes from the breakdown of organic fuel molecules, such as glucose.

❑   What is the name given to the chemical reactions in which molecules are broken down?

■   These are called *catabolic* reactions. (Book 1, Chapter 3)

So, ATP is formed when energy-providing molecules are broken down. ATP molecules are then used to provide energy to drive many other biochemical reactions of a different kind – those that require input of energy, such as the synthesis of new macromolecules. (You will recall that such reactions are known as anabolic reactions.) Many other cellular processes also require energy; examples of such processes which you have already encountered in earlier parts of this course include cell division, active transport and muscle contraction. ATP also provides the energy to drive these processes. Because of this universal role of ATP in the transfer of energy, it is often referred to as the 'energy currency' of the cell; ATP is continually being formed, and rapidly used, during cellular metabolism.

Energy is obtained from ATP when it is broken down to ADP and P_i. The breaking of the chemical bond that links ADP with P_i releases energy (the same amount as was needed to form ATP from ADP and P_i in the first place). Biochemical reactions that require energy are coupled to ATP breakdown. The formation and breakdown of ATP, coupled to catabolic and anabolic reactions respectively, is shown in Figure 4.3.

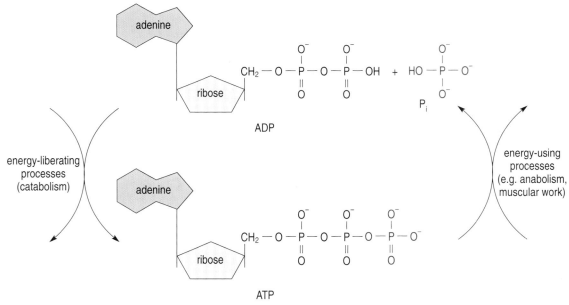

Figure 4.3   Energy economics of the cell, showing that the conversion of ADP and inorganic phosphate (P_i) into ATP is coupled to catabolic reactions, while the breakdown of ATP into ADP and P_i is coupled to anabolic reactions and other cellular processes that require energy.

Each ATP molecule typically exists for only a very brief period before being utilized to provide energy; the total amount of ATP in the body is sufficient to maintain the body, at rest, for a mere 90 seconds. ATP then, is constantly being made and broken down by the chemical reactions going on in our cells.

4.2.3   Oxidation and reduction

In Book 1 we referred to the process of glucose breakdown to carbon dioxide and water as oxidation. In order to understand how glucose oxidation generates energy for use by the cell, it is necessary to consider this process in more detail. In fact, the term **oxidation** has a more strict chemical definition, meaning the addition of oxygen atoms, the removal of hydrogen atoms or at its most fundamental, the removal of electrons.

The converse of oxidation, i.e. the addition of hydrogen, loss of oxygen, or addition of electrons, is defined as **reduction**. Every oxidation reaction is accompanied by a reduction reaction.

For example, consider the reaction of the metal magnesium (Mg) with carbon dioxide (CO_2) to form magnesium oxide (MgO) and carbon (C):

$$2Mg + CO_2 \longrightarrow 2MgO + C$$

The magnesium has become oxidized, i.e. *gained oxygen*, the carbon has become reduced, i.e. *lost oxygen*. Notice too that in becoming MgO (i.e. the ionic compound $Mg^{2+} O^{2-}$) the Mg atom has *lost electrons* and the O atom has *gained electrons*.

Oxidation and reduction reactions are of great importance in energy metabolism. Glucose molecules are gradually broken down, or oxidized, by sequential removal of hydrogen atoms. The hydrogen atoms join with (i.e. reduce) special carrier molecules, called **nicotinamide adenine dinucleotide** (derived from the vitamin, niacin, and abbreviated to NAD^+) and **flavin adenine dinucleotide** (FAD, a derivative of vitamin B_2, or riboflavin). NAD^+ and FAD are both **coenzymes**, i.e. non-protein molecules which are closely associated with enzymes and which help catalyse chemical reactions.

❑   What is the significance of the plus sign on NAD^+?

■   The molecule has an overall positive charge.

Both NAD^+ and FAD react with pairs of hydrogen atoms released during the catabolism of glucose, becoming NADH and $FADH_2$ respectively. In so doing, they accept and carry electrons (see Box 4.1). As you will see shortly, during the last part of the sequence of reactions by which glucose is oxidized, these reduced coenzymes pass on their hydrogen atoms, and so become reoxidized; the H atoms combine with molecular oxygen, forming water. (Thus the oxygen we breathe in is converted *not* to CO_2, as is often thought, but to H_2O.) The energy released via the reoxidation of NADH and $FADH_2$ in this way is used to generate ATP.

Box 4.1   The role of the coenzyme NAD$^+$ as a hydrogen carrier

Cells derive energy from the oxidation of glucose and other fuel molecules; under aerobic conditions the oxidizing agent, or ultimate electron acceptor, is oxygen. In the course of their oxidation, these fuel molecules donate pairs of hydrogen atoms ('2H', which is equivalent to two H$^+$ ions plus two electrons, e$^-$) to either nicotinamide adenine dinucleotide (NAD$^+$) or flavin adenine dinucleotide (FAD). The reduced coenzymes (NADH or FADH$_2$) then pass the pair of electrons to oxygen via the electron transport chain, located in the inner membrane of the mitochondrion (Section 4.2.8); in this way, NADH and FADH$_2$ are reoxidized to NAD$^+$ and FAD respectively.

Part (a) shows the molecular details of the reduction of NAD$^+$ by two H atoms from a substrate molecule. Notice that both electrons but only *one* H$^+$ are transferred to the nicotinamide ring; the other H$^+$ is free in the solution. (Here, to save space, the convention of representing the phosphate groups in the molecule as the letter 'P' in a circle is used.)

Part (b) shows an example of an oxidation reaction in which NAD$^+$ is the hydrogen acceptor; for simplicity, only the group of atoms in the substrate molecule that is involved in the reaction is shown.

4.2.4   Energy-generating reactions

The main source of ATP is glucose. The breakdown of glucose involves a complex series of chemical reactions. While it is not necessary for you to memorize all the steps of these reactions, it is important to realize that a linked sequence of three distinct metabolic pathways is involved, and that these take place in different parts of the cell, as summarized in Figure 4.4. Another important point is that most of the reactions that make up these these metabolic pathways do *not* generate ATP, and a few steps actually *use* ATP. Furthermore, it is not only glucose that can provide energy; it is simply that *most* of the cell's energy is derived from glucose. In fact, as you will see, fatty acids and glycerol (from triacylglycerols and other lipids) and amino acids (from proteins) can be converted into molecules which can enter the sequence of catabolic pathways at particular points. This is also shown in Figure 4.4.

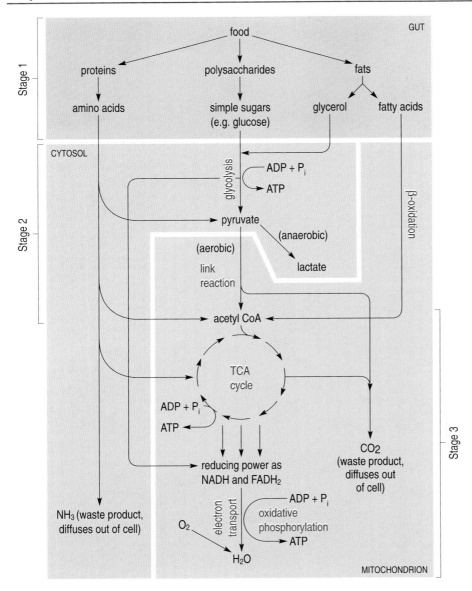

Figure 4.4   Schematic summary of the three consecutive linked pathways involved in the breakdown of glucose to produce energy:(i) *glycolysis*, then (via the *link reaction*) to (ii) the *TCA cycle* and finally to (iii) *electron transport* coupled to *oxidative phosphorylation*. The entry points of molecules derived from fats (triacylglycerols) and proteins into the energy-producing pathways are also shown. Stage 1: the breakdown of large molecules into simple subunits; Stage 2: the breakdown of simple subunits to acetyl CoA, accompanied by the production of limited amounts of NADH and ATP; Stage 3: the complete oxidation of acetyl CoA to CO_2 and H_2O, accompanied by the production of large amounts of NADH, $FADH_2$ and thereby most of the cell's ATP. Notice that: Stage 1 occurs in the gut; Stage 2 begins in the cytosol and is completed in the mitochondria; and all of Stage 3 occurs in the mitochondria.

We will now look at these three pathways more closely. For some of you the chemical reactions may look formidable; or you may enjoy following them through. We will need to refer to some of the details given in boxes, because this will help you to understand the processes involved.

4.2.5   Glycolysis

The first pathway involved in the breakdown of glucose is called the glycolytic pathway or **glycolysis**; this takes place in the cytosol. Glycolysis involves a stepwise conversion of glucose to a substance called *pyruvate*. Each step in the conversion is catalysed by a different enzyme. The reactions (which you do *not* need to memorize) are shown in full in Box 4.2. For each molecule of glucose entering the glycolytic pathway, there is a net formation at the end of the pathway of two molecules of ATP, two molecules of NADH and two molecules of pyruvate.

Box 4.2   Glycolysis (the glycolytic pathway)

The first pathway in the catabolism of glucose is known as glycolysis. This is a sequence of reactions by which each molecule of glucose (C-6) is converted into two molecules of pyruvate (C-3).

Note that three of the 10 reactions which make up this sequence (those numbered 1, 3 and 10)

are irreversible. This means that, in most cells, the route from glucose to pyruvate is always one-way, so glucose cannot be synthesized from pyruvate. However, some cell types which have appropriate enzymes can bypass the three irreversible reactions, and so produce glucose from pyruvate. (The relevance of this glucose synthesis will become clear later in the chapter.)

The first reaction in the glycolytic pathway is the conversion of glucose into a molecule called glucose 6-phosphate:

$$\text{glucose} + \text{ATP} \longrightarrow \text{glucose 6-phosphate} + \text{ADP}$$

This reaction is catalysed by an enzyme called *hexokinase* (or, in liver cells, a very similar enzyme called *glucokinase*) and actually uses up a molecule of ATP; a phosphate group is transferred from ATP to the carbon-6 position of the glucose molecule – Figure 4.1 shows the carbon atom numbers. (The addition of a phosphate group to a molecule is called *phosphorylation*; phosphorylation reactions are very important in biological systems.) This first reaction is of particular importance because glucose 6-phosphate cannot pass out of cells. Furthermore, in most cells the reaction is irreversible; thus once converted to glucose 6-phosphate, glucose is effectively trapped within the cell. It is only in liver cells and epithelial cells of the kidney (and also the intestine) that the enzyme necessary for the conversion of glucose 6-phosphate back to glucose occurs. Later we will look at the significance of this *reversal* of glycolysis in the maintenance of blood glucose levels.

How are two molecules of pyruvate formed from a single glucose molecule? You will remember that glucose is a *hexose*, i.e it contains six carbon atoms (Figure 4.1). Pyruvate, on the other hand, contains only three carbon atoms. During glycolysis each glucose molecule undergoes a stepwise conversion into another 6-carbon molecule (called fructose 1,6-bisphosphate). This molecule is then split into two molecules, each containing three carbon atoms. The split occurs at the reaction numbered 4 in Box 4.2. The two molecules formed after this reaction both continue along the glycolytic pathway.

You have seen that not all the reactions of the glycolytic pathway generate ATP, and indeed, that some of them, such as the conversion of glucose to glucose 6-phosphate, actually *use* ATP. So how is ATP generated? Look again at Box 4.2, and you will see that later in the pathway there are two reactions (7 and 10) in which ATP is formed.

❑   How many molecules of ATP will be formed at each of these steps for a single molecule of glucose entering the pathway?

■   Two ATP molecules will be formed at each step, because both of the molecules formed by the splitting of the 6-carbon molecule into two 3-carbon molecules (at step 4) continue along the glycolytic pathway.

So, for each molecule of glucose that enters the glycolytic pathway, four molecules of ATP are formed (two each at steps 7 and 10). However, since two molecules of ATP are used (one each at steps 1 and 3), there is a *net* formation of two ATP molecules for each glucose molecule entering the pathway.

On further inspection of Box 4.2, you will notice that the phosphate group which combines with ADP to form ATP at steps 7 and 10 comes from the substrate (Book 1, Chapter 3) of that particular reaction. This type of ATP formation is hence called **substrate level phosphorylation**. (The other, very important type of phosphorylation, oxidative phosphorylation, was introduced in Figure 4.4 and is discussed in detail later.)

In addition to the formation of ATP and pyruvate, another very important transformation, that of the coenzyme NAD^+ to its reduced form, NADH, occurs during glycolysis, at step 6 of the pathway. For each molecule of glucose entering the pathway, two molecules of NADH are formed (because two 3-carbon molecules are produced from each glucose molecule). Each NAD^+ reacts with two hydrogen atoms released by the oxidation and phosphorylation of the intermediate molecule at step 6. The two hydrogen atoms removed from the substrate can be considered as two hydrogen ions (H^+) and two electrons (e^-). In the process of gaining these two electrons some of the energy from the substrate is transferred to the NAD^+ molecule; NAD^+ is regenerated from NADH later, when it transfers this pair of electrons to an *electron carrier*. (Notice that both electrons but only one of the hydrogen ions combine with the NAD^+– the 'spare' H^+ is free in solution: Box 4.1.)

$$NAD^+ + 2H \text{ (from substrate)} \longrightarrow NADH + H^+$$

Some of the energy released by the oxidation of the intermediates in the glycolytic pathway is thus carried by NADH. NADH molecules give up these electrons, and *hence this additional energy*, in the last of the three pathways involved in glucose breakdown, which (not surprisingly) is called the *electron transport chain* – to be described shortly.

So, to recap, during glycolysis, for each glucose molecule entering the pathway, two molecules each of ATP and NADH are formed in addition to two molecules of pyruvate. The pathway can thus be summarized in a simplified flow diagram (Figure 4.5). Note also that the rate of glycolysis, and hence the amounts of glucose broken down and of products formed, is controlled by feedback inhibition of enzymes early on in the pathway, as described in Book 1, Chapter 3. In this way, appropriate amounts of ATP are made for the needs of each individual cell.

There is one more point that needs to be made about the reactions of the glycolytic pathway. This is that many, but not all of the reactions are reversible. In certain tissues, the non-reversible reactions can be bypassed, thereby enabling glucose *synthesis* to take place. This is of importance in the regulation of blood glucose levels, which we will come to shortly.

4.2.6 The link reaction and lactate formation

Pyruvate formed during glycolysis has two alternative fates. In the presence of oxygen (i.e. under aerobic conditions), it is converted, in the mitochondria, by the so-called link reaction to a molecule known as acetyl coenzyme A (usually abbreviated to acetyl CoA). It is called the 'link reaction' because it

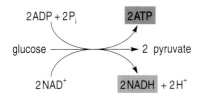

Figure 4.5 Summary diagram of glycolysis – the first of the three consecutive pathways by which glucose is catabolized.

Box 4.3   Alternative fates of pyruvate: the link reaction and lactate formation

The fate of pyruvate, the end-product of glycolysis, depends on the availability of oxygen in the cell. In the absence of oxygen (i.e. under anaerobic conditions), pyruvate is reduced by NADH to *lactate*, thereby regenerating the NAD^+ required to allow glycolysis to continue (used in reaction 6, Box 4.2). When oxygen is present, (i.e. under aerobic conditions), pyruvate (C-3) is oxidized further, to acetyl CoA, in the *link reaction*. In this reaction, NAD^+ is reduced to NADH and an atom of carbon is lost as CO_2. The acetyl CoA is further catabolized via the TCA cycle.

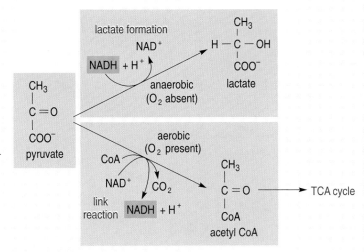

serves to connect two consecutive metabolic pathways. In this reaction, one carbon atom is lost from the pyruvate molecule, as CO_2, and the remaining 2-carbon molecule unit (known as an acetyl group) joins with CoA. At the same time, one molecule of NAD^+ is reduced to NADH. The acetyl CoA then enters the *TCA cycle*, the second of the three pathways involved in glucose catabolism (see below). This is what occurs in most cells. However, under anaerobic conditions (i.e. if oxygen is *not* present) – for example, in muscle during vigorous exercise – pyruvate is instead converted to lactate; this is a reduction reaction so NAD^+ is regenerated in the process. We return to this later. (The link reaction and the reduction of pyruvate to lactate are both shown in Box 4.3.)

Some microbes, such as yeasts, regenerate NADH by converting pyruvate to alcohol (C_2H_5OH) and carbon dioxide in the absence of oxygen. This process is known as *fermentation*.

4.2.7   The TCA cycle

If you look back to Figure 4.4, you will see that the second pathway in the production of energy from glucose takes place in the interior of the mitochondria, and is called the **TCA cycle**. (TCA stands for 'tricarboxylic acid', meaning an acid with three carboxyl, –COOH, groups; the cycle was so named because some of the intermediates in the cycle are tricarboxylic acids.). It is also called the *citric acid cycle* (citric acid is one of the tricarboxylic acids in the cycle) or the *Krebs cycle* (after the scientist Hans Krebs, who worked out the details of the reactions of the cycle). You have seen that the molecule that enters the TCA cycle is acetyl CoA. This molecule can also be produced from fatty acids, which can therefore also contribute to energy production via the TCA cycle. Box 4.4 shows the iterative sequence of reactions by which fatty acids are catabolized to acetyl CoA, and the calculation of the associated ATP yield; you do *not* need to memorize this information.

Box 4.4   Catabolism of fatty acids to acetyl CoA

The first step in the catabolism of a fatty acid is its 'activation' by linking to coenzyme A, a reaction in which energy as ATP is consumed (step 1). (Notice that the ATP molecule is split into AMP, adenosine *mono*phosphate, and two P_i units – not ADP and one P_i, which is much more common.) The fatty acyl CoA is oxidized by successive removal of pairs of H atoms to FAD and NAD^+ (steps 2 and 3). The molecule is then split by reaction with a further CoA at the second carbon atom back from the original acyl carbon, resulting in the formation of an acyl CoA that is two carbon atoms shorter than the original fatty acid substrate and a molecule of acetyl CoA (step 4). The former is further catabolized via successive repeats of steps 2–4; the latter goes on to be broken down completely via the TCA cycle. Because it is the CH_2 group two positions back from the end carbon, i.e. at the beta (β) position, that becomes oxidized (to C=O), the sequence of reactions in steps 2–4 is often referred to as *b-oxidation*. You can see that fatty acid catabolism yields very large amounts of energy. For the complete catabolism of the C_{18} fatty acid shown, there will be 8 $FADH_2$ and 8 NADH plus 9 acetyl CoA produced; each of the latter will yield 1 $FADH_2$ and 3 NADH via the TCA cycle, a total of 17 $FADH_2$ + 35 NADH, which will give $(17 \times 2) + (35 \times 3) = 139$ ATP molecules via oxidative phosphorylation (see later, in Section 4.2.8 for the relationship between $FADH_2$ and NADH, and ATP production). The initial activation of the fatty acid molecule consumes the equivalent of 2 ATPs, and 9 ATPs are produced by substrate level phosphorylation during the 9 turns of the TCA cycle, thus making a net yield of: $139 - 2 + 9 = 146$ ATPs.

As its name implies, the TCA cycle is a cyclic series of chemical reactions. The acetyl group of the acetyl CoA produced from pyruvate via the link reaction (or from fatty acids as shown in Box 4.4) combines with a 4-carbon molecule, called *oxaloacetate*, to form *citrate*. This 6-carbon molecule is then sequentially transformed via the reactions of the cycle, resulting in the regeneration of oxaloacetate. Two carbon atoms are lost during the cycle, as carbon dioxide (CO_2). Once again, each reaction in the TCA cycle involves a different enzyme. The details are shown in Box 4.5.

You are not expected to learn all the steps in the TCA cycle. The important points to remember are that, for each turn of the cycle, three molecules of NAD^+ are reduced to NADH and one molecule of FAD is reduced to $FADH_2$. Like NADH, $FADH_2$ carries a pair of electrons, and thus acts as an energy carrier. In addition, one molecule of guanosine triphosphate (GTP, a molecule similar to ATP, but containing the base guanine instead of adenine) is formed from guanosine diphosphate (GDP) and P_i (in step 6 of the cycle, Box 4.5). GTP can also transfer energy in a similar way to ATP, although it is much less widely used than ATP. However, as shown in step 6, GTP can also readily transfer a phosphate group to ADP, to generate ATP, so its formation during the TCA cycle can effectively be considered as equivalent to the formation of ATP. The net result of the TCA cycle is summarized diagrammatically in Figure 4.6.

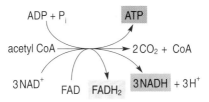

Figure 4.6   Summary diagram of the TCA cycle.

❑   For the complete catabolism of each molecule of glucose entering the glycolytic pathway, how many turns of the TCA cycle are required?

▓   Two. During glycolysis each glucose molecule is converted to two pyruvate molecules. Each of these pyruvate molecules is then converted to acetyl CoA. Thus two molecules of acetyl CoA enter the TCA cycle for each molecule of glucose entering the glycolytic pathway.

You have seen that acetyl CoA entering the TCA cycle can be derived from either glucose or fatty acids. Derivatives of some amino acids can also contribute to the TCA cycle. For example, the amino acid alanine can be converted into pyruvate, which can then be converted to acetyl CoA. Other amino acids derivatives can enter the TCA cycle at a later stage. For those of you who are interested in the details, some examples are given in Box 4.6.

Box 4.5   The TCA cycle

Acetyl groups (carried by coenzyme A as acetyl CoA molecules), produced by catabolism of glucose and fatty acids (and also some amino acids) are catabolized to CO_2 via a cyclic sequence of reactions called the TCA cycle. The acetyl group (C-2) combines with a molecule of oxaloacetate (C-4) to form a citrate molecule (C-6). The reactions that follow involve oxidation (removal of hydrogen atoms

in the formation of NADH and $FADH_2$) and molecular cleavage (loss of two C atoms as CO_2), and result in the regeneration of oxaloacetate, ready to start the cycle again.

Note: We show carboxylic acid groups in their ionized, i.e. *carboxylate*, form; hence the use of $-COO^-$, *not* $-COOH$, in this and subsequent figures. The molecular structure of the $-COO^-$ group is shown on the right.

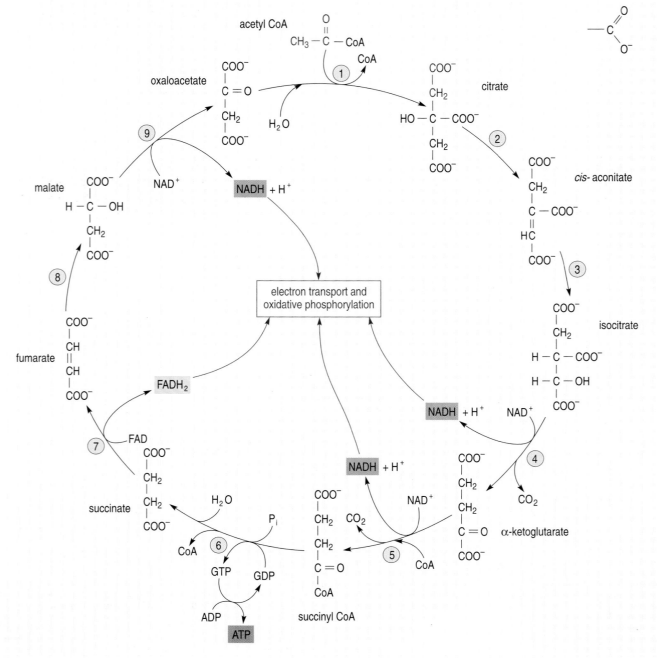

Box 4.6   Some reactions of amino acid catabolism

Part 1

The common types of reaction in which amino acids are broken down are *transamination* and *oxidative deamination*. These processes are important because they allow entry of amino acids into the energy-producing pathways.

Transamination involves the transfer of the amino ($-NH_2$) group from an amino acid to a so-called *keto acid*. In the equation below, R^1 and R^2 are different R

groups (Book 1, Chapter 3). Note that we have shown amino acids in their ionized form – in Book 1, Chapter 3 we showed them in the unionized form. (See opposite.) The former is the more accurate represent-ation, but the latter is generally used for simplicity and is quite acceptable.

$$R - CH - COO^-$$
$$|$$
$$^+NH_3$$

$$R - CH - COOH$$
$$|$$
$$NH_2$$

transamination

$$R^1 - CH - COO^- \; + \; R^2 - \overset{\overset{\displaystyle O}{\|}}{C} - COO^- \; \rightleftharpoons \; R^1 - \overset{\overset{\displaystyle O}{\|}}{C} - COO^- \; + \; R^2 - CH - COO^-$$
$$\quad\quad | \qquad\qquad\qquad\qquad\qquad\qquad\qquad\qquad\qquad\qquad\qquad | $$
$$\quad\;\; ^+NH_3 \qquad\qquad\qquad\qquad\qquad\qquad\qquad\qquad\qquad\qquad\; ^+NH_3$$

amino acid 1   keto acid 2   keto acid 1   amino acid 2

In oxidative deamination the amino group is removed, as ammonia (NH_3), and a molecule of NAD^+ (or the related molecule, $NADP^+$, which is NAD^+ with an extra phosphate group) is reduced in

the process. The ammonia is excreted at the kidneys, mainly after conversion to urea. Notice that, in solution, NH_3 molecules combine with H^+ ions to form *ammonium* ions (NH_4^+).

oxidative deamination

$$R - CH - COO^- \; + \; H_2O \; + \; NAD(P)^+ \longrightarrow \; R - \overset{\overset{\displaystyle O}{\|}}{C} - COO^- \; + \; NH_4^+ \; + \; NAD(P)H \; + \; H^+$$
$$\quad\; | $$
$$\;\; ^+NH_3$$

amino acid   keto acid   ammonium ion

Part 2

The figure opposite shows two examples of keto acid production from the corresponding amino acids, by transamination (alanine → pyruvate) or oxidative deamination (glutamate → α-ketoglutarate). Pyruvate can be catabolized via the link reaction to acetyl CoA which can then be broken down completely via the TCA cycle; α-ketoglutarate can be broken down even more directly, as it is itself an intermediate in the TCA cycle (see Box 4.5).

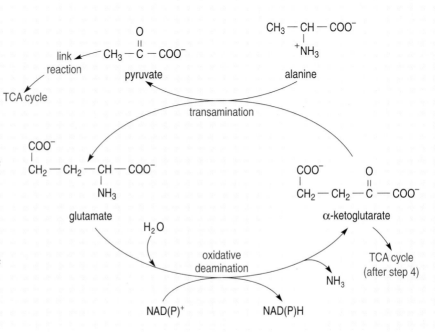

4.2.8 Electron transport coupled to oxidative phosphorylation

As you have seen, relatively little ATP is produced by glycolysis and the TCA cycle (Figures 4.5 and 4.6).

❑　　　For each molecule of glucose catabolized, how many molecules of ATP are produced by glycolysis and the TCA cycle?

■　　　Four. Two ATP molecules per glucose are formed during glycolysis; and catabolism of the *two* acetyl CoA molecules produced from each molecule of glucose yields a further two ATPs.

Much of the energy released by the breakdown of glucose is carried by the reduced coenzymes NADH and $FADH_2$. It is in the final pathway involved in the production of energy from glucose and other organic molecules that this energy is 'harnessed' to produce more ATP. This ATP production pathway (i.e. ADP *phosphorylation*), which is coupled to the *oxidation* of (transfer of electrons from) reduced coenzymes, is called **oxidative phosphorylation** – in contrast to the substrate level phosphorylations of glycolysis and the TCA cycle. Oxidative phosphorylation takes place at the inner membrane of the mitochondria. For each molecule of glucose catabolized, oxidative phosphorylation produces 32 molecules of ATP. This is why the mitochondria are often referred to as the 'powerhouses' of the cell.

Oxidative phosphorylation generates ATP as a result of the reoxidation of the NADH and $FADH_2$ produced during glycolysis and the TCA cycle (and also in substantial quantities by fatty acid catabolism – Box 4.4). The electrons carried by these two reduced coenzymes are transferred along a chain of molecules (which includes several iron-containing proteins called *cytochromes*). These are present as molecular complexes on the inner mitochondrial membrane. The complete series of electron carriers is known as the **electron transport chain** and the final electron acceptor in this chain is oxygen. The hydrogen ions also released from the coenzymes (remember each H atom is H^+ with an electron, e^-) remain in the mitochondria and finally join with the oxygen which has gained electrons, resulting in the formation of water, as summarized in the equation below. This reaction is catalysed by the last electron carrier complex in the chain, called cytochrome oxidase.

$$O_2 + 4H^+ + 4e^- \longrightarrow 2H_2O$$

How is it that electron transport is able to fuel ATP production? The transfer of electrons along the chain of carrier molecules involves a sequential reduction in *energy*; the electrons effectively pass down an *energy gradient*. A proportion of the energy released as they do so is used to generate ATP. In common with all energy transfer processes, some of the energy is also released as heat. The process of electron transport coupled to oxidative phosphorylation is summarized diagrammatically in Figure 4.7.

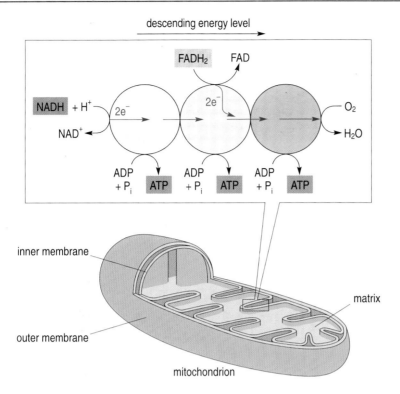

Figure 4.7   Electron transport coupled to oxidative phosphorylation. This process takes place at the inner mitochondrial membrane. Each coloured circle represents a different electron-carrier complex in the electron transport chain; the last one, which transfers the electrons to oxygen, is called cytochome oxidase. ATP synthesis at each of the three complexes is catalysed by molecules of a membrane-bound enzyme complex called ATP synthetase (not shown).

So, how do we arrive at the figure of 32 molecules of ATP generated by oxidative phosphorylation for each glucose molecule entering the glycolytic pathway? First, consider the reactions that take place in the mitochondria.

❑   Which series of reactions in glucose catabolism take place in the mitochondria?

■   The link reaction, the TCA cycle, and electron transport coupled to oxidative phosphorylation.

❑   For each glucose molecule that enters the glycolytic pathway, how many and which coenzyme molecules are reduced in the link reaction and in the TCA cycle?

■   For each glucose molecule, two molecules of NAD^+ are reduced during the link reaction; six molecules of NAD^+ and two of FAD are reduced during the TCA cycle.

Thus a total of eight molecules of NADH and two of $FADH_2$ are produced in the mitochondria for each glucose molecule completely catabolized. If you look again at Figure 4.7, you will see that the two types of coenzyme enter the electron transport chain at different points (corresponding to different 'energy levels'), so that each molecule of NADH produces *three* molecules of ATP, while each molecule of $FADH_2$ produces *two* ATP molecules.

❑   From the above information, work out how many molecules of ATP will be formed from eight NADH and two FADH$_2$ molecules.

■   Eight NADH molecules will generate $8 \times 3 = 24$ molecules of ATP. Two FADH$_2$ molecules will generate $2 \times 2 = 4$ molecules of ATP. Thus $24 + 4 = 28$ molecules of ATP will be formed by the reoxidation of the reduced coenzymes produced during the link reaction and the TCA cycle.

So, the link and TCA cycle reactions, which take place in the mitochondria, generate a total of 28 molecules of ATP. The remaining 4 ATP molecules produced by oxidative phosphorylation come from the 2 NADH formed during glycolysis, which, you will remember, takes place in the cytosol. Cytosolic NADH cannot pass across the mitochondrial membrane directly into the interior of the mitochondria. Instead, the electrons carried by this NADH are transferred by 'shuttle' molecules, which we will not describe here, to FADH$_2$ in the mitochondria. The two molecules of FADH$_2$ thus formed will then generate a further 4 ATP molecules. This gives us the total of 32 ATP molecules produced by oxidative phosphorylation for each molecule of glucose catabolized aerobically. This is summarized in Table 4.1.

Table 4.1   ATP formation by the different pathways in the catabolism of glucose.

Reaction or pathway	ATP formed by substrate level phosphorylation	Coenzyme molecules reduced per glucose molecule	ATP formed by oxidative phosphorylation	Total ATP (i.e. by oxidative and substrate level phosphorylation)
glycolysis (cytosol)	2	2 NADH → 2 FADH$_2$ (mitochondria)	4	6
link reaction (mitochondria)		2 NADH	6	6
TCA cycle (mitochondria)	2	6 NADH 2 FADH$_2$	18 4 } 22	24
Total ATP formed	4		32	36

To recap, glucose is broken down by a series of metabolic pathways known as glycolysis, then (following the link reaction) the TCA cycle and electron transport coupled to oxidative phosphorylation. The coenzymes NADH and FADH$_2$ formed via glycolysis and the TCA cycle give up electrons to oxygen via a chain of carriers and this electron transport is coupled to the production of ATP. Breakdown of a single glucose molecule results in the production of 36 ATP molecules: 2 (from glycolysis) + 2 (from the TCA cycle) + 32 (from oxidative phosphorylation). Fatty acids, glycerol and some amino acids can also be converted into molecules which can enter the TCA cycle. These processes are summarized in Figure 4.8.

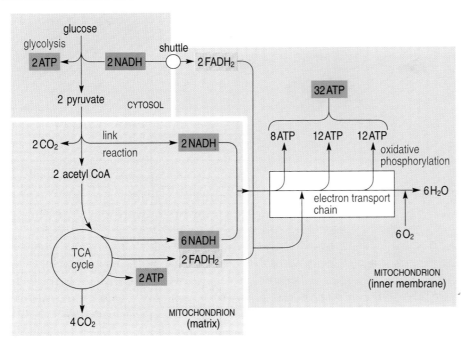

Figure 4.8   Summary of the consecutive pathways involved in the production of ATP from glucose, showing where they occur in the cell and also the yields of reduced coenzymes and ATP: glycolysis (in the cytosol); the link reaction and the TCA cycle (in the mitochondrial matrix); electron transport coupled to oxidative phosphorylation (at the mitochondrial inner membrane).

$$C_6H_{12}O_6 + 6\,O_2 + 36\,ADP + 36\,P_i \longrightarrow 6\,CO_2 + 6\,H_2O + 36\,ATP$$

ATP is generated in all cells, and the energy released when ATP is broken down to ADP and P_i is used to fuel chemical reactions in the cell. However, only a part of the energy released upon breakdown of each molecule of ATP is used to drive biochemical reactions; the remainder is released as heat. When glucose is catabolized to carbon dioxide and water, by no means all the energy stored in the glucose molecule is used to produce ATP; some 60% of this energy is released as heat. In fact, *all* processes in which energy transfer occurs are associated with loss of a proportion of that energy as heat. We will return to consider the physiological implications of metabolic heat generation in the second part of this chapter.

4.2.9   Energy metabolism in skeletal muscle

So far, we have considered the supply of energy as ATP from a general point of view, for a 'stereotype' cell. In most cases, the amounts of ATP formed in each cell are appropriate to the energy needs of that cell; the metabolic reactions involved are regulated by feedback inhibition (see Book 1, Chapter 3). However, in skeletal muscle (Book 2, Chapters 2 and 4), where ATP plays an essential role in muscle contraction, sudden and extreme changes in ATP demand can occur. A sudden demand for high levels of ATP for muscle contraction cannot be rapidly met by the metabolic pathways described in the previous section, so an alternative source of ATP is used.

This source of ATP is a molecule called **creatine phosphate**, which is formed, from creatine and ATP, by the action of an enzyme called creatine kinase. (Notice that phosphorylation reactions are catalysed by so-called *kinase* enzymes. Another example is hexokinase, which catalyses the first reaction in the glycolytic pathway – Box 4.2.) The phosphorylation of creatine is reversible:

$$\text{creatine} + \text{ATP} \rightleftharpoons \text{creatine phosphate} + \text{ADP}$$

So, when skeletal muscle is at rest, and levels of ATP are greater than those of ADP, the above reaction is driven to the right. When there is a sudden demand for ATP, ATP levels drop, and the reaction moves to the left, producing more ATP for use in muscle contraction. This source of ATP is usually sufficient for the initial few seconds of muscle activity, by which time the rate of ATP formation (by glycolysis, the TCA cycle and oxidative phosphorylation) is increased, and can match the demands of the active muscle. Most of the energy required for very brief exercise, such as jumping or initial lifting of a weight, comes from creatine phosphate breakdown. However, if muscle activity is intense and longer lasting, i.e the muscle is performing vigorous exercise, another factor comes into play, and that is an insufficiency of oxygen supply.

During longer-lasting intense exercise, the increased demands for oxygen cannot always be met by increased ventilation, so skeletal muscle cells cannot continue to respire aerobically.

❑　　How will energy (ATP) production be affected by anaerobic conditions?

■　　The link reaction, in which pyruvate is converted to acetyl CoA, requires oxygen to reoxidize the NADH produced. In the absence of oxygen, the NADH instead reacts with pyruvate, converting (i.e. reducing) it to lactate and regenerating the oxidized form of the coenzyme, NAD^+. Therefore no acetyl CoA, the 'substrate' of the TCA cycle, is produced. The electron transport chain and hence oxidative phosphorylation also require oxygen. So, in anaerobic conditions, the link reaction, TCA cycle and oxidative phosphorylation do not operate and glycolysis is the only source of ATP.

What is special about skeletal muscle that enables it to continue to perform intense activity in the absence of oxygen, when the major ATP-generating pathways are inoperative? The answer is that skeletal muscle contains reserves of glycogen – the storage form of glucose – and as long as sufficient glycogen, appropriate enzymes and NAD^+ are present, enough ATP can be generated by glycolysis alone. (You will learn about how glucose is released from glycogen later in this chapter.) The formation of lactate from pyruvate, which occurs under anaerobic conditions, serves to regenerate the NAD^+ necessary for continued glycolysis. Note that only short bursts of vigorous exercise, such as a 100 m sprint, can be sustained in this way. This is because the build-up of lactate and H^+ ions produced by the exercising muscle leads to a lowering of blood pH (i.e. the blood becomes more acidic). This accumulation of lactate is what causes the feeling of discomfort which occurs during, and for some time after, vigorous exercise and is known as *muscle fatigue*. Endurance activity, such as long-distance running, involves mainly *aerobic* muscle respiration. Since ATP is generated more slowly by aerobic respiration than by the creatine phosphate system and anaerobic respiration, the pace of endurance activity is relatively slow.

At the end of a period of vigorous exercise, creatine phosphate reserves must be replenished and the accumulated lactate must be metabolized. Thus there is an increased demand for oxygen after exercise, or, to put it another way, the *oxygen debt* (Chapter 2) must be repaid. This is why we continue to breathe heavily for some time after intense exercise.

Energy is constantly required to drive the chemical reactions that are continually going on in our bodies. You have already seen that ATP is a very short-lived molecule, and must be manufactured continuously, so it is important that molecules used to generate ATP are available all the time. Since food is not eaten constantly, this means that there must be some control of the supply of energy-providing molecules. As you have seen, the main molecule used to provide energy is glucose. The way in which glucose is supplied to the tissues is thus of great importance. This is what we turn to next.

Summary of Section 4.2

1   The main molecule from which energy is generated is glucose – the stepwise catabolism of glucose releases energy stored in the bonds holding its component atoms together. Some of the energy released by these catabolic reactions is used in the formation of ATP. This is a short-lived intermediate molecule which acts as the cell's energy currency; the breakdown of ATP is coupled to anabolic (energy-using) reactions and other energy-requiring cellular processes.

2   Glucose is broken down by a series of three consecutive metabolic pathways: first by glycolysis, which takes place in the cytosol; then, after the link reaction, by the TCA cycle, which takes place in the mitochondria; and finally by electron transport coupled to oxidative phosphorylation, which takes place at the inner mitochondrial membrane. For each molecule of glucose completely catabolized, 36 molecules of ATP are formed.

3   Other organic molecules (e.g. fatty acids, glycerol and certain amino acids) can be converted into molecules that can enter the TCA cycle and so be used to produce energy.

4   Skeletal muscle has a special requirement for a rapid supply of ATP to drive muscle contraction. This is met by the release of ATP from stores of creatine phosphate, built up during periods of rest. During short bursts of intense exercise, skeletal muscle respires anaerobically, i.e. it derives energy from glycolysis alone. During endurance exercise, skeletal muscle respires aerobically.

4.3 Energy storage and supply

4.3.1 Storage of energy-producing molecules

You have seen that glucose is the molecule that is transferred around the body in the circulation as a source of energy. However, since cells require a continuous supply of energy, if glucose were simply transported throughout the body after absorption from the digestive system and used as required, there would be a serious problem.

❑ Can you think what this might be?

■ There would be a shortage of glucose between meals; this would result in periods during which blood glucose levels would be very low, for example, overnight.

A steady supply of glucose is essential to an extremely important group of cells. These are the neurons of the central nervous system which, unlike other cell types, can utilize *only* glucose to provide energy (except under very rare circumstances) and do not store glucose. Hence these cells rely on a continuous supply of glucose from the circulation.

Clearly, glucose is present at higher levels in the circulation when it is being absorbed from the gut after meals; this is known as the **absorptive state**. An average meal usually takes about four hours to be fully digested and absorbed. During the **post-absorptive state** glucose is *not* entering the circulation from the gut, but is, instead, supplied from energy stores laid down during the absorptive state.

In fact, the levels of glucose in the bloodstream are regulated, i.e. held within a narrow range, and do not rise dramatically after a meal. In an individual who has not eaten for several hours, the blood glucose level will be typically in the range 80–90 mg per 100 ml of blood. After a meal, this level rises, but seldom to over 140 mg per 100 ml, even if a large amount of carbohydrate has been eaten. Moreover, blood glucose levels return to their typical values within about two and a half hours after a meal, even though absorption from the gut is continuing. Elevation of glucose levels above this range is known as **hyperglycaemia**; reduced levels (below about 70 mg per 100 ml) are known as **hypoglycaemia**. Between meals, as the levels of glucose in the bloodstream drop, glucose is rapidly released from the body's energy stores. Before going on to deal with the control of glucose storage and release, it is necessary to look at how and where glucose is stored.

Glucose that is not utilized immediately to provide energy is converted into other types of molecule for storage. One of these storage molecules is **glycogen**, a polysaccharide made up of many individual glucose units linked together. The other main type of storage molecules are triacylglycerols (fats), which can be synthesized from glucose. Although both kinds of molecule can be made in most cell types, stores of glycogen or fats are laid down in three main tissues: glycogen is stored in the liver and skeletal muscle, whereas fat is stored in **adipose tissue**, which is made up of *adipocytes* (fat cells). We will now go on to describe the fate of ingested glucose in these tissues during the absorptive state.

❑   Polysaccharides are digested into monosaccharides in the gut. What happens to these simple sugars after digestion?

■   Monosaccharides are absorbed into the circulation via the small blood vessels in the villi. These vessels link with the hepatic portal vein, which passes to the liver.

The liver is an organ with many different roles. These not only include exocrine functions, some of which you have already met in the previous chapter, but also some metabolic and excretory functions and even some other roles that are endocrine in nature.

❑   Can you recall the exocrine function of the liver in digestive processes?

■   The liver produces bile, which is involved in the digestion of fats.

The many functions of the liver are summarized in Table 4.2.

Table 4.2   Functions of the liver.

Digestive	• synthesizes and secretes bile salts • secretes bicarbonate ions
Metabolic	*During the absorptive state*: • converts glucose into glycogen and triacylglycerols (fats) • converts amino acids to fatty acids • synthesizes triacylglycerols and secretes these in a modified form as lipoproteins *During the post-absorptive state*: • produces glucose from glycogen and other sources • converts fatty acids into ketones during fasting • produces urea (from amino acid catabolism) and releases it into the bloodstream *Cholesterol metabolism*: • synthesizes cholesterol and releases it into the bloodstream • converts plasma cholesterol into bile salts
Plasma formation	• produces plasma clotting factors • produces plasma proteins (e.g. globulins, albumin, lipoproteins, binding proteins for hormones and trace elements)
Excretory	• destroys old red blood cells • secretes bilirubin and other bile pigments • excretes many unwanted exogenous molecules • transforms endogenous and exogenous organic molecules (see Chapter 5)
Endocrine	• secretes insulin-like growth factors (see Book 1, Chapter 6) in response to growth hormone • produces erythropoietin (a hormone important in the formation of red blood cells – see Chapter 5) • contributes to the activation of vitamin D (see Chapter 3) • forms tri-iodothyronine from thyroxine (these are the thyroid hormones – see Book 2, Chapter 2)

The liver has a profound effect on the molecular composition of blood. On entering the liver, via the hepatic portal vein from the intestine, the blood flows through numerous small channels (called *sinusoids*) which maximize the contact of circulating molecules with the liver cells (also known as *hepatocytes*). This arrangement allows ample opportunity for exchange of substances between the circulating blood and the hepatocytes.

During the absorptive state, some of the glucose reaching the liver in the hepatic portal vein is taken up by the liver cells. The remainder stays in the circulation and is taken up by all other cells in the body and used to provide energy, as described in Section 4.2.1 above. In the liver, the glucose has several fates: some of it is used immediately as a source of energy by the liver cells, but any that is surplus to immediate requirements is converted into glycogen and triacylglycerols. These processes are summarized in Figure 4.9.

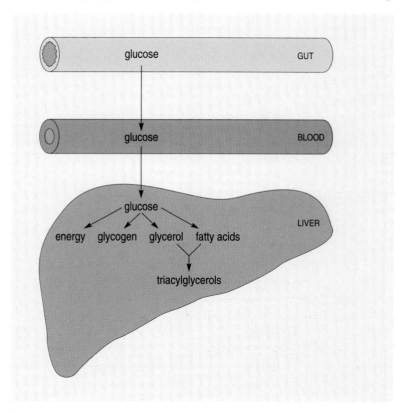

Figure 4.9 Fate of glucose taken up from the circulation by the liver.

The glycogen is then stored in the liver, but most of the triacylglycerols are exported to be stored in other parts of the body in adipose tissue. Before being exported from the liver, the triacylglycerols are assembled, together with proteins, into aggregates. These aggregates contain much more lipid that protein and so, since fat is less dense than protein (remember that it floats), are called **very low density lipoproteins (VLDL)**. The VLDL are secreted by the liver cells into the bloodstream.

The VLDL in the circulation are too large to penetrate the walls of capillaries. Instead, they are broken down to release fatty acids by an enzyme on the lumenal surface of the the endothelial cells lining the capillaries (Chapter 2). This enzyme, called **lipoprotein lipase**, is especially abundant in the blood vessels that supply adipose tissue, so much of the fatty acid released from the VLDL diffuses into the adipocytes. Once in the adipose tissue, the fatty acids are used to form triacylglycerols once more. This process is summarized in Figure 4.10.

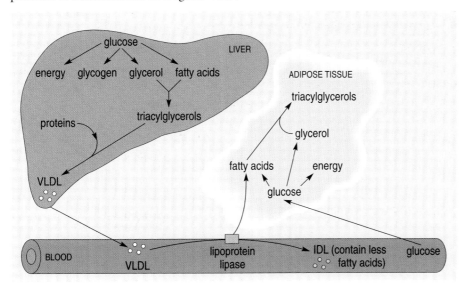

Figure 4.10   VLDL are produced in the liver and enter the circulation. Fatty acids from the VLDL are taken up into adipose tissue and converted to triacylglycerols. The lipoproteins that remain in the circulation after this uptake contain a smaller proportion of fatty acid; they are therefore less dense and for this reason are called intermediate density lipoproteins (IDL).The uptake of circulating glucose by adipose tissue is also shown.

Adipocytes, like all cells of the body, also take up glucose during the absorptive state. Again, they use some of this glucose for their own immediate energy needs; the remainder is converted, by the action of enzymes within the cells, to glycerol and fatty acids, which are then combined to form triacylglycerols (Figure 4.10). Adipose tissue, then, stores both fats produced from glucose within the tissue itself and those that are synthesized by and exported to it from the liver.

The third main storage site for molecules derived from glucose is skeletal muscle. You will remember that skeletal muscles are the striated muscles which produce voluntary movements of the body (Book 2, Chapters 2 and 4). Skeletal muscle forms the greatest tissue mass of the body, and is also the main consumer of glucose. However, the glucose taken up by skeletal muscle is not only used as an immediate source of energy, but is also converted to glycogen for storage. This process is summarized in Figure 4.11.

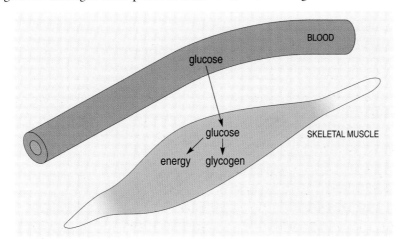

Figure 4.11   Fate of glucose taken up from the circulation by skeletal muscle.

Thus you have seen that, in addition to its immediate use as a fuel for all cells in the body during the absorptive state, glucose is converted into other molecules which are stored in the liver, adipose tissue and in skeletal muscle. Figure 4.12 summarizes these different processes.

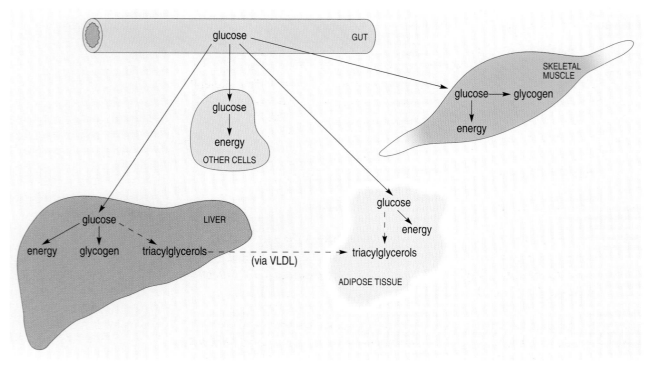

Figure 4.12 Summary diagram showing the fate of glucose entering the circulation from the gut during the absorptive state. The dashed lines indicate that several processes have been summarized on the diagram. For example, VLDL (synthesized in the liver) deliver fatty acids to the adipose tissue cells, where they are subsequently combined with glycerol to form triacylglycerols. The production of triacylglycerols from glucose in the liver and adipose tissue – shown here as a single step – occurs via the separate synthesis of glycerol and fatty acids.

4.3.2   The post-absorptive state: energy provision from stores

During the absorptive state, glucose is available to all cells, but what happens during the post-absorptive state, when no glucose is entering the circulation from the gut? As you have seen, it is essential not only that glucose is continually present in the circulation, but that glucose levels in the circulation are regulated. During the post-absorptive state, the reserves built up during the absorptive state are broken down to release glucose into the bloodstream.

❏   What molecules do you think will be broken down to produce glucose during the post-absorptive state?

■   Two important molecules which are used to produce glucose during the post-absorptive state are glycogen and triacylglycerols.

Glycogen breakdown is known as **glycogenolysis** and the breakdown of fats is known as **lipolysis** (lysis = breakdown).

The first glucose released into the circulation during the post-absorptive period, when none is being absorbed from the gut, comes from reserves of glycogen in the liver. The breakdown of glycogen and subsequent release of glucose occur fairly rapidly, but the amount of glycogen stored in the liver is only sufficient, under normal circumstances, for about four hours supply of energy. Moreover, not all the glycogen stored in the liver is actually broken down; some is retained, even during prolonged periods without food. Other reserves must therefore be tapped in order to maintain circulating glucose levels.

Skeletal muscle stores of glycogen are also broken down during the post-absorptive period. However, skeletal muscle does not have the necessary enzymes to complete the conversion of glycogen to glucose. Thus skeletal muscle glycogen cannot be used *directly* to resupply the bloodstream with glucose. Instead, skeletal muscle glycogen is converted to glucose 6-phosphate, which then enters the glycolytic pathway in the muscle cells. (If you look back to Section 4.1.2, you will see that glucose 6-phosphate is the first intermediate formed from glucose during glycolysis.)

❑   Can you recall the end-products of glycolysis?

■   The end-products of glycolysis are: pyruvate, ATP and NADH (Figure 4.5). In aerobic conditions, pyruvate is then converted by the link reaction, to acetyl CoA; in anaerobic conditions, pyruvate is reduced by NADH to lactate (Box 4.3).

Some of the pyruvate produced via glycolysis continues into the link reaction and then the TCA cycle and is thereby utilized to provide energy for the muscle. In addition, some pyruvate and lactate are released from skeletal muscle into the circulation. They are taken up by the liver and converted into glucose which is then released into the circulation and is thus made available to the rest of the body. This synthesis of glucose, from other molecules such as pyruvate (as opposed to the release of pre-existing glucose units by the splitting of polysaccharide chains) is called **gluconeogenesis**.

The quantity of glycogen stored in skeletal muscle is only roughly the same as that available in the liver. However, there is another important source of circulating glucose during the post-absorptive state: lipolysis (fat breakdown) in adipose tissue releases glycerol and fatty acids which enter the circulation. On reaching the liver, the glycerol is taken up and converted to glucose (another example of gluconeogenesis), which is then released into the bloodstream. Fatty acids, however, *cannot* be converted to glucose. You will learn how these fatty acids are used later.

One other process which contributes to the supply of glucose to the circulation during the post-absorptive state, occurring after a few hours of fasting, is the catabolism of protein. A significant amount of protein, from many cell types, but particularly muscle, can be broken down without causing cell or tissue damage. Breakdown of proteins releases amino acids, which pass to the liver, where some are converted to glucose, via intermediates known as keto acids (Box 4.6).

❑   This last source of glucose cannot be used indefinitely. Why is this?

■   Proteins play essential structural and functional roles in all cells. If protein breakdown were to continue unchecked, cells would not be able to function normally, and would eventually die.

The different ways in which glucose is supplied to the circulation in the post-absorptive state are summarized in Figure 4.13.

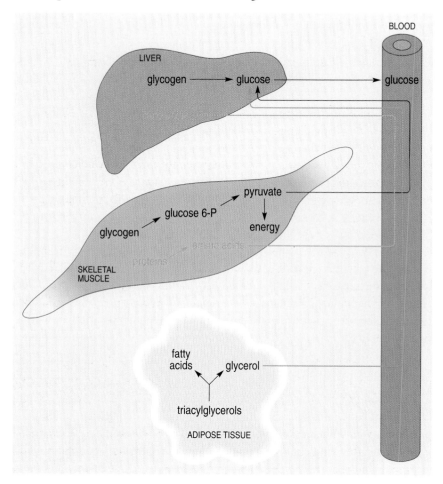

Figure 4.13   Summary diagram showing the sources of glucose entering the circulation during the post-absorptive state (in aerobic conditions).

The liver, then, plays a crucial role in the maintenance of steady levels of glucose in the bloodstream. When levels of glucose in the circulation are high, glucose is taken up and converted into glycogen and triacylglycerols. When glucose levels drop, reserves of glycogen in the liver are broken down to release glucose. Moreover, other molecules, such as pyruvate, lactate, glycerol and amino acids, released by other cell types, are taken up by liver cells and used to synthesize glucose, which is then released into the circulation. There is one other organ that can synthesize glucose in this way, and that is the kidney. However, gluconeogenesis occurs in the kidney only during prolonged fasts.

Despite these various sources of glucose, all the energy needs of the body cannot be met by gluconeogenesis and glycogenolysis alone. Another important process comes into play during the post-absorptive state, which, rather than releasing glucose into the bloodstream, has the result of *reducing the use* of glucose by many cell types. This process thus saves circulating glucose for use by the central nervous system, and is called **glucose sparing** (or fat utilization). As its name implies, this process involves the reduction of the catabolism of glucose as the main cellular source of energy. Instead, energy is derived from the breakdown of fat molecules (lipolysis).

The breakdown of each molecule of fat yields three molecules of fatty acid and one molecule of glycerol.

❑   The breakdown (digestion) of fats in the gut by pancreatic lipase results in rather different products. What are these?

■   Pancreatic lipase digests fat molecules into *two* fatty acid molecules and one monoacylglycerol molecule (i.e. removal of the fatty acid units is incomplete: one of them remains in combination with glycerol).

The fatty acids produced by cellular lipolysis are catabolized to acetyl CoA via a sequence of reactions known as β-oxidation (Box 4.4). These reactions yield large amounts of the reduced coenzymes NADH and $FADH_2$, which are used to produce ATP via oxidative phosphorylation and the electron transport chain. The acetyl CoA also produced is then further catabolized via the TCA cycle.

A proportion of the fatty acids are also released into the bloodstream; these are taken up by other cells and catabolized by β-oxidation. However, fatty acid catabolism does not occur in the cells of the central nervous system which, as we have already stressed, are dependent upon glucose. A somewhat different chemical reaction occurs in the liver; here fatty acids are metabolized to molecules called *ketones*, which are in turn released into the circulation for use by other tissues. Ketones play an important role in the provision of energy during extreme fasting or starvation. This is because, unlike fatty acids (which are bound to plasma proteins in the blood), they are free in the bloodstream and so can cross the blood–brain barrier and thus be used as an energy source by the central nervous system. These processes are summarized in Figure 4.14.

You have seen that there are a number of processes which come into play to maintain glucose levels in the circulation during the post-absorptive period, thereby conserving available glucose for use by the central nervous system. However, in extreme situations, if fasting is prolonged, changes in the metabolism of the brain can also occur, so that many brain areas utilize ketones as an additional source of energy. This conserves proteins, so that tissue damage resulting from protein breakdown is kept to a minimum.

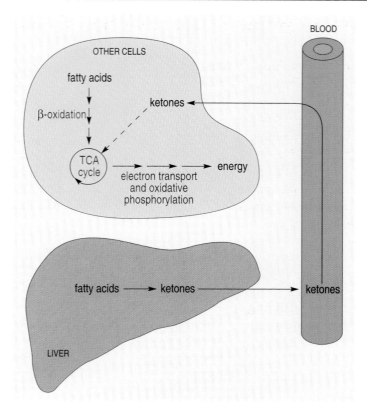

Figure 4.14 Summary diagram showing glucose sparing (fat utilization) during the post-absorptive period.

Summary of Section 4.3

1   Glucose levels in the circulation are regulated. Metabolic processes are controlled in order that appropriate glucose levels in the circulation are maintained.

2   The period during which glucose enters the bloodstream from the gut, after a meal, is known as the absorptive state. The period when glucose is *not* entering the bloodstream from the gut, but is instead released from stores laid down in the liver, skeletal muscle and adipose tissue, is referred to as the post-absorptive state.

3   During the absorptive state, glucose that is not immediately used to provide energy is converted into and stored as glycogen and triacylglycerols (fats). Glycogen is synthesized and laid down in the liver and in skeletal muscle; triacylglycerols are formed from glucose in adipose tissue cells, and also in the liver, which exports triacylglycerols to adipose tissue to be stored.

4   During the post-absorptive state, glycogen and fats are broken down (glycogenolysis and lipolysis) and in the liver there is synthesis of 'new' glucose (gluconeogenesis), which is released into the circulation. After several hours of fasting, proteins may be catabolized and used by the liver to produce glucose. During the post-absorptive state, the use of glucose by many types of cell is also reduced, and fatty acids are metabolized to provide energy.

4.4 Fate of amino acids absorbed from the gut

In the absorptive state, amino acids are absorbed from the gut and enter the circulation. Most circulating amino acids are taken up by cells and used for the synthesis of new proteins. Amino acids that are not used for protein synthesis are converted, by removal of the amino group, into *keto acids*, which can either be used to synthesize fatty acids or catabolized by entry into the TCA cycle (see Box 4.6). The amino groups ($-NH_2$) combine with a hydrogen atom to form ammonia (NH_3). Ammonia is extremely toxic at high levels; however, it is converted in the liver to the much less toxic substance, **urea**, which is excreted by the kidneys. These reactions are shown in Figure 4.15.

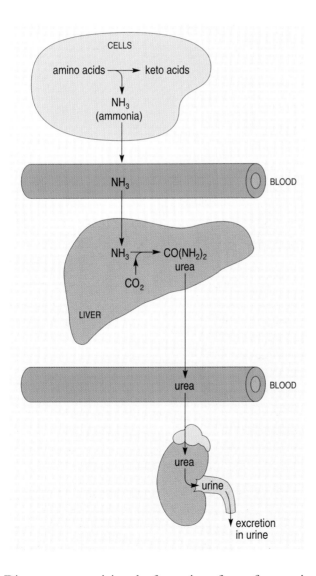

Figure 4.15   Diagram summarizing the formation of urea from amino acids and its subsequent excretion via the kidneys.

Although proteins are synthesized during the absorptive period, stores of protein are *not* laid down in the way that glycogen acts as a store of glucose. The synthesized proteins only *replace* those catabolized during previous periods of fasting between meals and those broken down as a result of the continual metabolic processes going on in cells (protein turnover – Book 1, Chapter 3). Excess amino acids are catabolized to provide energy or converted to carbohydrates (via gluconeogenesis) or to fats. It is only at times of growth, such as in childhood or during 'bodybuilding', that increases in body protein occur. As you have already learnt in Book 2, Chapter 2, hormones play an important role in the regulation of protein synthesis.

Summary of Section 4.4

1   Most amino acids absorbed from the gut are used for protein synthesis; those that are not are converted into keto acids which can be converted into fatty acids or catabolized to provide energy.

2   The amino groups released as ammonia on formation of keto acids are converted into urea, which is excreted via the kidneys.

4.5 Fate of fats absorbed from the gut

You will recall from the previous chapter that the absorbed fats leave the intestinal epithelial cells and enter the lymph as chylomicrons. From there, they enter the bloodstream, where they are processed in a similar manner to the VLDL described above.

❑   What are VLDL, and what happens to them in the circulation?

■   VLDL are very low density lipoproteins, which are manufactured in the liver and released into the bloodstream. They are broken down by the enzyme lipoprotein lipase (which is located on the membrane of capillary endothelial cells), releasing fatty acids. The fatty acids so released enter the tissues to combine with glycerol and so re-form triacylglycerols.

You have also seen that triacylglycerols are stored, mainly in adipose tissues, and are broken down during the post-absorptive state. The fatty acids so released are utilized as a source of energy by many cell types; the glycerol also produced is converted to glucose in the liver.

Although triacylglycerols are the major dietary lipids, there are – as you know – two other major classes of lipids: phospholipids and steroids. One steroid which has received a great deal of attention in the context of health, and so should perhaps be mentioned here, is cholesterol. In particular, cholesterol is thought of in the context of atherosclerosis, in which fatty deposits are laid down in blood vessels, leading to vascular damage and disease (see Chapter 2).

❑   Cholesterol is not used as a metabolic fuel, but is involved in other vital processes. Can you list three important roles of cholesterol?

■   Cholesterol plays an essential role in cell membrane structure (Book 1, Chapter 3), in the synthesis of steroid hormones (Book 1, Chapter 4) and in the synthesis of bile salts (Chapter 3 of this book).

In humans (unlike many animals, e.g. dogs) all cells can synthesize cholesterol but, in general, the amount they produce is insufficient for their needs. Additional cholesterol is manufactured by the liver and transported to the rest of the body in the circulation. Thus no cholesterol is actually required in the diet.

Although some dietary cholesterol is absorbed from the gut, much of it passes though the digestive system and is excreted in the faeces. The levels of circulating cholesterol are regulated by control of cholesterol synthesis in the liver. When blood cholesterol levels are high, for example if dietary intake is high, synthesis by the liver is reduced. Thus under 'normal' circumstances, cholesterol levels are kept within an appropriate range, and (contrary to popular belief) variations in dietary intake of cholesterol for most individuals do not have much affect on circulating levels.

There are, however, other factors that can influence cholesterol levels. One of these is fatty acid intake. Polyunsaturated fatty acids (present at high levels in many vegetable oils) and mono-unsaturated fatty acids (found in meat and dairy produce, as well as in many vegetable oils) reduce plasma cholesterol levels, while saturated fatty acids (found at high levels in meat and dairy produce, and some vegetable oils) increase levels of plasma cholesterol. Animal fats contain a much higher proportion of saturated fatty acids than vegetable oils.

These effects of different types of fatty acids occur because of the way in which cholesterol is transported in the circulation. Like the majority of lipids, cholesterol is transported in the blood together with other lipids and proteins, in lipoprotein complexes. There are a number of different types of lipoprotein complex. Two that you have already encountered are the chylomicrons, in which absorbed fatty acids are transported from the gut (see Chapter 3) and VLDL, produced in the liver. Both chylomicrons and VLDL are broken down by the enzyme lipoprotein lipase. However, this breakdown is incomplete, and the residual complexes are known as intermediate density lipoproteins (IDL). Further degradation of these IDL by lipoprotein lipase produces **low density lipoproteins (LDL)**. (See Figure 4.16.)

LDL are important because they are the main carriers of cholesterol in the blood; they are composed of about 20% protein and 80% lipid, around half of which is cholesterol. The LDL supply cholesterol to the tissues; this cholesterol uptake occurs both by *passive endocytosis* (Book 1, Chapter 3) and after binding to a specific receptor on the cell surface which recognizes the protein component of the LDL (this is an example of a process known as *receptor-mediated endocytosis*). Cholesterol is removed from cells by incorporation into **high density lipoproteins (HDL)**, which return cholesterol to the liver to be degraded and excreted in bile, or to be repackaged (in VLDL). HDL are composed of 50% protein and 50% lipid, of which only two-fifths is cholesterol. These processes are summarized in Figure 4.16.

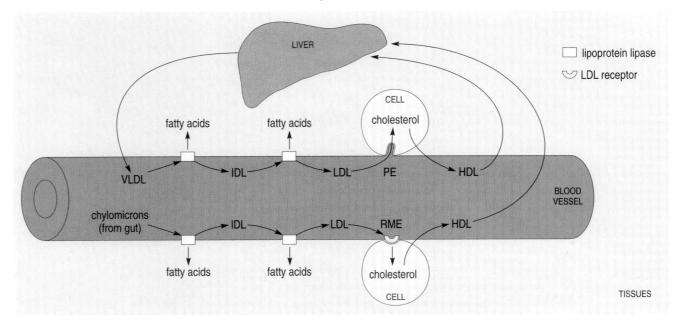

Figure 4.16 Summary diagram showing cholesterol transport. (PE = passive endocytosis; RME = receptor-mediated endocytosis.)

It is the *ratio* of LDL cholesterol to HDL cholesterol in the circulation which is thought to be the best indicator of the risk of developing atherosclerosis; the greater the proportion of HDL, the lower the risk. Dietary fatty acids influence the relative proportions of LDL and HDL in the circulation; unsaturated fatty acids increase the proportion of HDL, while saturated fatty acids increase the proportion of LDL. Cigarette smoking, an established risk factor, causes a reduction in plasma HDL, whereas exercise increases HDL. Oestrogens, interestingly, cause an elevation of HDL and a reduction of both total cholesterol and LDL. This is one possible reason why the incidence of cardiovascular disease is lower in pre-menopausal than post-menopausal women (see Book 4, Chapter 2).

❑   A small number of individuals, who have a particular genetic abnormality, lack LDL receptors. What would you expect the effect of this to be on circulating cholesterol levels?

◼   Absence of LDL receptors prevents the specific uptake of cholesterol into cells (receptor-mediated endocytosis) and results in elevated levels of circulating cholesterol. (This condition is known as *hypercholesterolaemia*.)

After this diversion into the biology of cholesterol which, as you have seen, is very important to health, we now return to energy metabolism. You have followed the fate of the major components of the diet and have seen that these are different in the absorptive and post–absorptive states. This is summarized in Figure 4.17.

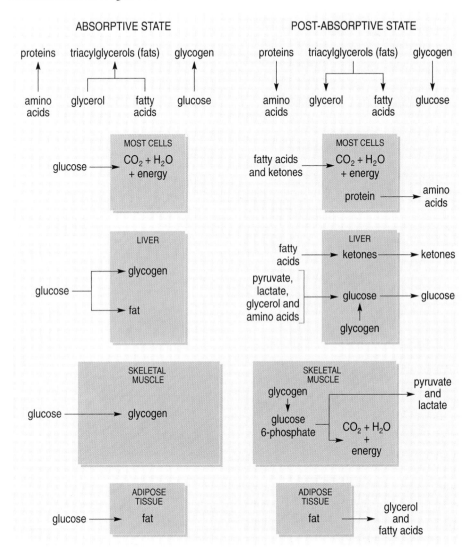

Figure 4.17   Summary of the events occurring in different tissues in the absorptive and post–absorptive states.

You have seen that maintenance of glucose levels in the circulation is of crucial importance for the energy supply to the central nervous system. You have examined the various ways in which circulating glucose levels are regulated, so the obvious question now is, *how* are these processes, which result in the regulation of glucose levels, themselves controlled? We will go on to describe this in the next section.

Summary of Section 4.5

1   Lipids, including cholesterol, circulate as lipoprotein aggregates. These are broken down by lipoprotein lipase, releasing fatty acids which enter cells, particularly adipocytes, where they are reconverted into triacylglycerols and stored. The action of lipoprotein lipase is incomplete, and residual complexes – in particular, low density lipoproteins (LDL) – are produced.

2   The LDL are the main carriers of cholesterol in the circulation; uptake of cholesterol from LDL into cells occurs both passively and via a specific LDL receptor. Cholesterol leaves cells and is returned to the liver by incorporation into high density lipoproteins (HDL). A high proportion of HDL in the circulation is associated with a reduced risk of developing cardiovascular disease.

4.6 Endocrine and neural control of the processes regulating blood glucose levels

The changes in metabolism that occur at the transition between the absorptive and post-absorptive states are controlled by hormones and by nerves. The hormonal component is the major control system, and the main hormone involved, insulin, is one that was first introduced in Book 1, Chapter 3. Insulin, which can perhaps best be described as a 'storage hormone', has many other actions; in addition to its metabolic functions, which we are about to describe, it also has growth-promoting actions, which we will not go into here.

Insulin is produced by endocrine cells in the islets of Langerhans, which, as you will recall from the previous chapter, are located in the pancreas. The islets contain four different types of endocrine cells; called alpha, beta, delta and PP cells. Insulin is secreted by beta cells; another important hormone, **glucagon**, which also plays a role in controlling the metabolic changes we have just described, is produced by alpha cells. A number of other hormones are produced by the pancreatic islet cells. In some cases, the function of these molecules is not yet fully understood, and we do not have space to describe them all here. One of these hormones, somatostatin, which is produced by the delta cells, inhibits the release of both insulin and glucagon; this example illustrates the complexity of the control mechanisms involved in the regulation of blood glucose levels, and the central role played by the pancreas.

How does insulin contribute to the homeostatic regulation of blood glucose levels? As discussed in Book 2, Chapter 3, a clue to the answer is that insulin release is triggered by an increase in the levels of glucose in the blood supply of the pancreas. Insulin release is thus stimulated during the absorptive state. The main metabolic effect of insulin is to increase glucose uptake and utilization, its main target cells being those of the liver, skeletal muscle and adipose tissue. Insulin acts by binding to specific receptor molecules on the target cell membrane. This causes a change in the receptor molecules which, in turn, begins a chain of intracellular reactions. These reactions culminate in changes to some of the components and events in the cell that are involved in glucose uptake and metabolism.

One of the actions of insulin is on glucose transport proteins. You will recall from the previous chapter that glucose can cross cell membranes in two ways: it is taken up from the intestinal lumen into intestinal epithelial cells by active transport, but its release from these cells into the bloodstream occurs by facilitated diffusion (Chapter 3). Facilitated diffusion is the mechanism by which glucose enters most cell types.

❑   Can you recall the main features of facilitated diffusion?

■   Facilitated diffusion involves a transport protein, but is not dependent on energy; the molecules move down their concentration gradient. Facilitated diffusion thus depends on the existance of such a gradient, and the availability of transport proteins.

Insulin affects glucose transport in skeletal muscle and adipose tissue, and a few other cell types, by increasing the *number* of molecules of transport protein that are actually present in the cell membrane. This allows more glucose to enter these cells. The transport system for glucose uptake in the liver, however, is *not* sensitive to insulin. So you would expect insulin to have no effect on glucose transport into the liver. Nevertheless, insulin *does* cause an increase in glucose uptake by the liver. It does this by causing activation of glucokinase (the form of hexokinase that is present in liver cells). This enzyme acts on glucose when it enters the liver cells, converting it to glucose 6-phosphate. Thus insulin speeds up the conversion of glucose to glucose 6-phosphate. This has the result of *lowering* the glucose concentration inside the liver cell.

❑   What effect would you expect this to have on facilitated diffusion?

■   It will *stimulate* facilitated diffusion, because this process is driven by the difference in concentration of glucose on each side of the cell membrane.

Insulin also increases the *utilization* of glucose, stimulating the intracellular reactions that are going on during the absorptive state.

❑   Apart from serving as a fuel for energy production, what is the fate of glucose during the absorptive state?

■   In the liver, glucose is converted to glycogen and to triacylglycerols; in adipocytes, glucose is converted to triacylglycerols; and in skeletal muscle, glucose is converted into glycogen.

Insulin not only stimulates these reactions, but also inhibits the reactions that occur during the post–absorptive state.

How does insulin have these effects on the reactions going on within cells? Insulin acts by altering the amounts and/or the activities of the enzymes involved in these reactions. For example, insulin promotes glycogen formation by increasing the activity of one of the enzymes involved in the conversion of glucose into glycogen (glycogen synthetase), while also inhibiting the activity of an enzyme (glycogen phosphorylase) that is involved in the breakdown of glycogen. Some of the metabolic processes influenced by insulin are summarized in Table 4.3.

Table 4.3 Some effects of insulin at the liver, adipose tissue and skeletal muscle.

Liver	Adipose tissue	Skeletal muscle
increases glucose uptake	increases glucose uptake	increases glucose uptake
increases glycogen synthesis	increases triacylglycerol synthesis	increases glycogen synthesis
increases triacylglycerol synthesis	decreases breakdown of triacylglycerols	increases protein synthesis
decreases breakdown of glycogen, triacylglycerols and protein		decreases breakdown of glycogen and protein
inhibits ketone formation		

You have seen that insulin release is triggered by increasing glucose levels in the circulation, and that its effects are to increase glucose uptake and utilization. This in turn results in a *lowering* of glucose levels in the bloodstream, and a corresponding reduction in the release of insulin.

❏   This is an example of a form of regulation you know about already. Can you say what it is?

■   Negative feedback, shown in Figure 4.18.

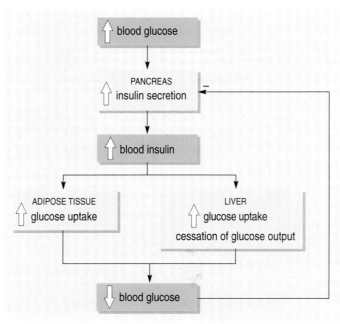

Figure 4.18 Summary diagram showing how insulin acts on adipose tissue and the liver to regulate blood glucose levels. The levels of insulin are controlled by negative feedback of lowered blood glucose on insulin secretion.

❑   When insulin levels are lowered, what would you expect the effects
        to be?

■   A reduction in circulating insulin levels causes effects opposite to
        those already described, i.e. glucose uptake and utilization are
        reduced.

You have seen that insulin release is controlled by the levels of glucose in
the circulation. Some other factors also affect insulin secretion. One such
factor is a gastrointestinal hormone, **gastric inhibitory peptide** or **GIP**.
GIP is released by endocrine cells in the small intestine in response to the
presence of fats and glucose; it stimulates insulin release, in anticipation
of the arrival of glucose in the circulation. This is an example of
feedforward control (Book 2, Chapter 3). This feedforward control is
useful because, when glucose begins to enter the bloodstream after a
meal, insulin levels are already raised, so glucose uptake by cells is
maximized. If this feedforward does not occur and blood glucose levels
rise too rapidly, excess glucose is excreted in the urine (Chapter 5) and is
therefore wasted. The effects of elevated blood glucose levels on health
are discussed in Chapter 7.

The nervous system also influences insulin release; nerves of the
parasympathetic system that innervate the islets of Langerhans are
activated during ingestion and stimulate insulin release.

Sympathetic nerves, on the other hand, inhibit insulin release. This effect
of sympathetic nerves is of importance at times of stress, during exercise
and when blood glucose levels are low. At these times, sympathetic nerves
are active and so insulin levels are reduced.

❑   What effect will this have on circulating levels of glucose?

■   It will make more glucose available in the circulation (since insulin
        acts to stimulate glucose uptake, and to inhibit glycogenolysis and
        gluconeogenesis). Thus an increased supply of glucose is available
        to cells at times when they will be needing increased amounts of
        glucose to provide energy. A good example of this is our well-used
        situation of what happens when we are faced with a charging bull
        – clearly, a stressful experience, and one in which the skeletal
        muscles will need extra energy for the exercise necessary to effect
        escape.

Circulating adrenalin and noradrenalin, which are released from the
adrenal glands (Book 2, Chapter 3) at times of stress, also inhibits insulin
secretion. These hormones have the same effect as sympathetic nerves,
which release noradrenalin as a neurotransmitter. The different ways in
which insulin secretion is controlled are shown in Figure 4.19.

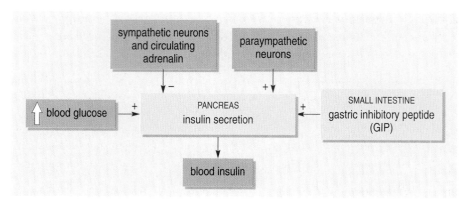

Figure 4.19 Summary of the major factors influencing insulin secretion.

You have seen how insulin regulates blood glucose levels during the absorptive state, and how the levels of insulin in the circulation are controlled. Now we will turn to how glucose levels in the circulation are regulated during the post-absorptive state.

The changes that occur as a result of a lowering of insulin levels are essentially those that occur on the transition from the absorptive to the post-absorptive state. Lowering of insulin levels, however, is only partly responsible for this transition; another pancreatic hormone, *glucagon*, is also involved. As the glucose circulating in the blood is taken up by cells, so blood glucose levels fall. This fall in circulating glucose levels is thought to act as a stimulus for the release of glucagon.

Glucagon acts largely on the liver to stimulate glycogenolysis, gluconeogenesis and ketone synthesis. These actions all have the effect of increasing the blood levels of both glucose and ketones. Since these effects of glucagon are opposed to those of insulin, they are often referred to as *glucose counter-regulatory controls*. The release and actions of glucagon are summarized in Figure 4.20.

Glucagon is not the only molecule which acts to increase glucose levels in the blood. You have seen that both circulating adrenalin and noradrenalin and the sympathetic nervous system inhibit insulin release, which has the effect of raising blood glucose levels. Adrenalin and noradrenalin and the sympathetic nervous system also increase the levels of circulating glucose more directly, by stimulating glycogenolysis, gluconeogenesis and lipolysis. These mechanisms are triggered by activation of neurons in the central nervous system, which respond to decreased glucose levels by activating the sympathetic nerves supplying the liver, adipose tissue and adrenal medulla. Thus there are several mechanisms to counteract decreased availability of glucose in the circulation. Figure 4.21 summarizes these other main glucose counter-regulatory controls.

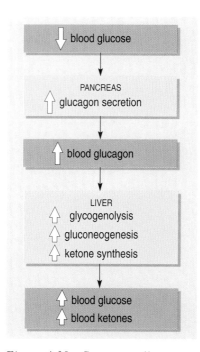

Figure 4.20 Summary diagram showing the actions of glucagon and the factors affecting its release. Adapted from Vander, A. J., Sherman, J. H. and Luciano, D. S. (1994) Human Physiology, Sixth International Edition, copyright © 1994, 1990, 1985, 1980, 1975, 1970 by McGraw-Hill, Inc., with permission of the McGraw-Hill Companies.

One group of hormones which have important effects on blood glucose levels are the glucocorticoids. These are a type of corticosteroid hormone. The corticosteroids are produced by the adrenal cortex at times of physical and mental stress (in response to adrenocorticotropic hormone (ACTH) secreted by the pituitary gland – Book 2, Chapter 3). The main glucocorticoid is cortisol (also known as hydrocortisone). Glucocorticoids have many important actions in the body, which we do not have space to detail here, but include stimulation of an increase in gluconeogenesis, reduction in glucose utilization by cells and release of fatty acids from adipose tissue.

A number of other hormones can also affect the metabolic processes which we have described, although these effects are secondary to their major roles in the body, and again their levels do not vary according to the absorptive/post-absorptive states. Two such hormones are thyroid hormones and growth hormone, which have been described in Book 2, Chapter 2. These hormones mobilize glucose at times of increased need.

So far, we have mainly focused on the regulation of glucose levels during 'normal' or resting conditions. But as you have already seen, there are times, for example during exercise, when extra demands for glucose are made. This extra requirement is provided by appropriate responses in the glucose regulatory systems, similar to those occurring during the post-absorptive state.

❑   Describe the processes that come into play when glucose levels in the circulation fall.

■   Blood glucose levels can fall either as a result of reduced supply of glucose from the gut, or as a result of increased demand for and uptake of glucose by skeletal muscle. A decrease in circulating glucose causes a decrease in insulin secretion and an increase in glucagon secretion. Low blood glucose levels cause activation of the sympathetic nervous system, and this further inhibits insulin release. These hormonal and neural events cause increases in glycogenolysis, gluconeogenesis and lipolysis.

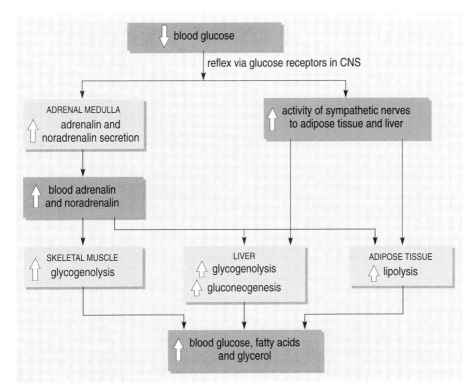

Figure 4.21   Effects of the nervous and endocrine systems in glucose counter-regulatory control. Adapted from Vander, A. J., Sherman, J. H. and Luciano, D. S. (1994) *Human Physiology, Sixth International Edition*, copyright © 1994, 1990, 1985, 1980, 1975, 1970 by McGraw-Hill, Inc., with permission of the McGraw-Hill Companies.

These responses are all similar to those that occur during fasting between meals.

❑ There is, however, one major difference between the events that occur during fasting and those that occur during exercise. Can you work out what this is?

■ The skeletal muscles need additional glucose during exercise, so glucose uptake and utilization must remain high in this tissue. During fasting, however, there is a decline in the uptake and utilization of glucose.

How are the additional requirements for glucose by skeletal muscle met when the regulatory conditions are such that, at times of rest, the uptake and utilization of glucose by this tissue would be *reduced*? Part of the answer lies with the skeletal muscle stores of glycogen, but it is also thought that there may be other factors which affect glucose uptake by skeletal muscles during exercise.

4.6.1 Diabetes mellitus

Although this is a course about health, there is one disorder we should perhaps mention here, and that is **diabetes mellitus**; this is a common condition in the West, affecting approximately 2% of the population. The name diabetes refers to the copious production of urine, and was first used by the Greeks. Mellitus refers to the sweet nature of the urine produced (*mellitus* is from the Latin word for honey). Diabetes mellitus should not be confused with diabetes insipidus (about which you will learn something in the next chapter), in which copious amounts of insipid (i.e. not sweet) urine is produced.

Diabetes mellitus results from either a deficiency (or complete lack) of insulin or from a lowered response of cells to insulin (to which we will return shortly). Thus diabetes mellitus is classified into one of two types, depending on whether insulin is produced. Type I, **insulin-dependent diabetes mellitus (IDDM)**, affects around 15% of diabetic individuals. In IDDM, insulin is lacking (completely or almost completely) because of the destruction of the pancreatic beta cells by an autoimmune reaction (see Book 2, Chapter 5), which is thought to be triggered after a viral infection. Insulin treatment is essential for individuals with IDDM and must be by injection, as insulin cannot be given orally.

❑ Can you suggest a reason why oral insulin treatment is not possible?

■ Insulin is a protein so would be broken down by the proteolytic digestive enzymes in the gut.

In type II, **non-insulin-dependent diabetes mellitus (NIDDM)**, the responsiveness of cells to insulin is diminished. Thus, although insulin may be present at normal or even at elevated levels, it is not able to effect its normal regulatory role. This is termed **insulin resistance** and can be due to alteration in the insulin receptors on the cell membrane or to disruption to the normal intracellular signalling by these receptors. NIDDM usually occurs in middle age or later and is associated with obesity, although other factors may be involved. It is typically treated by dietary controls and exercise.

The absence or ineffectiveness of insulin in diabetes mellitus results in elevation of blood glucose levels. Some of this excess glucose is excreted by the kidneys (which you will learn about in the next chapter), hence the sweet urine. Fat mobilization is also increased in diabetics, so leading to elevated levels of lipids in the circulation. Prolonged exposure, over many years, to raised levels of circulating glucose and lipids causes tissue damage. This is thought to contribute to at least some of the chronic conditions associated with the diabetes: atherosclerosis, peripheral nervous system damage, blindness, kidney damage and susceptibility to infection. You will learn more about this in Chapter 7.

IDDM can cause other severe problems if not treated. In IDDM, blood glucose levels are always elevated, not only because glucose uptake is disrupted, but also because glycogenolysis and gluconeogenesis continue. Lipolysis also continues, so that levels of circulating fatty acids and glycerol are also increased. In extreme instances, this can lead to a potentially fatal disruption in the balance of body fluids and salts.

Unfortunately, insulin treatment can also be hazardous.

❑   If too much insulin is present, what do you think the consequences would be?

◼   If excess insulin is administered, blood glucose levels could drop too low, resulting in insufficient glucose being available for the brain. This can result in a potentially fatal coma.

Although in this section we have painted a somewhat depressing picture, we should remember that a great many diabetic individuals are very successfully treated.

Summary of Section 4.6

1   The changes in metabolic processes which occur at the transition between the absorptive and post-absorptive states are controlled by hormones and by nerves.

2   During the absorptive state, increased levels of glucose trigger the release of the hormone insulin from the beta cells of the pancreatic islets. Insulin release is also stimulated by the gastrointestinal hormone, GIP, and by parasympathetic nerves. Sympathetic nerves and circulating adrenalin and noradrenalin inhibit insulin release.

3   Insulin increases glucose uptake and utilization, particularly in the liver, skeletal muscle and adipose tissue, where it stimulates the formation of stores of glycogen and triacylglycerols. It also inhibits the breakdown of these reserves.

4   During the post-absorptive state, decreased glucose levels stimulate the release of the hormone glucagon from alpha cells of the pancreatic islets. Glucagon release is also stimulated by sympathetic nerves and by circulating adrenalin and noradrenalin.

5   Glucagon stimulates gluconeogenesis and also the breakdown of glycogen and triacylglycerols (glycogenolysis and lipolysis).

4.7 Metabolic rate

Energy is released when metabolic fuel molecules are catabolized, but only some of this energy is used to power new chemical reactions and other cellular processes. The remainder is released as heat. This can be represented by the following equation:

energy generated = energy used + heat released

The energy provided by catabolism can be used to perform *work*. The scientific meaning of the term 'work' is not the same as the everyday one. In the present context, we mean such *internal* energy-requiring activities such as active transport, secretion, muscular contraction, as well as the *external* work involved in moving objects in the environment, e.g. during activities such as carrying suitcases, or hanging out the washing. So when any type of work is performed, some energy is released and dissipated as heat. The *total* energy being used by the body in a particular period of time is termed **total energy expenditure** and can be represented by:

$$\text{total energy expenditure} = \text{heat generated} + \text{external work done} + \text{energy stored}$$

Energy is measured in either of two units, which you learnt about in Book 1, Chapter 6: kilojoules (abbreviated to kJ) or kilocalories (kcal). (A kilocalorie is the the same as the older – and rather confusing – unit of energy, the Calorie.) One kcal is approximately 4.2 kJ and is defined as the amount of energy required to increase the temperature of 1 litre of water by 1 °C.

How much energy is provided by one glucose molecule? The amounts of energy released by reactions of individual molecules is tiny; it takes 6×10^{23} (i.e. $6 \times 10 \times 10 \times 10 \times 10 \ldots$ 23 times) molecules of glucose (which would weigh 180 g) to produce 686 kcal. Conversion of 6×10^{23} ATP molecules to the same number of ADP molecules produces a mere 7 kcal of energy. The amount of energy released by the breakdown of food molecules, then, can be measured in kcal.

The rate at which energy is used by the body, i.e. the amount of energy used per unit time, is known as the **metabolic rate**; it is usually expressed as kcal per hour.

❏   Many factors influence an individual's metabolic rate. Can you list some of these?

■   Activity, body size, age, sex, external and internal temperature, intake of food, infection, pregnancy, lactation, menstruation, emotional state, sleep.

The metabolic rate of an individual who has not eaten for 12 hours, is at rest and at a comfortable temperature, is known as the **basal metabolic rate (BMR)**. This is *not* a measure of the lowest metabolic rate, which occurs during sleep. A measure of BMR is useful, because it allows comparison of metabolic rates between individuals. The BMR of an individual varies during the lifespan; taking relative body weights into account, that of a child is greater than that of an adult. This is because, in a child, much more molecular synthesis is needed for the formation of new tissue. In contrast, BMR decreases with advancing age. There are also individual variations in BMR, not only the obvious differences associated with size and sex (the BMR of women typically being less than that of men of the same size), but also between individuals of the same sex and a similar height or weight.

However, the main influence on BMR comes from the thyroid hormones produced by the thyroid gland, an endocrine gland located in the neck, which you learnt about in Book 2, Chapter 2. Thyroid hormones have a marked effect on BMR. They act to increase oxygen consumption and heat production by many parts of the body, an exception being the brain. The *way* in which thyroid hormones exert this stimulatory effect on BMR is not understood. The levels of circulating thyroid hormones, however, are the main regulator of the BMR. Conditions in which the levels of thyroid hormones in the circulation are elevated or depressed can occur. An excess of thyroid hormone is known as *hyperthyroidism*.

❏   From what you have learnt, can you predict what the effects of hyperthyroidism on BMR might be, and what symptoms would result?

■   Elevated levels of thyroid hormones would increase the BMR. Symptoms would include an increased rate of catabolism, increased appetite and food intake, but loss of weight.

Correspondingly, reduced levels of thyroid hormones *(hypothyroidism)* cause a low BMR, i.e. reduction in catabolism and appetite and weight gain despite low food intake.

Two other hormones which increase metabolic rate are adrenalin and noradrenalin which, as you know, are released at times of stress.

❏   Can you explain the effects of adrenalin and noradrenalin on metabolic rate? (Look back to Section 4.2.5.)

■   Adrenalin and noradrenalin increase the levels of circulating glucose directly, by stimulating glycogenolysis, gluconeogenesis and lipolysis. These hormones also inhibit insulin release. This removes the insulin stimulation of glycogen and triacylglycerol synthesis and the insulin inhibition of glycogen breakdown. So this has the effect of increasing the catabolism of glycogen and triacylglycerols, i.e. it causes metabolic rate to increase.

You have seen that increased physical activity causes an increase in metabolic rate. The energy expended during different activities is shown in Table 4.4.

Table 4.4   Energy expenditure during different activities for a 70 kg person.

Form of activity	Energy expended /kcal per hour
lying still, awake	77
sitting at rest	100
typing rapidly	140
dressing or undressing	150
walking on level at 4.8 km per hour	200
cycling on level at 9 km per hour	804
walking up an 8% gradient at 4.8 km per hour	357
sawing wood or shovelling snow	480
jogging at 9 km per hour	570
rowing at 20 strokes per min	828

The balance of energy storage and utilization for an adult usually fluctuates only slightly around a constant level. A significant change in lifestyle, such as a change in diet, or in the level of physical activity, will change this energy balance. An example of this is seen if there is a dramatic reduction in food intake, which tends to have an initial effect of causing a rapid weight loss. This loss does not continue, however, but weight stabilizes at a new, lower level. This is a result of the body reaching a new energy balance, at a new, lower BMR.

Summary of Section 4.7

1   The rate at which energy is used by the body is known as the metabolic rate.

2   Basal metabolic rate (i.e. that at rest and after fasting for 12 hours) varies between individuals and changes during the lifespan. It is influenced by the thyroid hormones.

4.8 Metabolism and liver function in the new-born baby

After birth, until feeding is established, the infant depends on the stores of glycogen and fat laid down during the later stages of gestation, for energy and raw materials for growth. The size of these reserves will depend upon factors such as the length of the pregnancy, the state of the placenta and maternal nutrition. If feeding is delayed too long after birth, hypoglycaemia can occur, and can be severe. Although insulin and glucagon (and the other pancreatic hormones) can be detected in the islets of Langerhans well before birth, it seems that neither hormone is involved in the regulation of glucose levels in the fetus. The insulin response to an increase in blood glucose levels only develops some weeks after birth, but since babies have small frequent meals of a consistent nutritional composition, the response is not needed until later. However, insulin does act as an important growth factor for the developing fetus (Book 1, Chapter 6).

Fats (triacylglycerols) play an important role in the nutrition of new-born babies. Fats are a major component of milk and the major source of energy in the new-born; fatty acid levels in the circulation rise from about two hours after birth, diminishing slowly to adult levels over a period of about a year. High triacylglycerols levels in milk are also needed for gluconeogenesis to maintain blood glucose levels in the new-born baby – glucose is synthesized from glycerol, derived from triacylglycerols.

The liver functions of a new-born baby are similar to those of an adult, but less well-developed, for some liver enzymes are absent – or only present at low levels – at birth. The process of glycogen formation in both the fetus and new-born baby differs from that of the adult. In the new-born, galactose (derived from lactose in milk) is converted, via glucose, into glycogen at times of excess. (You will recall that lactose is a disaccharide made up of glucose and galactose units and that galactose is an isomer of glucose.) In adults, who have a varied diet in which milk is usually a minor component, galactose is *not* likely to be in excess. So, after conversion to glucose, it is catabolized by the same biochemical pathways as glucose.

Summary of Section 4.8

1   Although insulin and glucagon are present at birth, the insulin response is not established until some weeks later.

2   Fats (triacylglycerols) are important for the provision of energy and for the maintenance of blood glucose levels in young babies.

PART II
THERMOREGULATION

4.9 Introduction

Humans have the ability to tolerate great variations in the temperature of their external environment. Human populations can survive, and indeed communities live, in parts of the world where the temperature may reach as low as $-65\,°C$ or as high as $+50\,°C$. In some other parts of the world there are daily temperature changes of as much as $35\,°C$. Severe damage would result if the temperature inside the body were allowed to become too high or too low. For example, protein three-dimensional structure, and therefore function, would be altered by high temperatures, and freezing of body water would cause damage to the tissues. Survival in extremes of climate is only possible because in humans mechanisms have evolved that allow body temperature to be regulated.

Humans, like other 'warm-blooded' (or *homeothermic*) animals, have control mechanisms that allow them to regulate body temperature within a narrow range. This enables extremes of temperature to be tolerated without damage to the internal organs. However, humans are exceptional in their ability to cope with the great extremes of temperature already mentioned. This is largely because of our ability to plan and to use components of our environment to help maintain body temperature and is a result of the evolution of the human brain.

Body temperature is regulated by control mechanisms such as shivering and sweating, in response to fluctuations in the external temperature of our surroundings, and also in response to internal variations in the rate of heat production in the body. But how is heat produced by the body? By now you know the answer to this; it is generated by metabolic reactions. The bonds which hold the component atoms of molecules together store energy. When these bonds are broken, energy is released. Some of this energy is used to fuel chemical reactions and other activities such as muscle contraction and active transport across membranes. The remainder is released as heat.

The amount of heat released inside the body is not constant. This is because there are variations in the metabolic activities going on at different times. For example, the chemical reactions going on in the body are different during the absorptive and post-absorptive states, or during rest and exercise. The amount of heat generated in the body can therefore vary considerably.

Physical processes going on inside the body also generate heat. The obvious example is that of muscle contraction during exercise, but there are other examples, such as the flow of blood through blood vessels causing friction which in turn generates heat.

Under normal circumstances, internal body temperature is regulated at between 36 and 38 °C. Skin temperature, however, can vary a good deal more than this, as you will see later. The temperature of other parts of the body also varies somewhat; for example, rectal temperature measurements (i.e. temperature measured in the rectum) are slightly higher than oral measurements. Body temperatures also vary during the course of the day, being lowest during sleep. Typical variation in body temperature (rectal) during a 24-hour period is shown in Figure 4.22.

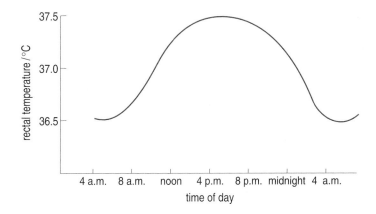

Figure 4.22   Typical variation in body temperature (rectal) during a 24-hour period. Adapted from Vander, A. J., Sherman, J. H. and Luciano, D. S. (1994) Human Physiology, Sixth International Edition, copyright © 1994, 1990, 1985, 1980, 1975, 1970 by McGraw-Hill, Inc., with permission of the McGraw-Hill Companies.

❑   There is another example of a cyclical variation in body temperature. Can you recall what this is?

■   The change in temperature that occurs during the menstrual cycle (discussed in Book 1, Chapter 4).

The ways in which body temperature is regulated will be examined later in this section. You will see that new-born babies have particular problems in maintaining body temperature and a different, but more limited range of strategies to enable them to cope with fluctuations in environmental temperature. First, though, we will look at how metabolism affects heat production.

Summary of Section 4.9

Humans are able to regulate their internal body temperature within a narrow range, despite variations in the temperature of their external surroundings and changes in the rate at which heat is generated inside the body. Normal body temperature varies during the day, and (for females) during the menstrual cycle.

4.10 Regulation of body temperature

In the preceding section, you saw that humans can regulate their body temperature, despite extremes in temperature of their external environment. Variations in temperature also occur inside the body, as a result of variations in metabolic rate; a good example is the rise in body temperature caused by the increased rate of heat production that accompanies strenuous exercise. What then are the mechanisms which enable body temperature to be regulated?

Heat is lost and gained from the body in the same ways as it is from other objects. So, processes such as *radiation* (the emission of heat as electromagnetic energy), *conduction* (the direct transfer of heat from molecule to molecule), and *convection* (the transfer of heat by movement of air or water past the object or body), are all involved. *Evaporation* (the loss of water from the skin and respiratory tract) also plays an important role in reduction of body temperature. This is because evaporation involves conversion of water to the gaseous state which requires a significant amount of energy.

The above processes are all involved in thermoregulation, but how are they controlled? In fact, thermoregulation is the classical example of a homeostatic mechanism (Chapter 1). There are continual changes to the temperature of both the internal and external environment; these are detected by temperature-sensitive receptors in the body, called thermoreceptors. The thermoreceptors activate effector systems, which act to return the temperature of the body to normal. It should be stressed that the body temperature, as already described, normally undergoes moderate fluctuations, and that 'normal' temperature is between 36 and 38 °C, not precisely 37 °C.

The location of the thermoreceptors permits the detection of temperature changes occurring both inside and outside the body. Peripheral thermoreceptors (i.e. those outside the central nervous system) are present in the skin and also deeper in the body, e.g. in the abdominal organs; central thermoreceptors are present in the spinal cord and hypothalamus. The thermoreceptors in the skin detect temperature changes near the surface of the body; those in the abdominal organs, the spinal cord and the hypothalamus detect core temperature changes. Information about temperature changes are conveyed from the peripheral thermoreceptors to the hypothalamus, which integrates the information, and in turn activates the effector systems.

There are different levels of thermoregulation. The obvious one is the voluntary action taken to move to or from an area of warmth, and the putting on or removal of clothes. There are a number of other similar actions which humans can take to regulate body temperature. However, autonomic events also play an essential role in temperature regulation. The systems that actually effect the required temperature change are the sweat glands, the blood vessels in the skin and the involuntary movement of skeletal muscles (shivering). The first two are activated via autonomic nerves, the latter via somatic motor nerves.

❑   What are the ways in which excess heat from metabolic activity is lost from the body?

■   Excess heat is lost by sweating and by dilation of blood vessels near the surface of the skin.

During sweating, body heat is lost because of evaporation. Sweating is the production of watery fluid from the sweat glands, which are located all over the body, in the skin (Book 1, Chapter 3). These glands are similar in structure to the glands in the wall of the digestive system (Chapter 3 of this book). Sweat glands secrete what is essentially a dilute solution of sodium chloride ('salt'). Some areas of the body have a greater density of sweat glands, not only the armpits and feet, but also the forehead and scalp, and the palms of the hands. It is estimated that an adult human has some 2.5 million sweat glands. Body heat is lost during sweating because, as we have seen, conversion of liquids to gases requires energy. The liquid on the surface of the skin takes up heat from the underlying tissue and when sufficient heat is taken up, the liquid evaporates.

Fluid lost during sweating is *additional* to a continual low level of fluid loss, which is occurring constantly, by diffusion through the skin and subsequent evaporation. This passive loss, together with fluid lost from the lungs when breathing, is referred to as **insensible water loss** and totals around 0.6 litres per day. In contrast, sweating is an active secretory process; that is, it requires energy. It results in a much greater fluid loss; levels of loss of up to 4 litres per hour have been reported during exercise at high temperatures.

Another important way in which body temperature can be prevented from getting too high is by the dilation of peripheral blood vessels. These are the many small vessels in the skin and are an effective means of conveying internal heat to the surface of the body, where it can be lost to the external environment. This is why a hot person has a flushed appearance.

❑   Thinking back to the ways of transferring heat described earlier, which processes are involved in heat lost in these circumstances?

■   Conduction and radiation. Heat is conducted from the blood in the vessels in the skin to the surrounding tissue, and thence to the body surface, from which it is radiated.

How is body temperature maintained in cold environments? One mechanism, which will almost certainly be obvious after reading the previous section, is by constriction of blood vessels. Constriction of peripheral blood vessels reduces the circulation of blood at the body surface, thereby reducing heat loss by conduction and radiation, so conserving body heat.

The methods of thermoregulation described so far involve either conserving or losing heat, according to the circumstances. Another way of maintaining body temperature in cold conditions is to increase the rate of heat production in the body.

❑   Can you suggest some ways that this might be achieved?

▉   By increasing muscle contraction and, in some circumstances, by increasing basal metabolic rate.

We have already seen that muscular activity generates heat. In addition to voluntary actions, such as rubbing one's hands or stamping the feet, there is an *involuntary* increase in the state of contraction of skeletal muscle in the cold. This increase is gradual and can lead to shivering, in which there are rhythmic contractions alternating with relaxations of the muscle, at a rate of about 10–20 times per second. Shivering is a very effective means of increasing body temperature, and because it involves no external work (i.e. no energy is expended in making changes in the external environment, for example as would be in carrying suitcases), all the heat generated is available for the body.

We have described the ways in which body temperature is regulated by the loss, conservation or generation of heat. Which parts of the nervous system transmit the instructions to the effectors? In fact, from information which you have learnt in earlier parts of the course (Book 2, Chapter 3), you already have the answer to at least part of this question. The sympathetic nervous system controls the activity of both the blood vessels and the sweat glands. Motor neurons of the somatic nervous system control the contraction of the skeletal muscles. The reflexes involved are shown in Figure 4.23.

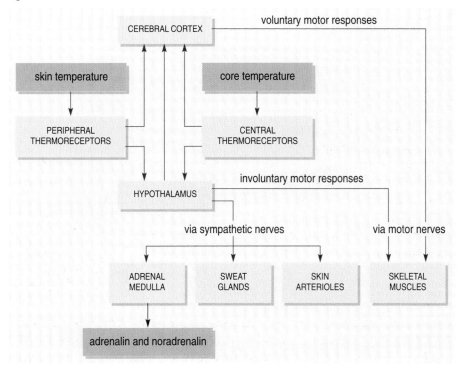

Figure 4.23 Summary of the mechanisms and reflexes involved in thermoregulation. Adapted from Vander, A. J., Sherman, J. H. and Luciano, D. S. (1994) Human Physiology, Sixth International Edition, copyright © 1994, 1990, 1985, 1980, 1975, 1970 by McGraw-Hill, Inc., with permission of the McGraw-Hill Companies.

The responses to temperature changes are dependent upon the environmental conditions; small changes in body temperature can be adjusted back to normal by changes in the supply of blood to the skin alone (by alteration of the state of contraction of the blood vessels). This is possible within the temperature range of 25–30 °C, which is called the **thermoneutral zone**. At lower temperatures, additional measures must be taken to increase body heat; the usual response is to conserve heat by putting to put on more clothes. At higher temperatures, greater heat loss is necessary, so sweating increases. The efficiency of sweating, however, is greatly affected by the humidity of the environment, since evaporation is much reduced, or even abolished, if there is already a large amount of water vapour in the air.

4.10.1   Temperature acclimatization

Humans are able to adapt very well to changes in climate. Adjustment to a different environmental temperature is known as **temperature acclimatization**. Acclimatization to high temperatures involves a more rapid sweating response, and an increase in the volume of sweat produced. This occurs after several days. Another change that occurs in heat acclimatization is that there is a reduction in the amount of sodium chloride eliminated. This avoids the possibility of a depletion of sodium (due to loss in an increased volume of sweat) which would have serious effects, as you will see in the next chapter. The composition of sweat that is produced is not changed upon acclimatization; rather, a proportion of the secreted sodium ions secreted by the sweat glands are *reabsorbed* by the epithelial cells lining the sweat ducts. This activity is stimulated by the action of an adrenal hormone called *aldosterone*, about which you will also learn in Chapter 5. Acclimatization to cold also occurs, but less is known about this.

4.10.2   Fever and hyperthermia

An increase in body temperature which most of us will have experienced is that of a **fever**. During fever, thermoregulation still occurs, but around a higher set-point temperature. This involves a change in the firing rate of the thermoreceptor cells in the hypothalamus. Fever usually occurs as a result of an infection, but can also be caused by physical trauma and stress. Fever is induced by the release of a factor (or possibly factors) by cells of the immune system (macrophages and monocytes). These factors are known as *endogenous pyrogens* (literally, 'internal fire-producers'); examples include *interleukins* (one of which you met in Book 1, Chapter 3), and a molecule called *tumour necrosis factor (TNF)*. These factors act on the thermoreceptors in the hypothalamus, altering their activity and raising the set-point. This, in turn, causes a sudden activation of autonomic mechanisms to conserve or generate heat, such as shivering and narrowing of the arterioles by vasoconstriction (Chapter 2) so that less warm blood reaches the body surface. Appropriate voluntary responses occur too, such as curling up (which cuts down heat loss by reducing the area of exposed body surface) and pulling on extra covers. This is accompanied by a feeling of cold. These heat generation/conservation measures continue until the new set-point temperature is reached. Later in the course of a fever, when the pyrogen is removed or inactivated, the hypothalamus is 'reset' to the normal level, the individual feels hot, and mechanisms to reduce temperature, such as sweating and vasodilation are brought into play. This change can be abrupt and used to be known as the 'crisis' or 'flush'.

Does fever have a function? We are commonly advised to reduce the fever that accompanies infections such as flu with drugs such as aspirin or paracetamol. Certainly, a greatly increased temperature can lead to convulsions and brain damage. This is of particular importance in infants and young children, where infection can lead to a very rapid and extreme rise in temperature. However, a moderate increase in body temperature during an infection makes the body less hospitable to many types of bacteria and may improve the effectiveness of the immune response.

Fever is one example of a state of the body called **hyperthermia**. Other examples of this are *heat exhaustion* and *heat stroke*. Moderate rises in temperature during exercise can normally be dealt with in the usual manner. Heat exhaustion results when excessive demands are placed on the thermoregulatory systems, and can be caused by failure to replenish water lost by sweating, or by salt deficiency. Heat stroke, on the other hand, is a result of the complete failure of the thermoregulatory control system. It usually occurs as a result of over-exertion in a hot climate. Although sweating occurs initially as normal, after a prolonged period the body temperature rises, sweating stops, and so body temperature increases still further. Heat stroke is extremely serious and can cause delirium, convulsions and prolonged unconsciousness. If treatment is not given to lower body temperature, this series of events is fatal.

4.10.3   Hypothermia

Reduction of body temperature below the normal range of values is known as **hypothermia**. It is actually fairly difficult to reduce body temperature below about 35.5 °C because of the effectiveness of the homeostatic controls of body temperature, but once temperature does drop below this level, mechanisms such as shivering are not possible because of muscular weakness. This causes a more rapid drop in temperature; below 34 °C, mental processes are affected, resulting in confusion. Loss of consciousness occurs at temperatures between 30 and 32 °C. At body temperatures below 28 °C, the cardiovascular system is affected, and blood flow to the brain and coronary circulation may be inadequate. However, people can recover from hypothermia surprisingly well. Individual variation, and factors such as age and fitness, affect the ability to survive hypothermia, as do the conditions in which it occurs. Immersion in cold water, for example, accelerates hypothermia, because of a reduction of insulation, which is normally provided by the air surrounding the body.

Summary of Section 4.10

1   Thermoreceptors in the skin detect temperature changes at the periphery (surface) of the body, those in the abdominal organs, spinal cord and hypothalamus detect core temperature changes.

2   Heat is lost and gained from the body by radiation, conduction, convection and evaporation. The main effector systems which act to reduce temperature are the sweat glands and peripheral blood vessels. The muscle activity of shivering raises body temperature. Behavioural responses also play an important role in thermoregulation.

3   Fever is caused by pyrogens released from cells of the immune system. These act on the thermoreceptors in the hypothalamus, resulting in an elevation of the set-point temperature and activation of mechanisms that raise body temperature.

4.11 Thermoregulation in the new-born baby

Infants are very vulnerable to changes in temperature, but are unable to take voluntary action to gain or lose body heat. Furthermore, the thermoneutral zone in new-born babies is higher than that of adults, being between 32 and 36 °C. New-born babies are also unable to shiver, although the reason for this is uncertain. They do, however, have an additional involuntary mechanism to generate heat; this is called **non-shivering thermogenesis**. This heat production occurs in a specialized type of adipose tissue, known as **brown adipose tissue (BAT)**, which is distributed as shown in Figure 4.24.

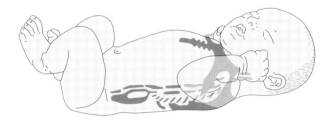

Figure 4.24   Distribution of brown adipose tissue (BAT) in a new-born baby.

BAT is so named because the fat cells in BAT, unlike those in ordinary 'white' adipose tissue, are densely packed with mitochondria, giving them a dark appearance when viewed by microscopy. BAT also has a much greater blood supply than white adipose tissue. Without going into great detail, BAT generates heat by the action of a protein called *uncoupling protein*, which as its name suggests reduces the normally tight 'coupling' of electron transport to oxidative phosphorylation in the mitochondria.

❏   How will this 'uncoupling' increase the rate of heat production?

■   The energy released by electron transport will *not* be used to fuel the synthesis of ATP from ADP and P$_i$, but instead will be liberated as heat.

Once the stores of BAT have been used, they cannot be renewed. BAT is utilized mainly during the first six months of life; although some remains even in adolescents. Non-shivering thermogenesis is stimulated in response to cold by the activity of the nervous system.

Mechanisms for *losing* heat are not well developed in new-born babies, and heat loss mainly occurs by vasodilation, i.e. widening of the arterioles, allowing more blood to be brought to the surface and so cooled; this is why Caucasian babies look pink! Sweat glands, although present in babies, are not as numerous as in adults; the number of sweat glands only reaches that of adults at around two years of age. Also, a much greater increase in body temperature is required to stimulate sweating in infants than in adults.

Summary of Section 4.11

New-born babies are vulnerable to change in temperature, since they cannot take voluntary action to conserve or lose heat. However, they do have a specialized mechanism to generate heat, known as non-shivering thermogenesis, in which electron transport is uncoupled from oxidative phosphorylation. This occurs in brown adipose tissue, which, once utilized, cannot be renewed.

4.12 Conclusion

In this chapter, you have learnt how cells derive energy from glucose (and also from other fuel molecules). You have also learnt about two fundamental examples of homeostasis: the regulation of blood glucose level and temperature regulation. You have seen that both the nervous and endocrine systems are involved in the control of the processes that keep these variables within their regulated range, and that many different organs and tissue types also play essential roles in these processes. Thus the maintenance of a stable internal environment requires the coordinated activity of the different systems of the body.

❏   What are the organs and tissues whose activities are integrated by the nervous and endocrine systems in the regulation of blood glucose levels?

■   The gut, the liver, adipose tissue and skeletal muscle (and during prolonged fasting, the kidney).

It should also have become clear to you during your study of this chapter that the activities of the different players – be they organ systems, organs, tissues or individual cells – in these homeostatic processes are continually changing. Also undergoing continual change are the levels and activities of many different types of molecule. For example, in glucose regulation, these include glucose itself, the glucose-regulatory hormones and neurotransmitters and the enzymes involved in glucose metabolism. So homeostasis can be examined at various levels within the hierarchy we first identified in Book 1, Chapter 1 – from the whole body down to individual molecules.

Objectives for Chapter 4

After completing this chapter you should be able to:

4.1   Define and use, or recognize definitions and applications of, each of the terms printed in **bold** in the text.

4.2   Outline how energy is generated from glucose, and why fatty acids and amino acids can contribute to energy production. (*Questions 4.1–4.3*)

4.3   Compare and contrast the events of the absorptive and post-absorptive states. (*Questions 4.3 and 4.4*)

4.4   Describe how lipids are transported in the circulation, and taken up into cells. (*Question 4.4*)

4.5   Explain how blood glucose levels are regulated. (*Question 4.3*)

4.6   Describe the control mechanisms involved in temperature regulation. (*Question 4.5*)

Questions for Chapter 4

Question 4.1   (*Objectives 4.1 and 4.2*)

During cellular respiration, glucose is oxidized, in a sequence of steps, to the end-products CO_2 and H_2O. Each oxidation reaction in this sequence is accompanied by a reduction reaction.

(a) Define the terms 'oxidation' and 'reduction'.

(b) What are the two coenzymes that are reduced and later reoxidized during the aerobic catabolism of glucose?

(c) What is the significance of the reoxidation of these two hydrogen-carrying coenzymes in aerobic cellular respiration?

Question 4.2   (*Objectives 4.1 and 4.2*)

The following processes are involved in the production of energy from glucose: the TCA cycle; electron transport coupled to oxidative phosphorylation; the link reaction; glycolysis.

Complete Table 4.5 overleaf, listing these processes in their correct sequence, and then adding information in the other four columns, as appropriate. Assume that the sequence begins with *one* molecule of glucose.

Table 4.5   For Question 4.2.

Process	Starting molecule(s)	End-products (which proceed to the next stage)	No. and type of coenzymes reduced	Net no. of ATP molecules produced

Question 4.3   (*Objectives 4.1, 4.2, 4.3 and 4.5*)

Fasting is important to many people, for religous reasons.

(a) Describe what happens to blood glucose concentration during a day's fast.

(b) Outline the changes that will occur in the hormones that regulate blood glucose concentration. What will be the effects on energy metabolism of these hormonal changes?

(c) What happens to fatty acids and amino acids during a day of fasting?

Question 4.4   (*Objectives 4.1, 4.3 and 4.4*)

In biochemical terms, what will be the outcome of eating a diet containing high levels of animal fats and sugary foods?

Question 4.5   (*Objectives 4.1 and 4.6*)

What particular problems does the new-born baby have in temperature regulation, and how is the baby equipped to cope with these specific problems? Why is it important that BAT is well supplied with blood vessels?

CHAPTER 5
FLUID REGULATION AND
EXCRETION

5.1 Introduction

In the last chapter you learnt about the way in which organic macro-molecules are utilized to provide energy. You saw that the levels of some molecules – most notably glucose – in the circulation are regulated, and that homeostatic control mechanisms operate which ensure that these levels are maintained within a fairly narrow range. In this chapter, we turn to the regulation of the levels of the simple inorganic substances that are essential to life: water and salts. By now you are familiar with the fact that water is the major component of the intracellular and extracellular fluids, and thereby forms the basis of the body fluids. You are also aware of many of the essential roles played by ions such as sodium and potassium (and others). How the levels of these substances are maintained at a balance in the body is the subject of this chapter.

The kidneys play a major role in these homeostatic processes. In particular, the control of water and sodium excretion by the kidneys is crucial in the regulation of body fluid volume and therefore, importantly, of blood pressure, as you will see. However, the kidneys also perform a number of other essential functions, which include the excretion of unwanted or potentially harmful waste products (such as the end-products of metabolism), the regulation of pH and the production and activation of some hormones. In order to understand these processes, we will need to look at the kidney and its functions at different levels; not simply at the level of the types and arrangement of its constituent cells, or that of the mechanisms, molecules, and ions involved, but also at the interactions of the kidney with other systems of the body. Indeed, these interactions are fundamental to the roles played by the kidney in homeostasis. We will begin with an overview of the organization and function of the urinary system. In later sections, we will re-examine particular aspects of kidney structure and function in more detail, in order to explain how this organ carries out its essential role in homeostasis.

5.2 Overview of the organization and function of the urinary system

The kidneys are a pair of organs situated at the back of the body, behind the digestive organs. Urine produced in the kidneys is collected and transported via tubes called *ureters* to the *bladder* (where it is stored). Urine leaves the body

via the *urethra*. The positions of these organs are shown in Figure 5.1.
Collectively, they are referred to as the *urinary system*.

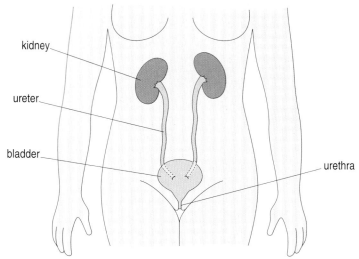

Figure 5.1 Diagram showing the position in the body of the kidneys, ureters,
bladder and urethra.

If one were to slice a kidney in half, one would be able to see an outer
capsule composed of connective tissue and three distinct inner areas, with
different coloration. These are an outer layer, or *renal cortex* (the term
'renal' meaning of the kidney), a middle layer, or *renal medulla*, and an
inner area, or *renal pelvis*, where the ureters widen to join the kidney, as
shown in Figure 5.2.

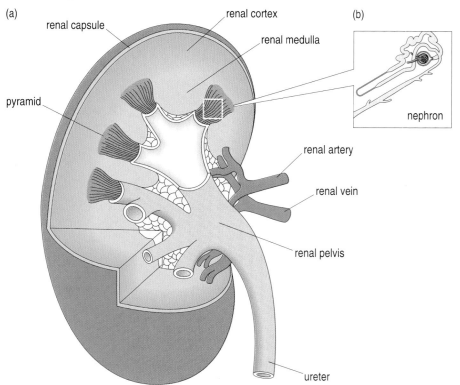

Figure 5.2 (a) Diagrammatic
representation of the kidney
structure. (b) An enlarged
diagram of a nephron.

Within each kidney there are around 1 million structures called **nephrons**. Each nephron acts as an independent filter and urine-processing unit. Individual nephrons are too small to be seen in Figure 5.2, but in order to give an idea of the position of nephrons in the kidney, an example has been shown, at an enlarged scale, on the right of the figure. The scale is further enlarged for the diagram of a nephron given in Figure 5.3.

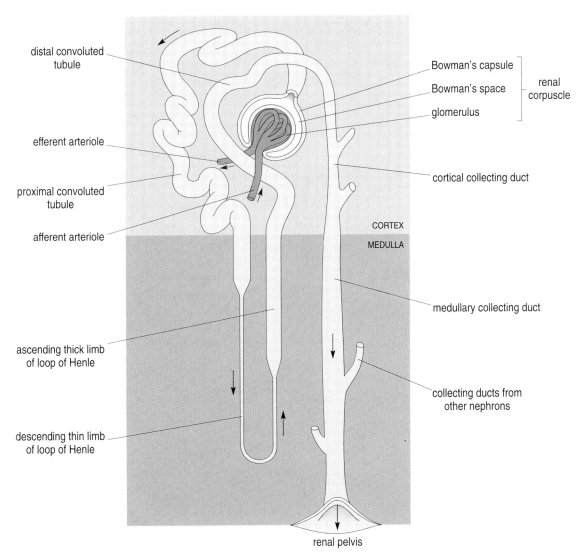

Figure 5.3 Larger-scale diagram of a nephron.

Each nephron contains a structure called a **renal corpuscle,** which acts as a filter, and lies in the cortex, and a long tube which collects and processes the filtered fluid, called a **renal tubule**. At the renal corpuscle, a network of very small-bore capillaries, known as the **glomerulus** (plural, glomeruli) comes into very close contact with the blind end of the tubule, which is composed of a single layer of epithelial cells. It is at this specialized region of close contact that fluid is filtered out of the blood capillaries, across the epithelial cells and into the lumen of the tubule. The filtered fluid, known as the **filtrate**, then passes along the tubule, which is rather convoluted (in some cases looping down into the medulla), before finally joining with the renal pelvis, where the urine is emptied into the ureters. It is during its passage along the tubule that the contents of the filtrate are processed, and urine is formed. Most of the filtered water, glucose, amino acids, sodium and other ions are reabsorbed by the epithelial cells of the tubule. Waste substances are either not reabsorbed at all, or only partially reabsorbed. Some molecules and ions are also secreted into the tubule by the epithelial cells, and, together with waste products which remain in the filtrate, are excreted in the urine. Although these sound like simple processes, they are closely controlled, so that the levels of water and salts in the body are regulated and wastes do not accumulate. In order to understand how this control is effected, we will need to look at the processes themselves in more detail.

Summary of Section 5.2

1   The functional unit of the kidney is the nephron; each of the two kidneys contains around one million nephrons.

2   Each nephron consists of a renal corpuscle, where fluid is filtered out of the blood, and a renal tubule, where the composition of the filtrate is modified, mainly by reabsorption of 'wanted' substances.

3   The processed filtrate forms the urine, which passes from the kidneys to the bladder via the ureters.

5.3 Processes involved in the formation of urine

Three main processes are involved in the formation of urine by the kidneys. These are glomerular filtration, tubular reabsorption and tubular secretion. Some metabolic reactions, which have an indirect effect on the formation of urine, also take place in the tubules. We will examine these different processes in turn.

5.3.1   Glomerular filtration

The first stage in the formation of urine is the filtration of fluid from the blood at the renal corpuscle. Blood enters the kidney via a blood vessel called the **renal artery** (see Figure 5.2) and travels through vessels of decreasing size to the renal corpuscle, where the **afferent arterioles** (i.e. those carrying blood *towards* the nephron, Figure 5.3) give rise to the capillaries of the glomerulus. Surrounding the glomerulus is the blind end of the tubule, which forms a hollow cup-like structure, known as **Bowman's capsule**. This arrangement is shown in Figure 5.4.

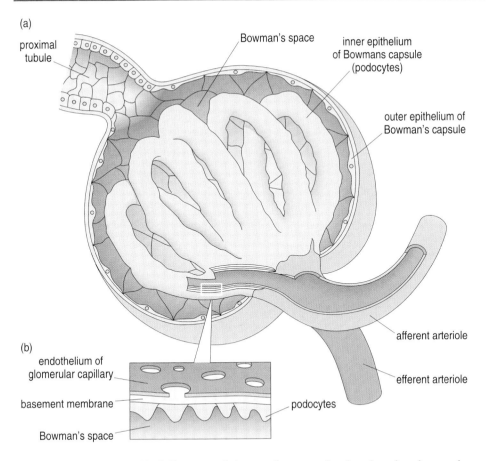

(a)

proximal tubule

Bowman's space

inner epithelium of Bowmans capsule (podocytes)

outer epithelium of Bowman's capsule

afferent arteriole

efferent arteriole

(b)

endothelium of glomerular capillary

basement membrane

Bowman's space

podocytes

Figure 5.4   (a) Simplified diagram of the renal corpuscle, showing the glomerular blood vessels and Bowman's capsule. (b) Enlarged diagram showing cellular specializations at the glomerulus.

During passage through the glomerulus, the pressure of the blood in the capillaries forces some water, small molecules and ions across the capillary and tubule walls, into the space in the middle of the blind end of the kidney tubule, known as *Bowman's space*. One way to visualize the arrangement of the corpuscle is to imagine a clenched fist (the glomerulus) pushed into the top of an inflated balloon (Bowman's capsule). The outer surface of the top of the balloon would be in close contact with the fist. This is also the case in the renal corpuscle – the epithelial cells of the inside of Bowman's capsule are in close contact with the endothelial cells which form the walls of the capillaries (Chapter 2). Fluid containing small molecules and ions is forced through the walls of the capillaries and of Bowman's capsule, into the tubule (in our analogy, this would be equivalent to the inside of the balloon).

The fluid filtered from the blood then passes along the tubule, via the renal pelvis, to the ureters; the unfiltered blood remaining in the capillaries leaves the glomerulus via the **efferent arterioles**.

The process of glomerular filtration is crucial to kidney function, yet fluid inside passes from the blood at capillaries all over the body (Chapter 2). So what is it that makes filtration from the glomerular capillaries in the kidney different from that occurring in other capillary beds? There are two main reasons for this difference. First, the pressure in the glomerular capillaries is high, so a greatly increased rate of filtration occurs in the kidney, and second, the filtered fluid is collected in the tubules, i.e. it is effectively removed from the internal environment of the body.

There are several special features of the arrangement at the glomerulus that makes this greatly increased rate of filtration possible. The pressure at the glomerular capillaries is much higher than that of other capillary beds because blood in the afferent arteriole supplying the glomerulus is at a higher pressure than that in other arterioles. Also, the arrangement and properties of the cells of the glomerulus are different from those of capillaries elsewhere in the body. This is not only because the walls of the glomerular capillaries and the Bowman's capsule are in close apposition, but also because the cells of the capillaries and capsule have some special structural properties. The endothelial cells lining these capillaries are unusual; they are extremely thin and have many pores (small holes), which are large enough to allow small molecules to pass through, but too small to allow filtration of very large molecules or, of course, blood cells. The extracellular matrix between the capillaries and the wall of the Bowman's capsule has an unusual chemical composition. It is thought that it, too, acts as a barrier to the passage of large molecules, including charged proteins. The epithelial cells of the inside of Bowman's capsule, which lie next to the capillaries are also unusual; they have foot-like processes (extensions) which leave spaces or channels, through which fluid can pass. The unusual shape of these cells has led to their being named *podocytes* ('foot cells'). The specializations of cells of the glomerulus are shown diagrammatically in Figure 5.4b, and in an electron micrograph in Figure 5.5.

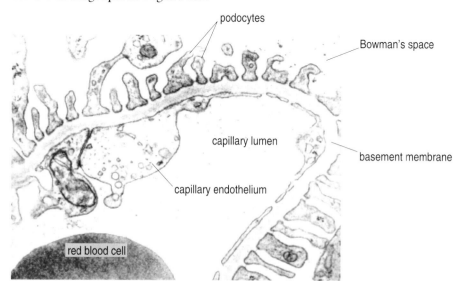

Figure 5.5 Electron micrograph of part of a glomerulus showing the structures illustrated schematically in Figure 5.4b.

You will recall that plasma is the liquid part of the blood and contains many different substances (see Chapter 2, Table 2.1). Around 20% of the plasma that enters the glomerulus is filtered out of the capillaries into Bowman's space. The liquid which passes out of the blood vessels, known as the *glomerular filtrate*, has nearly the same composition as plasma, except that it does not contain proteins. Another difference between plasma and the filtrate is due to the fact that some small molecules and ions remain bound to proteins in the plasma, and so these too are not filtered. Examples include plasma calcium, of which around half is bound to protein, and fatty acids, virtually all of which (as you learnt in the previous chapter) are in the form of lipoproteins.

The volume of fluid filtered per unit time is defined as the **glomerular filtration rate (GFR)**. For a 70 kg individual, this rate is around 180 litres per day, or 125 millilitres (ml) per minute. This contrasts with the total amount of fluid filtered by all the other capillaries in the body, which is around four litres per day. You may be interested to compare these values with those of the total blood volume, which of course varies between individuals but is about five litres, and the total plasma volume, which is about three litres. The massive rate of filtration by the kidneys is achieved not only because of the cellular specializations at the glomerulus, but also because the kidneys receive a large proportion (20–25%) of the cardiac output; this means that, at any moment, about 20–25% of the volume of blood pumped by the left ventricle passes to the kidney (*not* that 25% of the total blood volume circulates in the kidney).

❑   As stated above, the total amount of plasma in the circulatory system is around three litres. As about 180 litres of plasma are filtered by the kidneys each day, how many times is the entire volume of plasma filtered each day?

■   The total amount of plasma is filtered through the kidneys 180/3 = 60 times per day. (However, it is important to realize that, in order to achieve this high rate of filtration, the total volume of *blood* circulates far more often than this through the kidneys.)

❑   You have seen that, during filtration, fluid is forced through the blood capillary and tubule walls at the glomerulus; what factors do you think would influence the rate of this process?

■   The rate of filtration is influenced by the pressure of the blood in the afferent and efferent arterioles, and by the permeability of the walls of the glomerulus and Bowmans capsule. The relative concentrations of proteins in the glomerular capillaries and Bowman's space also have an effect on GFR.

It may help to think of a hose, leaking through a number of holes. The greater the number and size of the holes, the greater the rate at which water leaks out. However, factors such as pore size and number, and the composition of the extracellular matrix in the glomerulus do not undergo rapid or significant changes under normal circumstances (although they may be affected in some disease states). Returning to the hose, water will also leak faster if the tap is turned on further, increasing the water pressure. A similar effect would be achieved by squeezing the hose beyond the holes. Similar mechanisms operate in the kidney; GFR is affected by factors that affect blood pressure in the afferent and efferent arterioles. We will return to this later.

There is another factor affecting the filtration rate in the kidney, which is not so easily compared with our analogy of the hose; this is the relative concentration of proteins in the glomerular capillaries and in Bowman's space. As water and small molecules and ions filter out of the blood, so the protein concentration in the glomerular capillaries increases and osmotic pressure tends to 'pull' the water back into the capillaries (osmosis was described in Book 1, Chapter 3 and also in Chapter 3 of this book). This exerts a negative effect on filtration rate. However, this influence on filtration rate is less significant than that of blood pressure in the glomerulus, which is high.

Under normal circumstances, GFR does not vary greatly despite changes in arterial blood pressure (*not* arteriolar pressure, mentioned above). We will return to why this is so when we look at the control of GFR later in this chapter.

The total amount of any substance filtered through the glomerulus (i.e. *not* proteins or protein-bound substances) per unit time can be measured by determining the plasma concentration of the substance, and multiplying it by the glomerular filtration rate. The resulting value is called the **filtered load** of the substance.

❑ If the concentration of substance X in the plasma is 0.8 mg (milligrams) per ml, and the filtration rate is 125 ml per min, what will be the filtered load of substance X?

■ The filtered load of substance X will be $0.8 \times 125 = 100$ mg per min.

This value, however, is *not* likely to be the same as the rate at which the substance is excreted. This is because the composition of the filtrate is modified as it passes along the tubules; this is what we turn to next.

5.3.2 Tubular reabsorption

After filtration at the glomerulus, the filtrate passes out of Bowman's space into the main part of the tubule, the walls of which are also composed of a single layer of epithelial cells. You will remember that the tubule has a complicated anatomy, looping down and back up again, as shown in Figure 5.3. During the filtrate's passage through the tubule, its composition is modified, predominantly by processes known collectively as *tubular reabsorption*, by which substances pass back across the tubular epithelium.

It is important to realize that, while the amounts of water and many ions that are reabsorbed are closely controlled in order that their levels in the body are regulated, not all reabsorption from the tubules is controlled. The reabsorption of organic nutrients, such as glucose, many amino acids and water-soluble vitamins, for example, is actually not controlled at all. This is because, under normal circumstances, virtually all of these physiologically useful organic molecules are reabsorbed, and so their levels in the circulation are not changed, but maintained, after passage through the kidney. As you have seen in the previous chapter, the levels of glucose are regulated elsewhere in the body, except under exceptional circumstances.

To understand *how* the reabsorption of water and salts is controlled, it is necessary to look in more detail at the reabsorption processes involved, and also at the organization of the nephron. First, we will consider how different molecules and ions are reabsorbed from the tubules.

Reabsorption of glucose and amino acids

Glucose and amino acids are absorbed by the epithelial cells of the kidney tubules in the same way that they are absorbed from the gut, i.e. by active transport, against a concentration gradient. In the tubule, as in the gut, glucose and amino acids are cotransported with sodium ions (Chapter 3). It is the concentration difference of sodium across the epithelium which is the direct driving force for the active transport of glucose and amino acids. This gradient is set up by an Na^+–K^+ ATPase (sodium pump), which was first described in Book 1, Chapter 3 (Box 3.3), and which you also met in Book 2, Chapter 3, and Chapter 3 of this book. As in the absorptive epithelia of the gut, in the kidney tubules the Na^+–K^+ ATPase molecules are localized on the basal and lateral sides of the epithelial cells (i.e. on the sides that are *not* facing the lumen). Consequently, sodium ions are pumped out of the cells into the interstitial fluid between them (as shown in Chapter 3, Figure 3.12, for the intestinal epithelium). This results in a lowering of the concentration of sodium inside the epithelial cells, so that it is less than the concentration in the lumen of the tubules. This gradient allows the active transport of sodium, together with a cotransported molecule such as glucose, into the epithelial cells from the lumen of the tubules.

When the levels of glucose and amino acids in the blood are within the normal range, these nutrients are reabsorbed completely during passage through the kidney.

❑   There is, however, a limiting factor in the reabsorption of glucose or amino acids. Can you work out what this is?

◼   The number of transporter molecules (transport proteins) in the lumenal membrane of the tubular epithelial cells.

When blood glucose levels are high, as occurs in diabetes mellitus (Chapter 4), then more glucose will be filtered, and the concentration of glucose in the filtrate will be increased. Under these circumstances, there can be too much glucose for the transport proteins to handle; the transport proteins may be constantly in use, so that not all the glucose present in the filtrate is able to bind to a free transport site. Another way to describe this is that the transporter molecules are *saturated*, that is, all the sites on the transport proteins which bind glucose may be filled. Under these circumstances, the excess glucose is not reabsorbed, but is excreted in the urine, making it sweet (hence the name *mellitus*, from the Latin word for honey).

Reabsorption of other organic molecules

Most other useful organic molecules, such as the vitamins, are also reabsorbed by active transport in the first part of the renal tubule. If excess amounts of water-soluble vitamins, such as vitamin C, are ingested, the excess is excreted, like excess glucose, because of the saturation of transport proteins. This is why it is not harmful to ingest large quantities of vitamin C. However, this is not the case for lipid-soluble vitamins (such as vitamins A and D) and other lipid-soluble chemicals, which can be toxic at high levels. Excess lipid-soluble molecules in the filtrate tend to diffuse passively into the epithelial cells lining the renal tubule; so, if ingestion continues, the levels of these molecules in the body rise. Such potentially toxic substances are, in some cases, modified (in the liver) to make them less lipid-soluble, and thus more readily excreted by the kidneys. They may also be excreted in bile. However, these modification processes are not totally efficient, so excretion remains incomplete, allowing accumulation of these substances in the body. This is one reason for the toxicity of chemicals such as DDT and *high* levels of vitamins A and D.

Organic molecules that are not useful, for example the end-products of some metabolic reactions, may also be partially reabsorbed by diffusion, although most are excreted. The main metabolic waste product in plasma is urea, which, as you may remember from the previous chapter, is a nitrogen-containing molecule formed during the catabolism of amino acids. Urea is a small molecule which is filtered at the glomerulus and is passively absorbed in the tubules. Around 40–60% of the urea that is filtered is reabsorbed, the remainder is excreted in the urine. Another important molecule excreted in the urine is creatinine, a waste product of skeletal muscle metabolism, also described in the previous chapter. Unlike urea, creatinine is not reabsorbed in the tubules.

Reabsorption of sodium

Sodium is reabsorbed both by active transport and by diffusion through protein channels in the cell membranes of the tubular epithelial cells (see Book 1, Chapter 3). Active transport of sodium is not only coupled to that of glucose and amino acids as described above; several other types of sodium transport molecules are also present in the epithelium of the kidney tubules. These transport other ions, such as bicarbonate or phosphate, together with sodium. Sodium reabsorption is also coupled to transport of hydrogen ions *out* of the epithelial cells by some cotransport proteins.

Ultimately, all absorption of sodium – by both active transport and diffusion – is dependent upon the decreased concentration of sodium inside the tubular epithelial cells, a result of the action of Na^+–K^+ ATPase.

The mechanisms by which sodium enters the epithelium varies according to the region of the tubule; this is because the epithelial cells of different regions have different transport proteins. Thus, different substances are cotransported with sodium in different parts of the nephron. For example, glucose is only reabsorbed in the first part of the tubule, while chloride and potassium are cotransported with sodium further along the tubule.

Reabsorption of ions other than sodium

You have seen how many ions, such as phosphate, are absorbed, with sodium, by active transport, and that the absorptive properties of the tubular epithelium varies in different parts of the nephron. Other ions are also absorbed by diffusion and, in the case of chloride ions, which, you will remember are negatively charged, by passive movement with the positively charged sodium ions.

Reabsorption of water

As in the gut, the absorption of water in the kidney tubules is a passive process, which occurs by osmosis and diffusion, because of gradients in the concentrations of other substances across the epithelium, most particularly sodium. You have seen that the action of the sodium pump creates a gradient of sodium concentration, which ultimately drives the active transport of many different molecules and ions. The reabsorption of sodium and these other substances has the effect of diluting the filtrate and raising the solute concentration of the surrounding tissue. Thus water tends to pass passively, by osmosis, out of the lumen into the epithelial cells and by diffusion through the junctions *between* the epithelial cells, which, in some parts of the tubule, are very leaky.

Now, we need to pause for a moment to consider the process of osmosis in a little more detail. You have learnt that osmosis is the passage of water across a semipermeable membrane from a region of low solute concentration to a region of high solute concentration, and that this process is important both in the absorption of water from the gut, and the reabsorption of water in the kidney. The osmotic strength of a solution is expressed as its **osmolarity**[*], which is the number of solute particles in a unit volume of solution. A solution that exerts a high osmotic pressure contains a large number of solute particles, and has a high osmolarity. Because osmotic pressure is dependent upon the *number* of particles in solution, substances that

[*]Another term frequently used in this context is that of 'osmolality', which refers to the number of solute particles per unit *weight* of water. Since 1 ml of pure water weighs 1 g, the osmolarity and osmolality of aqueous solutions are very similar, so the two terms are frequently used interchangeably. For convenience, we shall use the term 'osmolarity' throughout.

dissociate into ions in solution exert a higher osmotic pressure than those that do not, since they will contain more osmotically active particles (e.g. NaCl will dissociate into two ions: one Na^+ ion and one Cl^- ion).

So, water is absorbed from the filtrate by osmosis mainly as a result of sodium reabsorption. However, a crucial point is that water can only pass across the epithelium *if* the epithelium is permeable to water; in fact the properties of the tubular epithelium vary along the length of the tubule, so that, for example, while water is readily reabsorbed in the proximal tubule, it is not absorbed so readily in some other regions, as you will see.

5.3.3   Tubular secretion

During passage through the tubules, while some molecules and ions are removed from the filtrate by reabsorption, others are *added* to the filtrate. This occurs by secretion from the tubular epithelial cells, into the lumen of the tubules. The main ions secreted are hydrogen (H^+) and potassium, (K^+) by active transport coupled to sodium reabsorption. Some products of metabolism (metabolites) such as creatinine, and some ingested organic molecules, for example drugs such as penicillin, are also secreted into the tubules. Secretion is also a way in which molecules that are not filtered at the glomerulus can be excreted. Both active transport and facilitated diffusion are involved in secretion at the tubules.

5.3.4   Tubular metabolism

In addition to absorption and secretion, the tubule cells also carry out some important metabolic processes, which are given the general term **tubular metabolism**. These include the production of ammonia, which is important in the regulation of H^+ ion levels, as we will see shortly; another is the catabolism of some organic molecules such as peptides, taken up from the tubule or from nearby blood vessels. Such substances could be toxic at high concentrations; their catabolism is a means of eliminating them from the body.

5.3.5   Renal clearance

From the previous section, you should now realize that the amount of a substance excreted in the urine is a result of the combination of the processes of filtration, reabsorption and secretion. This can be expressed, for a substance X, by the equation:

amount of X excreted =
(amount of X filtered + amount of X secreted) − amount of X reabsorbed

The overall fate of substances in the tubule can be determined by measuring the amount present in the urine, and comparing this value with that of the filtered load. From this we can determine whether a substance undergoes net reabsorption (i.e. is not excreted) or net secretion (i.e. is excreted).

For clinical purposes, renal function is measured by determining the clearance of substances from the plasma. The **renal clearance** of a particular substance is defined as the volume of plasma from which the substance is completely cleared from the kidney per unit time. If a substance is neither secreted or reabsorbed, then the renal clearance of that substance will be equal to the glomerular filtration rate. In fact, there is no substance occurring naturally in the body that has these properties. A compound in the body that is not reabsorbed and undergoes only very little secretion is creatinine; this substance is therefore usually measured in order to assess the effectiveness of glomerular filtration.

So, in order to measure clearance of any substance, the amount of that substance in the plasma, and the amount excreted in the urine per unit time must be measured:

$$\text{clearance of X (ml per min)} = \frac{\text{amount of X excreted (mg per min)}}{\text{plasma concentration of X (mg per ml)}}$$

❑   What will be the clearance of urea if the plasma concentration is 0.26 mg per ml and the amount excreted is 18.2 mg per min?

◼   The clearance of urea will be 18.2/0.26 = 70 ml per min.

❑   What will be the clearance of glucose, which has a plasma concentration of 0.8 mg per ml, and is completely reabsorbed?

◼   Zero. No glucose is cleared from the kidney under normal circumstances (i.e. in the above equation, 0/0.8 = 0!)

5.3.6   Properties of different parts of the kidney tubule

As you have already seen, an important factor in the formation of urine is that the different absorption processes do not operate uniformly along the entire length of the tubule; particular specialized processes occur in different regions of the tubule. The structure of the epithelial cells in the different regions of the tubule reflects this (see Figure 5.6).

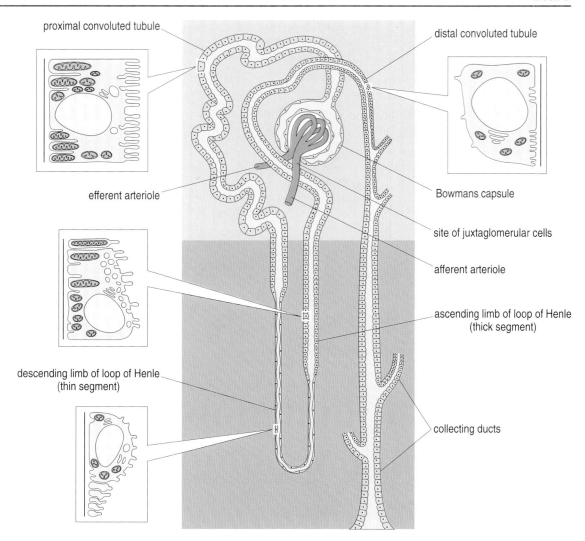

Figure 5.6   Diagram showing the main structural features of epithelial cells in different parts of a kidney tubule. (The black vertical line in each inset diagram denotes the basement membrane.)

The first part of the tubule, known as the **proximal convoluted tubule**, is where most reabsorption of glucose, amino acids and water occurs.

❑   Thinking back to the gastrointestinal system, what specializations would you expect the epithelial cells that line the inside wall of the proximal tubules to exhibit?

■   Microvilli, which increase the surface area available for absorption, and many mitochondria, as active absorption requires energy.

After passing through the proximal tubule, the filtrate reaches an area known as the **loop of Henle** (pronounced 'henlee'). The epithelial cells forming the first part of the loop are much thinner than those of the proximal tubule (see Figure 5.6) and they have no microvilli and few mitochondria.

❏   What does the relatively low number of mitochondria suggest about these cells?

■   That these are relatively inactive cells, metabolically.

❏   What sort of process, then, might go on in this area?

■   Passive or facilitated diffusion.

The first part of this so-called thin region of the loop of Henle, called the descending limb, is a site of passive movement of water, and to a lesser extent, of ions. The epithelium in this region is permeable to these substances and the filtrate is concentrated by the reabsorption of water by osmosis, since the osmolarity of the surrounding tissue is greater than that of the filtrate. However, the second thin part of the loop of Henle, the ascending thin limb, is less permeable to water.

The thickness of the tubule wall increases about half-way up the ascending limb; the epithelial cells here are much deeper, and contain more mitochondria (Figure 5.6). Na^+ and Cl^- ions are absorbed by active transport in the ascending limb. Other ions, particularly K^+ and H^+, are secreted into the tubule in this area. Upon returning to the area of the renal corpuscle, the ascending limb shows an extremely important anatomical arrangement, which is of fundamental importance in the control of kidney function. If you look at Figures 5.3 and 5.4, you will see that the tubule passes between the afferent and efferent arterioles. In fact, the tubule passes extremely close to the glomerulus. We will return to this point in the next section.

After the tubule passes close to the glomerulus, it is known as the distal convoluted tubule, which empties into the **collecting duct system**. The final control of urine composition occurs by reabsorption and/or secretion in this part of the nephron. Collecting ducts from several nephrons merge, and the filtrate is emptied into the renal pelvis.

At this stage, you may be wondering how the reabsorbed molecules are returned to the rest of the body. The answer is that there is another capillary network in the kidney, in addition to the glomerular system. This is known as the **peritubular capillary system**, and is illustrated in Figure 5.7 which shows how the capillaries surround the tubular system, allowing passage of reabsorbed substances back into the blood (substances that are secreted by the tubular epithelium pass *out* of the blood in this region). A loop of blood vessels, known as the *vasa recta*, follows the path of the long loops of Henle.

The processes described above explain how molecules and ions are filtered, reabsorbed and secreted, but offer no explanation of how these processes are controlled. What happens, for example, if excess fluid is drunk, or salt ingested? There are clearly great variations in the intake of these substances, and in their loss from the body by other routes, for example

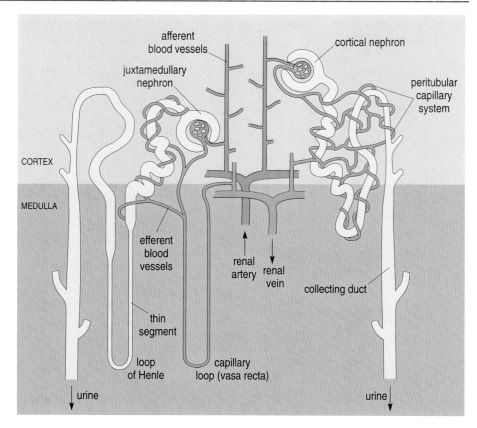

Figure 5.7 Diagram showing the peritubular capillary system and vasa recta.

during sweating. There are times when it is crucial that not all the filtered sodium and water are reabsorbed, but others when it is essential to conserve every last drop of water. In the following section we will see how renal processes are controlled, so that water and sodium levels, and also the levels of several other important variables, can be regulated.

Summary of Section 5.3

1   The main processes involved in the formation of urine are glomerular filtration, tubular reabsorption and tubular secretion.

2   Plasma is filtered out of the blood at the renal corpuscles, where the glomerular capillaries are surrounded by the epithelial cells of a special part of the kidney tubules, known as Bowman's capsule.

3   The high rate of filtration of plasma at the renal corpuscles is made possible by the high pressure of the blood in the glomerular capillaries, and by structural specializations of both the capillary endothelial cells and the tubular epithelial cells, and by the chemical properties of the extracellular matrix which lies between them.

4   Large molecules, such as proteins, and also protein-bound molecules, such as fatty acids, are not filtered at the renal corpuscle.

5   After filtration, the filtrate is processed as it passes along the tubule. Physiologically useful molecules, such as glucose, amino acids and many ions are reabsorbed, by sodium-coupled active transport. Sodium also crosses the tubular epithelium passively. Water is reabsorbed passively, by osmosis and diffusion, largely as a result of the movement of sodium ions. Waste organic molecules are reabsorbed to a varying extent.

6   Some substances are added to the filtrate by secretion from the tubular epithelial cells.

7   The tubular epithelial cells also have a metabolic role.

8   Renal function is assessed by measuring clearance, usually of creatinine, from the plasma.

9   Both the structure and the types of transport proteins of the tubular epithelial cells vary in different regions of the tubule; the substances reabsorbed in different parts of the tubule therefore also vary.

5.4 Overview of the control of renal processes

You have seen that the major processes involved in urine formation are glomerular filtration and tubular reabsorption and secretion. It is by control of these processes that regulation of variables such as body fluids, sodium, and pH occur. First we will look at the control of glomerular filtration.

5.4.1   Control of glomerular filtration

In Section 5.3.1, you learnt that the glomerular filtration rate, or GFR, is the volume of fluid entering the tubule per unit time. The main factor influencing GFR is the pressure of the blood in the afferent and efferent arterioles. Both the nervous and endocrine systems are involved in the control of the state of dilation of the renal arterioles, and hence in the control of GFR.

What, then, is the nature of the stimulus that results in changes in the pressure in the arterioles? In fact, there are several such stimuli, and they are not all fully understood. One important stimulus is blood pressure itself. In Section 5.3.1, we stated that GFR does not vary greatly with variations in arterial blood pressure. This is because, like other capillary systems, the glomerular system is *autoregulated* (Chapter 2). This means that when blood pressure in the afferent arteries increases, the arterioles undergo a contraction, reducing the pressure in the capillaries. This prevents sudden large increases in pressure in the capillary bed. However, a *persistent* increase in arterial pressure will result in a general increase in pressure in the arterioles and thus also in the glomerulus, and this will cause an increase in GFR.

This brings us to an important point. The kidney actually plays a vital role in the regulation of blood pressure. This is because an increase in blood volume will cause an increase in blood pressure. Blood volume, in turn, is related to the volume of water in the body. Since the kidney is the major route by which the levels of water in the body are regulated, its normal function is essential in the regulation of blood pressure.

Now let us return to how GFR is controlled. Apart from the effect of arterial blood pressure, there is a local stimulus, detected within the nephron itself, which influences GFR. Not all the details of the mechanisms involved in this local control are known yet, but it is made possible by the anatomy of the nephron. If you look back to Figure 5.3, you will see that after the loop of Henle, the tubule passes very close to the glomerulus, in between the afferent and efferent arterioles. This arrangement is called the **juxtaglomerular apparatus**, and is shown in more detail in Figure 5.8. There are two types of specialized cells which are found only in this area. These are a special type of tubular epithelial cells known as **macula densa cells**, which lie adjacent to the arterioles, and a second type of cells which lie around the arterioles, the **juxtaglomerular cells.** The latter cells produce an enzyme called **renin**, which has several actions, one of which results in the production of substances that decrease the diameter of blood vessels and so increase the blood pressure. The significance of this cell arrangement is that changes in the composition of the filtrate in the lumen of the tubule are detected by the macula densa cells which, in response, release factors (as yet unknown) that diffuse to the juxtaglomerular cells to effect changes in renin production and ultimately in the state of contraction of the arterioles, thus influencing filtration rate.

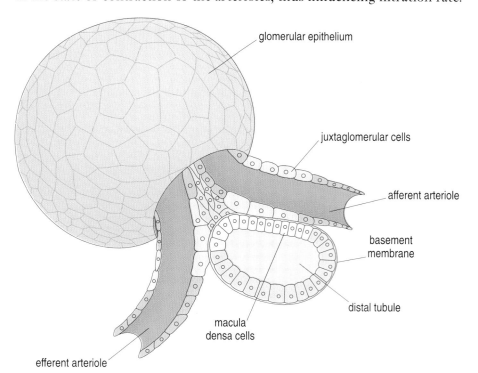

Figure 5.8 Simplified diagram showing the arrangement of the specialized cells in the distal tubule and the arterioles at the juxtaglomerular apparatus.

For example, if the concentration of ions detected in the filtrate by the macula densa cells is high, it would indicate that the flow through the tubule is too great to allow the 'normal' amount of reabsorption in the proximal tubule and loop of Henle. This could be compensated for by a reduction in renin release, causing a reduction in the pressure in the glomerular capillaries and a resultant reduction in the GFR. Thus the flow of filtrate through the tubule would be less, and increased reabsorption would be possible, returning the levels of ions in the filtrate to 'normal'. This is illustrated as a flow diagram in Figure 5.9.

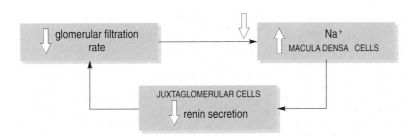

Figure 5.9   Simplified diagram showing an example of the control of GFR. An increase in Na⁺ levels in the distal tubule is detected by the macula densa cells and leads to a decrease in renin secretion by the nearby juxtaglomerular cells. Reduced renin levels cause a decrease in GFR, which in turn leads to a reduction in Na⁺ concentration at the macula densa.

We will return to a discussion of the regulation of GFR in more detail below, when considering the regulation of water and sodium levels in the body.

5.4.2   Control of reabsorption processes

You have seen that several different processes are involved in tubular reabsorption. What may not be clear is how these processes can be controlled in order to affect the *amounts* of different molecules and ions reabsorbed. The answer is that there are mechanisms which allow *changes* in the membrane properties of the epithelial cells in some parts of the tubules, in particular those of the distal parts of the tubule, and also those in the collecting ducts. One of these changes allows increased reabsorption of water when water needs to be conserved.

A second feature of the anatomy of the nephron plays an essential role in the control of reabsorption, this is the long loop of Henle. You have seen that the final control of water reabsorption is in the distal part of the tubules, in the collecting ducts. The changes in the collecting ducts that allow increased reabsorption of water are only effective because the osmolarity of the extracellular fluid in this region is elevated.

❑   Can you work out why this is important?

■   Because water is absorbed passively, by osmosis. If there were no osmotic gradient, even if the permeability of the ducts were increased, no increase in water reabsorption would occur.

As you have seen, absorption of water from the tubule is an entirely passive process, and is dependent upon the concentration of solutes in the epithelium and surrounding tissue being higher than that in the filtrate. A key factor in the control of water reabsorption, then, is the existence of a gradient of increasing osmolarity in the extracellular fluid of the medulla, as shown in Figure 5.10.

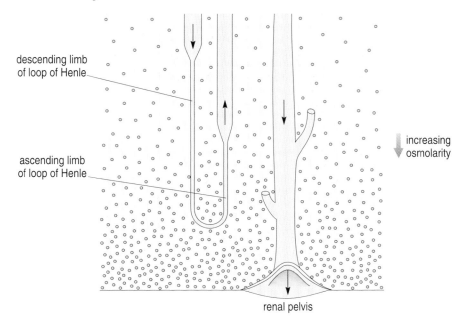

Figure 5.10   The gradient of osmolarity of the medulla. (Solute particles are shown as green circles.)

The osmolarity increases with distance into the medulla from the cortex. This gradient, to which urea makes an important contribution, is set up by a process known as the *countercurrent multiplier system* which comes into play as the filtrate passes along the long loops of Henle. The existence of the gradient means that, as the filtrate passes along the collecting ducts, the osmolarity of the extracellular fluid surrounding the ducts increases. This allows reabsorption of water, by osmosis, along the whole length of the ducts, when, under the influence of stimuli which you will learn about shortly, the ducts have increased permeability to water. If there were no gradient, although water could be reabsorbed in the first part of the ducts, the increase in the osmolarity of the filtrate caused by the loss of the reabsorbed water would soon prevent further water reabsorption, as the concentration of solutes in the filtrate would reach the same value as that in the extracellular fluid.

Summary of Section 5.4

1   Blood pressure in the afferent and efferent arterioles influences the rate of glomerular filtration, and the kidney plays an essential role in the regulation of blood pressure.

2   Control of GFR is made possible because of the arrangement of specialized cells at the juxtaglomerular apparatus.

3   The filtrate is monitored by the macula densa cells which send a chemical signal by diffusion to the juxtaglomerular cells.

4   The juxtaglomerular cells secrete renin, which starts a chain of events leading to a change in the diameter of the blood vessel walls, and so an alteration in the blood pressure and therefore the rate of filtration.

5   Reabsorption is controlled by mechanisms which produce a change in the membranes of tubular epithelial cells in the distal tubules and collecting ducts, and is dependent upon a gradient of increasing osmolarity in the extracellular matrix of the medulla, set up by the countercurrent multiplier system.

5.5 Regulation of body sodium and water levels

Now that you are familiar with the renal processes involved in the excretion and reabsorption of water and salts, and with the places at which these renal processes are controlled, we can turn to *how* the amounts of water and salts in the body are regulated. In this first section, we will consider the regulation of water and sodium content. Both these substances undergo only filtration and reabsorption in the kidney; they are not secreted. The control mechanisms in the kidney that are involved in water and sodium balance then, operate on these two processes.

Under 'normal' circumstances, the amounts of water and sodium taken in are the same as the amounts eliminated; there is no net loss or gain of these substances (see Table 5.1).

Table 5.1 Average daily intake and output of water and sodium chloride in adults. Adapted from Vander, A. J., Sherman, J. H. and Luciano, D. S. (1994) Human Physiology, Sixth International Edition, copyright © 1994, 1990, 1985, 1980, 1975, 1970 by McGraw-Hill, Inc., with permission of the McGraw-Hill Companies.

	Water	Sodium chloride
Intake		
drunk	1 200 ml	
in food	1 000 ml	10.50 g
metabolically produced	350 ml	
total	2 550 ml	10.50 g
Output		
insensible loss (via skin and lungs)	900 ml	
sweat	50 ml	0.25 g
in faeces	100 ml	0.25 g
urine	1 500 ml	10.00 g
total	2 550 ml	10.50 g

This table shows only average values, and as we are all aware, the amount of water and salts taken in and excreted vary considerably according to what we eat and drink. The homeostatic mechanisms that regulate water and sodium levels are able to deal with these variations, with resultant variation in the concentration and volume of the urine produced. For example, the volume of water excreted in the urine can be between 0.4 and 25 litres per day, depending on the volume of fluid ingested. Excretion of a large volume of urine is known as **diuresis**. At this point, some of you may be thinking of the effects of drinking lots of tea, or many pints of beer; in fact alcohol has a particular effect on the control mechanisms that regulate body fluid levels, as you will see.

❑   Can you think of some situations where increased volumes of water and sodium are lost from the body by routes other than the kidney?

■   In hot weather and/or during exercise, sweating may be greatly increased, leading to an increased loss of water and sodium. During a bout of vomiting or diarrhoea, extra water and salts are lost.

The regulation of the levels of water and salts is not only important in the circumstances we have just described, but goes on all the time, since, like everything else in the body, fluid and salt levels are in a dynamic state. You will see that the homeostasis of water and salts involves the interactions of many different systems of the body.

Water balance

The first step in the regulation of water levels is the detection of a change or deviation from the optimum levels of water in the body. As you know, water is the basis of all body fluids. Think, for a moment, of the fluid compartments of the body. You will remember that there are two body compartments in which fluid is present: inside cells (intracellular fluid), and outside cells (extracellular fluid). Extracellular fluid is present in the blood plasma, and also in the spaces between cells, where it is called interstitial fluid. As water can pass between these sites by osmosis and diffusion, a change in water levels will therefore affect the entire body. It will not surprise you to learn then, that changes in water levels are monitored in both fluid compartments of the body.

First, we will look at what happens if insufficient water is ingested.

❑   When the water content of the body decreases, what effect will this will have on the osmolarity of the intracellular and extracellular body fluids?

■   The osmolarity of the intracellular and extracellular body fluids will increase.

Any change in the osmolarity of the extracellular compartment is detected by a group of neurons in the hypothalamus, which are therefore known as **osmoreceptors**. When the osmoreceptors detect an increase in osmolarity of the interstitial fluid which surrounds them, they activate another group of hypothalamic neurons, which secrete **antidiuretic hormone (ADH)**. Since the hypothalamic neurons that produce ADH extend processes to the pituitary gland, this is where ADH enters the circulation, as shown in Figure 5.11.

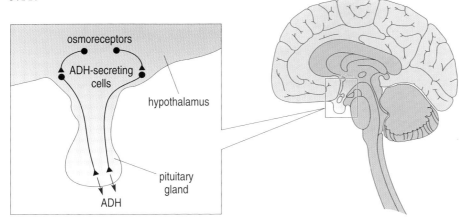

Figure 5.11   Osmoreceptors and ADH–secreting cells.

ADH stimulates changes in the membrane proteins of the epithelial cells of the collecting ducts. Specialized proteins which allow passage of water become incorporated into the membranes of these cells in response to ADH. This has the effect of increasing the permeability of this part of the tubule to water. Since the osmolarity of the extracellular fluid surrounding the collecting ducts is high (because of the countercurrent multiplier system), increased amounts of water are reabsorbed. Thus, if the levels of ADH in the circulation are high, water reabsorption is increased, and the urine becomes more concentrated.

Another stimulus for ADH release comes from vascular stretch receptors which detect changes in blood fluid levels. These are of two types: **volume receptors** at the venoatrial junctions (i.e. the junctions where the veins, the venae cavae, returning blood to the heart join the atria), which detect small changes in blood volume, and arterial baroreceptors (Chapter 2), which come into play when there is a severe loss of blood. Some of the vascular stretch receptors relay this information to the hypothalamus where they influence ADH secretion from nearby cells.

❑ You have already seen that fluid levels affect blood volume, and thus influence blood pressure. If water levels are low, what will be the effect on blood pressure?

■ It will be reduced. Blood pressure is reduced if blood volume is reduced. Blood volume will be reduced if water levels in the body are low.

A decrease in blood volume is detected by the vascular stretch receptors. The change in their firing in turn causes an increase in ADH release.

The control of ADH secretion is shown in Figure 5.12.

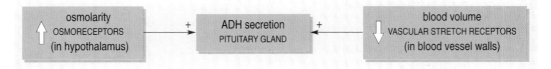

Figure 5.12 Diagram showing the factors controlling ADH secretion.

ADH, then, plays an essential role in the conservation of water at times when fluid intake is low, because it increases the reabsorption of water from the collecting ducts. As we have already stressed, however, there is another renal process which influences water levels, and that is filtration.

❑ You have seen that a lowering of fluid levels results in a decrease in blood pressure. How will this affect GFR, and water reabsorption?

■ A general reduction in blood pressure will cause a lowering of GFR. This will cause an increased reabsorption of sodium, and hence an increase in the passive reabsorption of water.

There is another important aspect of the control of water levels which does not take place in the kidney, and that is the process of drinking itself, stimulated by feelings of thirst. Another group of cells in the hypothalamus, sometimes called *thirst receptors*, are also activated by an increase in the osmolarity of the extracellular fluid. This stimulates a feeling of thirst, which results in increased intake of water. You will learn more about thirst in the following chapter.

ADH plays a key role in water balance. Substances that interfere with ADH production will thus cause disruption to the normal production of urine. A number of you may have experienced this. Alcohol inhibits the release of ADH. This is why consumption of alcoholic drinks seems to have a disproportionate effect on urine production, and also why, in excess, it leads to dehydration and subsequent feelings of thirst!

Diseases in which ADH production is affected also cause a disruption to the normal production of urine. Loss of the ability to synthesize ADH – for example, if the hypothalamus is damaged – is the cause of the condition known as **diabetes insipidus,** characterized by the formation of copious amounts of very dilute urine. It is usually treated successfully by the administration of ADH.

❑ Now that you have seen what occurs when water levels in the body are low, can you work out what will happen if water levels are high?

■ ADH will not be secreted, as the osmoreceptors and baroreceptors that project to the ADH-producing neurons in the hypothalmus will not be appropriately activated. If ADH is not present, the rate of water absorption in the collecting ducts will be very low, and increased volumes of dilute urine will be produced. Increased plasma volume occurs when water levels are high; this will result in an increased GFR, so that reduced amounts of sodium will be reabsorbed. This will lead to a reduction in the passive reabsorption of water, which further contributes to an increased excretion of water.

Regulation of sodium levels

Sodium, like water, is not secreted in the kidney, so the excretion of sodium is dependent upon only two factors: filtration and reabsorption. Both processes are controlled in the regulation of sodium levels.

First, we will look at what happens if sodium levels are low, for example, if insufficient salt is ingested. Under these circumstances, the osmolarity of the body fluids will decrease.

❑   What effect will a reduction of the sodium content, and thus of the osmolarity of the body fluids, have on blood pressure; how will this affect GFR?

◼   It will cause a reduction in blood pressure, because, when sodium levels in the body fall, the plasma volume falls. A reduction in blood pressure will cause a reduction in GFR, because the arterial pressure in the kidneys is lowered as part of the general reduction in blood pressure.

The reduction in GFR will allow increased reabsorption of sodium, and hence also of water, reducing further sodium loss. This is another example of negative feedback.

Other factors also act to reduce GFR when sodium levels are reduced. These involve the action of another group of hormones, and the special anatomical feature of the kidney tubule that was described earlier in this chapter. Thinking back, can you recall how the distal tubule returned to pass close to the glomerulus, and the special types of cell found there, in an arrangement known as the juxtaglomerular apparatus? This was shown in Figure 5.8.

The macula densa cells detect some aspect of reduced flow in the tubule. Although this is not yet fully understood, it is thought that this may be a lowered level of sodium ions, since more reabsorption of sodium is possible in the proximal tubule and loop of Henle if flow is reduced. Whatever the change detected, the macula densa cells respond by stimulating the juxtaglomerular cells to secrete renin into the blood. Renin does not act directly on blood vessels, but cleaves a small polypeptide, **angiotensin I**, from a precursor molecule called **angiotensinogen**, which is produced by the liver. (The word ending -*ogen* is often used in naming precursor molecules; you will remember from Chapter 3 that the pepsin and trypsin precursors are pepsinogen and trypsinogen, respectively.) Angiotensin I is then converted into **angiotensin II** by the action of **angiotensin converting enzyme**, which is located on the lumenal (i.e. inner) surface of capillary endothelial cells, particularly those of the lung. This complicated sequence of events, involving several different organs, is illustrated in Figure 5.13.

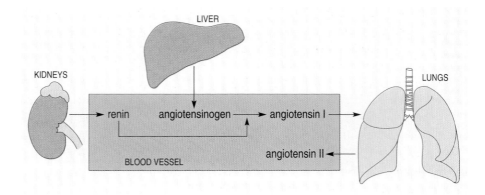

Figure 5.13   Diagram illustrating how the production of angiotensin II from angiotensinogen involves the kidneys, liver and lungs.

Angiotensin II is a hormone which is rapidly broken down in the circulation, but which, among other things, acts to change GFR. Angiotensin II causes a constriction of blood vessels and so an increase in blood pressure, and thus is important in the regulation of blood pressure. In the nephron, angiotensin II is particularly active on the efferent arterioles, thus causing an increase in GFR.

There is a third way in which GFR is increased, and that is in response to the activity of sympathetic nerves. When blood pressure is lowered, sympathetic nerves are activated, causing a constriction of blood vessels and the release of renin. The ways in which GFR is controlled are summarized in Figure 5.14.

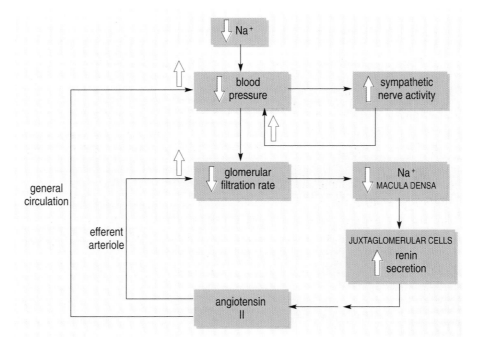

Figure 5.14   Control of GFR, shown in more detail than in Figure 5.9.

The other way in which sodium levels are regulated is by alteration to the process of reabsorption. This is achieved by the action of a steroid hormone called **aldosterone**. Aldosterone is produced by the adrenal glands situated at the top of the kidneys (Book 2, Chapter 3). This hormone increases sodium reabsorption from the collecting ducts. It does so by stimulating an increase in the synthesis of sodium transport proteins in the epithelial cells in this region. (Aldosterone also stimulates the production of sodium transport proteins in the intestinal epithelium and the epithelial cells lining the ducts which empty fluid from the sweat and salivary glands; this increases sodium reabsorption and reduces sodium loss from the gut and skin.) Angiotensin II stimulates aldosterone production. This is illustrated in Figure 5.15.

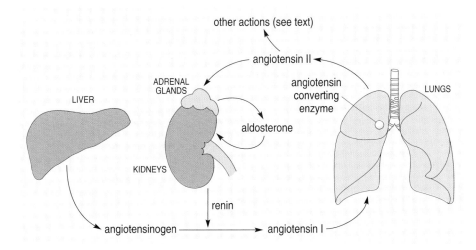

Figure 5.15   The stimulation of aldosterone release by angiotensin II.

Since angiotensinogen and angiotensin converting enzyme are always present, the levels of angiotensin II in the circulation are determined by the levels of renin in the circulation. Renin levels are determined by the kidney and are influenced by three factors. These are: sympathetic nerves; the juxtaglomerular cells (which act as pressure receptors in the blood vessels of the kidney); and the macula densa cells. So, lowering of blood pressure outside the kidney stimulates sympathetic nervous activity, which stimulates renin production; the juxtaglomerular cells also detect changes in blood pressure, this time within the kidney itself, and respond to lowering pressure by secreting more renin; and finally, the macula densa cells detect changes in the concentration of sodium in the ascending part of the loop of Henle, and respond to decreased salt concentrations by stimulating renin production. These control mechanisms are shown in Figure 5.16.

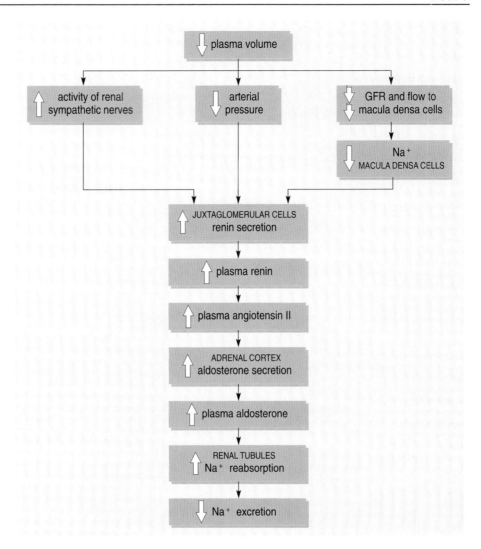

Figure 5.16 The control mechanisms acting to increase renin release, and hence release of aldosterone. Adapted from Vander, A. J., Sherman, J. H. and Luciano, D. S. (1994) Human Physiology, Sixth International Edition, copyright © 1994, 1990, 1985, 1980, 1975, 1970 by McGraw-Hill, Inc., with permission of the McGraw-Hill Companies.

Under normal circumstances these processes regulate the levels of sodium, and thus plasma volume. This influences blood pressure, helping to maintain it at appropriate levels. Abnormally high activation of the renin–angiotensin system can contribute to high blood pressure. This can occur, for example, when a renal artery becomes partially blocked.

When sodium levels are higher than optimal, another hormone also plays a role in the regulation of sodium balance. This is **atrial natriuretic factor (ANF)** which is produced by cells in the atria of the heart. ANF inhibits sodium reabsorption in the kidneys and also increases GFR by acting on renal blood vessels. ANF secretion is stimulated by increased atrial distension, which occurs because of the increased plasma volume when sodium levels are raised.

An essential factor in the consideration of the regulation of sodium balance is the control of intake. Salt appetite is stimulated by decreased blood volume. Both thirst and salt appetite are stimulated by angiotensin II, but salt appetite, unlike thirst, is not immediate, but takes several hours to develop.

❑   Why will excess dietary sodium cause an increase in blood pressure?

■   Excess sodium in the body fluids will cause an increased retention of
       water, because water will move, by osmosis, towards regions of high
       salt levels. Retention of water causes increased blood volume; this
       causes an increase in blood pressure.

Summary of Section 5.5

1   Water levels are monitored in both the intracellular and extracellular
       fluid compartments of the body.

2   When osmolarity of the body fluids increases, for example if water levels
       are low, osmoreceptors in the hypothalamus respond to the increased
       osmolarity of the extracellular fluid by stimulating nearby cells to
       secrete the hormone ADH. ADH increases the permeability of the
       collecting ducts to water. More water is therefore reabsorbed. This is
       possible because of the gradient of increasing osmolarity of the
       extracellular fluid around the ducts, set up by the countercurrent
       multiplier system.

3   Stretch receptors in the cardiovascular system detect changes in the
       distension of blood vessels and thus changes in blood volume. When
       distension is reduced, this too results in an increase in ADH secretion.

4   Thirst receptors (another type of cells in the hypothalamus), respond to
       increased osmolarity of the body fluids by stimulating a feeling of thirst.

5   Regulation of sodium levels is closely related to regulation of water
       levels. Increased sodium causes an increase in osmolarity, controlled in
       part by changes in water intake and excretion, already described.

6   Sodium levels are also monitored in the filtrate as it passes through the
       juxtaglomerular region of the renal tubule. Macula densa cells respond
       to conditions in which the sodium content in the filtrate is reduced by
       stimulating renin production by the juxtaglomerular cells. Renin
       production results in the formation of angiotensin II, which acts to
       constrict blood vessels, increasing blood pressure, and thus GFR. In the
       kidney the efferent arterioles are particularly affected by angiotensin II;
       their constriction therefore also increases GFR. Angiotensin II also
       stimulates aldosterone secretion from the adrenal gland. Aldosterone
       acts to increase sodium reabsorption in the collecting ducts.

7   Salt appetite is stimulated by a decrease in blood volume and by
       angiotensin II, which also stimulates thirst.

8   Increased distension in the atria of the heart, caused by increased blood
       volume, causes the release of atrial natriuretic factor (ANF). ANF
       inhibits sodium reabsorption and acts on renal blood vessels to increase
       GFR, thus accelerating sodium excretion.

5.6 Regulation of potassium levels

Potassium ions play an important role in all cells, and cross cell membranes to enter the cytosol by active transport, by the action of the Na^+–K^+ ATPase. It is thus essential that the K^+ concentration in the extracellular compartment is kept at an appropriate level, so that this pump can be effective. The regulation of appropriate extracellular K^+ levels is particularly important for the maintenance of membrane potentials in muscle and nerve cells (Book 2, Chapter 3). As for other ions, K^+ levels are regulated by the kidney: K^+ is filtered through the glomerulus, and most is then reabsorbed by the proximal tubule and the loop of Henle. In the cortical collecting ducts, however, K^+ may be secreted, and it is this process which is controlled to maintain potassium balance. The main factor affecting K^+ secretion is aldosterone, which, as you have already seen, also plays an essential role in the regulation of Na^+ levels. We do not have space to describe the details here.

5.7 Regulation of pH

You have already learnt something about pH, in Book 1, Chapter 3, and in Chapters 2 and 3 of this book. You will recall that acidity is expressed in terms of pH, and that pH is inversely related to the level of hydrogen (H^+) ions. The pH of most body fluids is near neutral; that is, they have a pH of around 7.4.

❏   Is a pH of 7.4 slightly acidic or slightly alkaline?

■   It is slightly alkaline. Acidity is determined by the concentration of hydrogen ions; a neutral pH is 7.0, acid pH values are less than 7 and alkaline solutions have pH values greater than 7.

As for all other ions in the body, the levels of hydrogen ions must be regulated, so that potentially damaging deviations from a neutral pH do not occur. An increase in levels of hydrogen ions in the circulation is known as **acidosis** (when the pH is reduced to below 7.4) and conversely, decreased hydrogen ion concentrations (when the pH is raised above 7.4) is known as **alkalosis**. Hydrogen ions may be lost or gained in the body by a variety of processes; for example, they may be produced as a by-product of various metabolic reactions and can be lost during vomiting.

❏   Why are hydrogen ions lost during vomiting?

■   Because of the high concentration of hydrogen ions in the stomach (Chapter 3).

Most hydrogen ions in the body result from the production of carbon dioxide, large quantities of which are produced during aerobic respiration (see Chapters 2 and 4). Carbon dioxide (CO_2) combines with water to form carbonic acid (H_2CO_3), which dissociates to form hydrogen ions and bicarbonate ions (HCO_3^-):

$$CO_2 + H_2O \rightleftharpoons H_2CO_3 \rightleftharpoons HCO_3^- + H^+$$

Hydrogen ions can bind, in a reversible manner, to bicarbonate ions and also to other molecules, including proteins such as haemoglobin. This has the effect of buffering (neutralizing) the hydrogen ions. The regulation of pH in the body then, occurs by buffering of hydrogen ions, until excess can be excreted by the kidney.

The regulation of the levels of circulating hydrogen ions which occurs in the kidney is actually achieved by changing the levels of bicarbonate ions in the plasma.

❑   What would you expect to happen to the concentration of hydrogen ions in the plasma if bicarbonate ions are removed and excreted in the urine?

■   Removal of bicarbonate ions would have the effect of 'pulling' the reaction shown above to the right, thus raising the levels of free hydrogen ions in the circulation. Conversely, if extra bicarbonate ions are added to the plasma, it has the effect of buffering an equal number of hydrogen ions in the circulation, thereby reducing the hydrogen ion concentration.

How, then, do these processes occur in the kidney? Bicarbonate ions are freely filtered through the glomerulus. Tubular epithelial cells produce hydrogen ions and bicarbonate ions. The hydrogen ions are secreted into the lumen, the bicarbonate ions move, down the electrochemical gradient produced by the active transport of sodium ions, into the circulation. This is shown in Figure 5.17. The bicarbonate ions that have been filtered into the lumen of the tubules then combine with the secreted hydrogen ions to form carbon dioxide and water (according to the equation above) which are reabsorbed into the epithelial cells. Thus, although the bicarbonate ions have not been reabsorbed as such, there is no net loss of bicarbonate ions from the circulation.

How does this process result in regulation of hydrogen ion levels in the circulation? Part of the answer is that when all the filtered bicarbonate is bound to secreted hydrogen ions, any extra hydrogen ions that are secreted bind to other, *non*-bicarbonate buffers in the filtrate. When this happens, there is a net *loss* of hydrogen ions, and a net *gain* of bicarbonate ions, from the plasma.

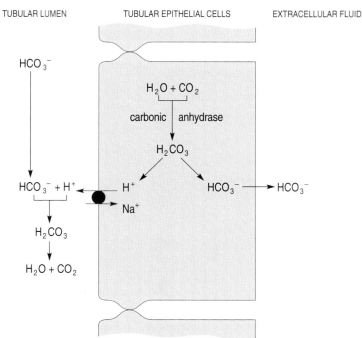

Another way in which bicarbonate levels in the plasma can be increased is by
the production of bicarbonate in epithelial cells of the proximal tubule, by a
chemical reaction involving the breakdown of the amino acid glutamine. This
was one of the processes referred to earlier in this chapter, in the section on
tubular metabolism. The resulting bicarbonate enters the circulation, while
ammonium ions are excreted. This is shown in Figure 5.18. Plasma pH is
hence regulated by control of these processes, but it is too complex to
concern us here.

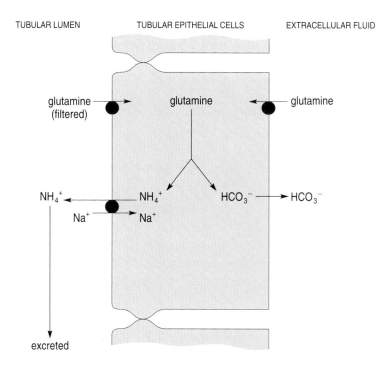

The respiratory system also plays an important role in pH regulation, as you saw in Chapter 2.

Summary of Section 5.7

1   The pH of body fluids is regulated by buffering of hydrogen ions and by secretion of hydrogen ions by the renal tubules.

2   Buffering of hydrogen ions in the circulation is mainly by bicarbonate ions, but also by other molecules such as proteins.

3   In the kidney, secreted hydrogen ions bind to filtered bicarbonate ions, excess hydrogen ions then bind to other components of the filtrate. Since the secretion of hydrogen ions by the tubular epithelial cells is accompanied by the production of an equal number of bicarbonate ions which return to the circulation, there is no net loss of bicarbonate.

4   Additional bicarbonate can enter the circulation as a result of the metabolism of glutamine by the tubular epithelium.

5.8 Movement of urine to the bladder and micturition

After passage through the tubules, urine is moved along the ureters to the bladder. The ureters are tubular structures, which are composed of smooth muscle and have an inner lining of epithelial cells. Movement of the urine is by a peristaltic type of action of the smooth muscle. The bladder is able to store quite large volumes of urine (300–400 ml); the smooth muscle which forms the major part of the bladder wall relaxes to accommodate the increasing volume of fluid. Under normal circumstances, urine does not leak out of the bladder, because of two specialized rings of muscle, the **internal urethral sphincter,** which is composed of smooth muscle, and the **external urethral sphincter** which consists of skeletal muscle (Figure 5.19). The anatomical arrangements of the muscles are such that the internal sphincter remains closed when the muscle of the main body of the bladder is relaxed. Both the bladder smooth muscle and internal sphincter muscles are under involuntary control, by neurons of the autonomic nervous system. The external sphincter, on the other hand, in most adults at least, is controlled voluntarily.

Emptying of the bladder is known as **micturition**. As the bladder fills, stretch receptors in the muscle are stimulated. These cause a reflex contraction of the main bladder muscle and relaxation of the sphincter. This is a local reflex, which occurs in the spinal cord. Messages from the bladder also reach the brain, giving the sensation of fullness. In adults, as the bladder fills, contraction of the bladder muscle is stimulated. Once a certain volume is reached (300–400 ml), the reflex contraction is strong enough to begin to open the internal sphincter. As this occurs, the nerves originating in the spinal cord that normally keep the external muscle contracted are inhibited, resulting in relaxation of the external sphincter. Once both sphincters are open, the contraction of the bladder muscle forces urine out of the urethra. The pathways involved in these processes are summarized in Figure 5.19.

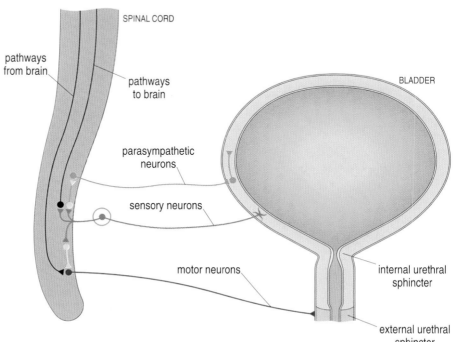

Figure 5.19   Diagram showing the nerve pathways involved in micturition. (The green circle denotes a dorsal root ganglion.)

During childhood, voluntary control of the external sphincter is learnt, by activation of pathways descending from the brain. These can cause initiation or prevention of urination, at will. If the spinal cord is injured, the ascending and descending pathways can be damaged, leading to loss of voluntary control of urination. Childbirth can cause a physical trauma of tissues that lie close to the birth canal, and involves stretching of the pelvic floor muscles. This can also lead to a loss of contractility of the external sphincter and surrounding muscles, but exercising the muscles of the pelvic floor can rectify this.

5.9 Kidney function in the new-born

The processes involved in the homeostasis of body fluids and salts are crucial not only for adults, but also for new-born babies. In fact they are particularly important for babies, for only small imbalances in the levels of water or salts, or accumulations of toxic substances can very rapidly have serious consequences.

Although much kidney development goes on in the fetus, not all glomeruli are functional at birth. The glomeruli deepest within the kidney are the last to develop. Although blood flow to the fetal kidneys is low, much urine is produced (see Book 1, Chapter 6), but this is not of a similar composition to that formed after birth, and it is the placenta, not the fetal kidneys, which is responsible for sodium and water balance.

After birth, glomerular filtration rate and sodium excretion fall, rapidly, but then slowly rise during the first post-natal week as the infant takes in fluid. The maturation of kidney function takes several years, adult rates of filtration and tubular function being reached at about two to three years of age. Babies are particularly vulnerable to dehydration, because their kidneys are not very efficient at producing concentrated urine. The water content of formula feeds is thus crucial.

5.10 Endocrine role of the kidneys

In addition to their major role in the regulation of levels of body fluids and salts and in acid–base balance, the kidneys also have an endocrine role. The hormone **erythropoietin** (which is also produced by the liver) is actually produced in and released from the kidney itself.

Erythropoietin stimulates the proliferation of undifferentiated precursor cells present in the bone marrow. These precursors give rise to red blood cells. Erythropoietin is released from capillary endothelial cells in the kidney; its release is stimulated by a decrease in oxygen concentration (P_{O_2}) in the blood supply to the kidneys.

The kidneys also play an important role in the hormonal control of calcium homeostasis.

❑   You have seen that about 50% of plasma calcium is filtered at the glomerulus. Can you recall why not all calcium is filtered?

◼   The remaining calcium in the plasma is bound to proteins which are too large to be filtered.

After filtration, calcium is reabsorbed in the tubules; it is not secreted. The levels of calcium in the plasma are, in part, regulated by control of the reabsorption process.

Two hormones play a major role in the regulation of plasma calcium levels, these are **parathyroid hormone**, and the active form of vitamin D (Chapter 3). Parathyroid hormone is produced by the parathyroid glands, which lie within the larger thyroid gland (Book 2, Chapter 2).

❑   Can you recall the relationship between parathyroid hormone production and blood calcium levels?

◼   When plasma calcium levels are decreased, parathyroid hormone secretion is stimulated.

Parathyroid hormone has several actions. In addition to increasing the reabsorption of calcium by the tubular epithelial cells, it increases calcium release from bone and activates vitamin D (which results in increased absorption of calcium from the gut). Thus plasma calcium levels are regulated, as shown in Figure 5.20.

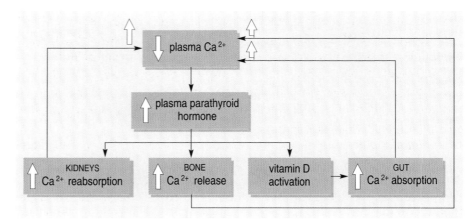

Figure 5.20   Regulation of plasma calcium levels.

The kidney also plays an important role in the activation of vitamin D. The key step in the activation of vitamin D occurs in the kidney, and is stimulated by parathyroid hormone.

5.11 Diuretics and kidney disease

Many diseases can affect the kidneys and, since this is a course about healthy humans, we will not examine these in detail here. However, a number of common conditions are treated by drugs that affect kidney function. One of the most commonly prescribed types of drugs are **diuretics**. These act to increase the volume of urine excreted, and do this by inhibiting sodium reabsorption.

❑   Can you explain how inhibition of sodium reabsorption results in an increase in the volume of urine excreted?

◼   Water is reabsorbed passively, by osmosis, largely as a result of sodium reabsorption, which raises the osmolarity of the extracellular fluid.

Diuretics are used to treat conditions in which sodium balance is disrupted because of a failure of the kidneys to excrete sodium normally. Such a failure results in an increase in water retention in the extracellular spaces; this is known as *oedema* (pronounced ee-dee-ma), and is, for example, a cause of swollen ankles. A common cause for the failure of the kidneys in this way is *congestive heart failure*, in which the contractility of the heart is reduced, resulting in a reduction of blood pressure, which, in turn, causes a reduction in GFR, reduced flow in the tubules and hence, via the renin–

angiotensin system, increased aldosterone production and sodium reabsorption.

Diuretics are also used to treat high blood pressure, or hypertension. Treatment results in lowering of the content of water and sodium in the body, and reduction in arteriolar dilation.

Diseases affecting the kidney itself are all too common. The treatment for these conditions is **dialysis**, which acts essentially as an artificial kidney system. The process involves diverting the blood from an artery into a semipermeable tubing. This tubing allows the passage of water, small molecules (e.g. urea) and ions but prevents the movement of large molecules (e.g. proteins). The tubing is immersed in a large volume of a salt solution with a composition similar to plasma, but without proteins. This is called the *dialysing fluid*. The composition of this fluid is crucial. It does *not* contain substances which are normally excreted at the kidney, and which build up in the plasma of individuals with kidney failure (e.g. urea, sulphate and phosphate ions). These substances therefore diffuse *out* of the blood into the dialysing fluid. The fluid contains *higher* levels of glucose and bicarbonate ions than those typical of a healthy individual. These substances then, *pass into* the blood from the dialysing fluid. Ions which do not build up in the plasma of people with kidney disease (e.g. Ca^{2+}, Mg^{2+}), and are at similar levels in the plasma and dialysing fluid simply exchange across the tubing; their levels in the blood are not altered much by dialysis. After dialysis, the blood is returned to the body, via a vein.

5.12 Excretion that does not occur via the kidneys

You have seen how 'unwanted' or excess substances that are filtered at the glomerulus are eliminated in the urine. You have also seen that others, for example hydrogen ions, can be eliminated by secretion into the filtrate. The other main way in which excretion occurs is in the faeces. The liver plays an important role in the breakdown of many substances, which are then secreted in the bile and eliminated, via the gut. Liver functions associated with its excretory role are listed below.

* Destroys 'old' red blood cells.
* Breaks haemoglobin down to form the waste product bilirubin.
* Detoxifies or transforms *endogenous* (i.e. made in the body, e.g. steroid hormones) and *exogenous* (i.e. ingested, e.g. drugs) organic molecules.
* Excretes trace metals.
* Excretes cholesterol.

This seemingly simple list includes functions which are essential to health; details of the biochemical processes involved are beyond the scope of this course and so are not described here. Liver failure results in the accumulation of toxic substances in the body, with potentially fatal consequences. Because the liver is involved in the detoxification of harmful substances, these substances can reach high levels in this organ. Thus it is frequently damaged by exposure to high levels of toxic substances. An example which may immediately spring to mind is that of alcohol. The effects of extreme and prolonged overconsumption of alcohol on the liver are well-known.

Most of you will be familiar with the condition called '*jaundice*'. This refers to a build-up in the body of bilirubin (an end-product of the breakdown of haemoglobin from red blood cells), which has a yellow colour, thus giving the yellowish, 'jaundiced' appearance of some individuals. Jaundice can occur for a number of reasons, including blockage of the bile duct, liver disease, and the presence of an elevated level of bilirubin in the blood because of abnormal breakdown of red blood cells. Jaundice is particularly common in new-born babies, because the capacity of the liver to secrete bilirubin is not fully developed at this stage.

In this chapter we have focused primarily on the role of the urinary system in homeostasis. You have seen that the kidney plays an essential part in maintaining the balance of fluids and ions in the body, and in the excretion of waste molecules. However, we hope that it has also become clear that the kidney does not function in isolation, nor simply under the influence of the nervous and endocrine systems. Normal kidney function, and hence the regulation of the amounts of water and other essential substances in the body, involves *interaction* with other organ systems, some of which might initially seem to be unlikely partners with the urinary system, such as the lungs. Another important point that should be stressed is the *dynamic* nature of the processes that have been described in this chapter, which are continually going on in our bodies.

Summary of Sections 5.8–5.12

1   Urine passes from the kidney to the bladder via the ureters. Urine is held in the bladder by the action of two specialized areas of muscle, the internal urethral sphincter and the external urethral sphincter. Micturition, or urination, is stimulated by distension of the smooth muscle of the bladder wall. This activates stretch receptors, which trigger a local reflex contraction of the bladder muscle and relaxation of the internal sphincter, and also a sensation of fullness, which leads to voluntary relaxation of the external urethral sphincter.

2   Maturation of kidney function takes some 2–3 years. Voluntary control of the external urethral sphincter is learnt during childhood.

3   The kidneys have endocrine functions. The hormone erythropoietin, which stimulates the proliferation of red blood cell precursors in the bone marrow, is produced in the kidneys.

4   The kidneys also play an important role in the control of calcium homeostasis, by activating vitamin D, which results in increased calcium absorption from the gut. Parathyroid hormone (produced in the parathyroid glands) stimulates this activation in the kidney, and also increases calcium reabsorption in the kidney tubules.

5   A number of common conditions, such as high blood pressure, are treated by substances called diuretics. Diuretics increase the amount of urine excreted, by inhibiting sodium reabsorption.

6   Individuals with kidney disease undergo dialysis, during which wastes are removed from the blood.

7   The liver plays an important role in the excretion of unwanted substances (such as organic molecules, trace metals and degraded red blood cells) which are not excreted at the kidney.

Objectives for Chapter 5

After completing this chapter you should be able to:

5.1   Define and use, or recognize definitions and applications of, each of the terms printed in **bold** in the text.

5.2   Outline the features of the main processes involved in the formation of urine, and relate them to the cell types found in the nephron. (*Question 5.1*)

5.3   Describe the fate of organic molecules, water, sodium and other ions that are filtered at the renal corpuscle, and how renal function can be assessed. (*Questions 5.1 and 5.2*)

5.4   Explain how the levels of water, sodium, potassium and calcium are regulated, referring to the control mechanisms involved. (*Questions 5.1 and 5.3*)

5.5   Show how acid–base balance is regulated. (*Question 5.4*)

5.6   Recall the processes and pathways involved in micturition.

5.7   Explain why the kidney can be said to have endocrine functions. (*Question 5.5*)

Questions for Chapter 5

Question 5.1   (*Objectives 5.1, 5.2. and 5.3*)

Substance X is present at a plasma concentration of 8 mg per ml and is excreted at a rate of 2 mg per min in the urine. Outline the possible fates of X in the kidney. What is the clearance of X?

Question 5.2 *(Objective 5.3)*

List the fates of (a) glucose, (b) sodium and (c) water in the kidney tubules.

Question 5.3 *(Objective 5.4)*

Complete Figure 5.21 to make a flow diagram. Show with arrows what will happen to the variables indicated after a period of severe sweating (draw arrows between appropriate variables). Which of the indicated variables must be confined within a narrow range (i.e. which are regulated variables)?

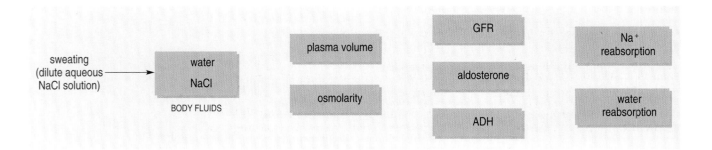

Figure 5.21   For Question 5.3.

Question 5.4 *(Objective 5.5)*

Severe diarrhoea results not only in the loss of water, but also of large amounts of bicarbonate ions. What effect would this have on the pH of the body fluids, and how would a balance be restored?

Question 5.5 *(Objective 5.7)*

What effect does decreased oxygen concentration in the circulation have on kidney function?

CHAPTER 6
COMMUNICATION AND
CONTROL IN THE REGULATION
OF THE INTERNAL
ENVIRONMENT

6.1 Introduction

This chapter returns to the theme of communication and control, which was covered in Book 2, Chapter 3. It revives some of the concepts you met there in the specific context of the regulation of the nutrient and fluid environment of the body. This regulation is achieved by exerting control over two things:

- behaviour, in the form of feeding and drinking;
- internal variables, such as insulin and urine production rates.

This chapter is concerned with how the nervous and endocrine systems exert such control, principally with respect to feeding and drinking. Of course, as you may have appreciated by now, everything you have met so far in Book 3 is, in a sense, about communication and control, e.g. insulin promoting glucose uptake and ADH promoting water reabsorption in the kidney. This chapter looks at the same processes, but at a higher level, that of the whole system, involving the integration of physiology and behaviour.

Before we go any further, this is an appropriate place to review briefly some concepts of communication and control that you learned earlier and which will be fundamental to the present chapter.

❏   What is a reflex?

■   A reflex is a relatively simple stereotyped piece of behaviour, triggered automatically by a particular stimulus (Book 2, Chapter 3).

We shall need to consider reflexes in the context of the present discussion.

❏   (a) What are the two means, discussed in the previous chapter, by which body fluids are regulated, and what is the principal hormone involved? (b) How are the internal control and the behavioural control activated?

■   (a) Both drinking and the kidneys contribute to the regulation of body fluids, whilst the hormone involved is ADH. (b) It appears that both ADH secretion and drinking are triggered by the activity of neurons in the brain that are sensitive to the local hydration state.

When previous chapters in the present book have looked at the physiological and biochemical processes involved in the regulation and control of the internal environment of the body, reference was made to the role of the nervous system in these processes. Although the bulk of the present chapter will discuss feeding and drinking, as the ADH example shows, the nervous and endocrine systems have a role in regulating the internal physiological processes of the body, in addition to their role in ingestive behaviour. The general principle of regulation and control by internal and external factors is summarized in Figure 6.1. Behaviour, determined by the nervous system in interaction with the external environment, affects the physiology of the body. Although this chapter is about regulation of nutrient and fluid levels, it is worth considering the similarities with temperature regulation.

❑   Can you relate Figure 6.1 to the regulation of temperature?

▦   There are involuntary controls such as shivering and voluntary controls such as putting on a coat or moving to a warmer place that serve to regulate body temperature (see Chapter 4).

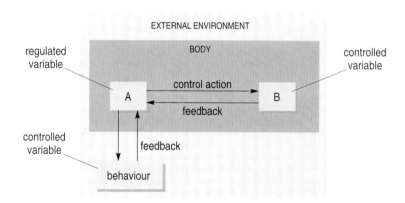

Figure 6.1   Controls exerted in the regulation of a physiological variable at A. These controls involve both involuntary physiological processes at B, whose consequences feed back to A, as well as behaviour.

Section 6.2 will look at the role of the nervous and endocrine systems in communication within the body, in a way that starts to make some links with the external environment and with behaviour. Section 6.3 will take a developmental perspective by looking at the way in which infant suckling, a means of deriving both water and nutrients, gives way to independent feeding and drinking. Sections 6.4–6.9 look at feeding and hunger and Section 6.10 at the ingestion of water and the thirst sensation. Throughout, you are advised to think of differences and similarities between types of ingestive behaviours.

Summary of Section 6.1

1   Regulation of internal variables (e.g. body fluid level) is achieved by exerting control over certain physiological variables (e.g. urine production rate) and behaviour (e.g. drinking).

2   Both nervous and endocrine systems have a role in the regulation of the internal environment.

6.2 Internal and external information and the physiology of the body

As represented in Figure 6.1, you have met examples of where information on an internal physiological event at one location in the body (A) is communicated to another location (B). At site B, action is effected in part on the basis of the information received from A. This action in turn regulates the physiological variable at A. For example, information on the state of hydration registered at the brain (A) is communicated to the kidney (B) by means of ADH, where control is exerted over urine production rate.

❑   Can you recall an example of where information received by the external sense organs is communicated to a physiological process and used to effect a control action in the interests of regulation?

■   In Chapter 3, Section 3.4.2, there was a discussion about the cephalic phase of digestion, where information about food being ingested is able to exert control over the secretion of juices in the stomach.

In other words, an important principle involved in the regulation of the internal environment is that of **anticipation**, which is illustrated with the help of Figure 6.2. The presence of food in the stomach triggers the secretion of digestive juices. However, observation of the timing of such secretion shows that rather than responding to the presence of food in the stomach, we normally start to respond before the food has even got into the stomach. In effect, we anticipate its arrival.

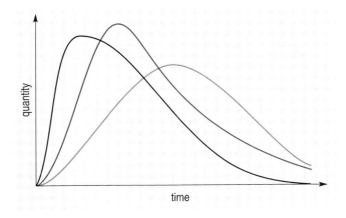

Figure 6.2   Representation of the quantity of food in the stomach (red), the amount of gastric juice if its secretion were a response to food in the stomach (blue) and when it is in response to the sight and taste of food (black).

❏   What is the biological advantage of such anticipation?

■   The food arrives in a stomach that is immediately able to start the digestive process. It avoids time delays. This might be of advantage at times when food is in short supply and the body is nutrient-deficient.

How do we explain such anticipation? One process that plays a role is that of **conditioning**, by which we can form associations between two otherwise unrelated events. Indeed, conditioning was first scientifically investigated in precisely the present context of digestion, by the Russian physiologist Ivan Pavlov. It is a concept that has now entered the popular vocabulary and imagination, e.g. 'it's all because of their conditioning'. But the term has a precise scientific meaning, as the following example will illustrate.

If food is placed in the mouth of a hungry dog, the animal will both salivate and produce gastric juices, two examples of reflexes. Pavlov observed both the secretion of saliva in a dog's mouth and the secretion of gastric juices in the stomach in response to the presence of food in the mouth. The food was said to be the **unconditional stimulus** (UCS), since it unconditionally elicited such secretion, which is the **unconditional response** (UCR). The logic underlying the term 'unconditionally' will become apparent in a moment. As you probably already know, Pavlov was famous for ringing bells at the time of giving his dogs food, or a second or so before presentation. Ringing a bell does not normally cause a dog to salivate and so would be termed a 'neutral stimulus' (NS). However, that all changed in the hands of Pavlov.

After a number of experiences of food accompanied by the sound of a bell, the bell on its own, i.e. even in the absence of food, acquired the capacity to elicit these oral and gastric secretions. The bell did not have the unconditional power of the food; it started out as a mere neutral stimulus. Rather its strength was *conditional* upon its association with food, and hence the appearance of the word 'conditioning' in our language. The bell was termed a **conditional stimulus** (CS) and the secretion in response to the bell was termed a **conditional response** (CR). Since the food did not require a conditioning procedure to elicit secretion of saliva, it was termed the unconditional stimulus. This is summarized in Figure 6.3. This phenomenon does not apply just to dogs. Humans also salivate in response to the sight and smell of food. The assumption is that they have been exposed to a long conditioning history in which these sights and smells have been followed by food in the mouth. Conditioning is one means by which we are said to form associations in our memory between two events that are associated with each other in the world. Thus Pavlov arranged an association between bell and food and the dog came to form a corresponding association.

A form of such anticipation applies also to the history of association between tastes and subsequent effects, post-absorption. As you have seen in Book 2, Chapter 3, and in the present book, if blood glucose levels rise, there will be increased secretion of the hormone insulin. This will promote the movement

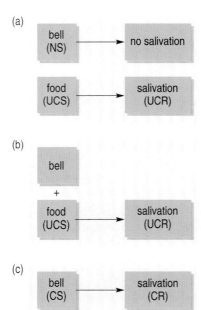

Figure 6.3   Representation of conditioning: (a) initially the bell (neutral stimulus, NS) does not elicit salivation but food (unconditional stimulus, UCS) does; (b) the bell is paired with presentation of food; (c) the situation after pairing in which the bell on its own, now a conditional stimulus (CS), can trigger salivation (conditional response, CR) even if the food is omitted.

of glucose into cells. However, since the ingestion of food (or even the sight and smell of food) is usually followed by the elevation of blood glucose levels, there is the possibility of a learned association between the two events, ingestion and post-absorptive consequences. Such an association, termed the 'cephalic' phase of insulin release, is indeed found in practice (Woods, 1991; Langhans and Scharrer, 1992). To what extent this is the outcome of conditioning is not entirely clear but doubtless conditioning plays an important role.

❏   Can you describe this effect in the terms of conditioning?

■   The rise in insulin secretion, as a result of rising blood glucose level, is termed the unconditional response. The sight and smell of food is the conditional stimulus. The rise in insulin level as a result of the presentation of food is the conditional response.

Thus the increase in insulin secretion occurs *before* the glucose reaches the circulation (see Figure 6.4). It is also found that glucose given orally stimulates a greater rise in insulin than does the same quantity given intravenously (Uvnäs-Moberg and Winberg, 1989).

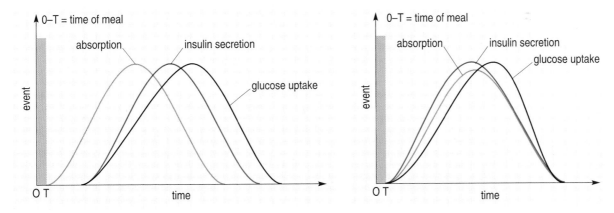

Figure 6.4   Anticipation within the insulin control system: insulin level in blood (red), glucose uptake by cells (black); absorption of nutrients from the gut (blue): (a) hypothetical response if there were no cephalic phase; (b) response with cephalic phase. The meal was eaten during time 0 to T.

❏   In the case of insulin secretion, can you see any advantage of such an anticipatory process?

■   It means that, shortly after encountering food, cellular absorption and metabolism of glucose from the bloodstream can proceed, since replenishment of the blood glucose is underway. It can also prevent the blood glucose level rising too sharply, a situation that might occur if insulin was produced only in response to an increase in blood glucose level.

Processes of anticipation illustrate a crucial feature of the system: although, for convenience, we speak of separate external and internal factors in the control of feeding, these are inextricably interdependent. External factors owe some of their potency to their effect on such internal factors as insulin level. An important message of Section 6.2 is that organisms have a history. You cannot simply take an organism at a single point in time and hope to get a full picture of the complex processes going on only in terms of what is happening at that particular time. Conditioning means that events that have happened in the past, e.g. a pairing of event X with event Y a number of times, will influence the present. This theme will be looked at further in the next section as we consider some of the factors that set the scene for adult ingestive behaviour, in terms of the development of feeding and drinking.

Summary of Section 6.2

1   Some control actions could be said to occur in anticipation of physiological changes to which they are appropriate. For example, secretion of gastric juices starts before food reaches the stomach and insulin secretion starts before nutrients reach the bloodstream.

2   Conditioning is a means by which such anticipation can occur.

3   If a neutral stimulus (e.g. a bell) is paired with an unconditional stimulus (UCS) that evokes a response (UCR), the neutral stimulus can become a conditional stimulus (CS) and evoke a conditional response (CR).

6.3 Suckling and the development of independent ingestive behaviour

The new-born human comes into the world equipped with a few innate reflexes (Book 1, Chapter 6 and Book 2, Chapter 3) that help it to survive (Booth, 1994). One such is the **suckling reflex**, consisting of orientation towards a nipple and sucking milk. The literature is a bit confusing here since the term 'suckling' is often used for the action of obtaining milk from the breast and to refer to both the infant and the mother. In humans, the infant's suckling is an example of a system that starts off being automatic and reflex-like in its organization but with experience comes under some voluntary control. Suckling has effects upon the activity of the digestive tract and is therefore important not only for the gain of nutrients but also for the development of the control of the motility (patterns of contraction) within the digestive tract.

In the transition from being simply a reflex to becoming part of a bigger system of voluntary behavioural control, suckling comes under some control from those parts of the brain that are concerned with energy balance. Thus the reflex can be modulated in such a way that it is particularly activated at times when ingestion is appropriate to energy needs.

The ability of the infant to exert control over suckling was demonstrated by means of some specially designed experiments done by psychologists (Bruner and Bruner, 1968). Equipment was built such that suckling was measured and it triggered effects in the environment, e.g. when infants sucked, illumination level was changed. Infants of 1–3 months learned to use sucking as a means to obtain such a result or to bring an out-of-focus picture into focus. So, even early on, learning processes are evident in relation to ingestive movements. The nervous system is able to associate oral factors with events as remote from nutrition as changes in room illumination. Therefore, considering the phenomenon of conditioning, one can imagine many possibilities for the development of complex associations involving normal suckling and its nutritive consequences.

In the overall context of this course, an important message of the present chapter is the need to take a holistic view of food intake and nutrient assimilation. In a system with interactions, tinkering with one part can have important implications at other parts of the system. A study by Marchini *et al.* (1987) illustrates this. They looked at the role of non-nutritive sucking (with a dummy) on the blood levels of insulin, gastrin and somatostatin. As discussed earlier in this book, these are hormones concerned with the metabolic state of the body. Some pre-term infants were fed by means of a stomach tube. This circumvents the suckling behaviour that would normally accompany the intake of nutrients. By-passing part of the normal system raises the question of whether there is normally a role of suckling behaviour *per se* that is missing in tube-fed infants. A pointer to the answer might be that an increased weight gain is observed in tube-fed infants who are allowed to suck a pacifier in association with tube feeding as compared to controls without such an opportunity for sucking. In the study of Marchini *et al.* infants were allowed to suck a non-nutritive pacifier and the effect on blood insulin levels observed. Such a procedure rapidly elevated blood insulin levels compared to those found in babies without a pacifier.

In a further experiment (Widström *et al.*, 1988), it was found that the process of digestion was assisted by endocrine and neural events triggered by the mechanics of sucking (e.g. enhanced rates of stomach emptying were seen). Widström *et al.* suggest that the normal development of feeding behaviour can be assisted by allowing the facility for sucking to occur.

You have already met the hormone cholecystokinin (CCK) in Chapter 3. Its role was described as a hormone that stimulates the secretion of various digestive juices. In this chapter another role is described: as a hormone that helps to switch off feeding. The secretion of CCK is stimulated by the suckling action of the infant (Uvnäs-Moberg and Winberg, 1989), another example of an association that might well be explained by conditioning.

The baby is motivated to ingest as a function of the length of time since last feeding. After a period of suckling at the breast there will be signs of **satiety**, meaning a state where ingestion cannot be aroused; the baby will be less likely to suckle. This example implicates a reflex organization of ingestion and a process that serves to switch off that ingestion. It appears that the stimulus that causes the baby to lose interest in further suckling is connected with the mechanical stretch of the stomach (Booth, 1994). This is an example of a negative feedback loop, as shown in Figure 6.5.

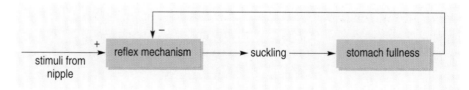

Figure 6.5   Control system underlying suckling.

Note that the infant is being exposed to the particular taste, texture and temperature of the milk accompanied by the mechanical acts of suckling and swallowing. It is known that infants have a rich capacity to form associations (Booth, 1994). Thus there might well be mother-specific or culture-specific tastes and odours associated with the milk that will form memories and which will play a role in subsequent diet preferences. Ingestion will be followed by filling of the stomach and by consequences for the physiology of the body of the digestion and absorption of the nutrients. The infant is equipped to respond positively to the taste of milk and to ingest it. It is from these interacting behavioural and physiological processes that the subsequent course of the development of ingestive behaviour, both feeding and drinking, is set. Subsequent preferences and aversions for particular foods will build upon the early experiences.

The stomach stretch factor also appears to play a role in terminating ingestion in adults, but in a complex combination with a variety of other factors, such as the events occurring after nutrients have left the stomach. Thus, as part of development, there is a complex elaboration of the kind of process represented in Figure 6.5. As the baby grows and experiences a wider range of different tastes, then so different associations will be made between the taste of these foods, their visual and tactile characteristics and the consequences of ingesting them (e.g. gastric secretions, gain of energy, correction of vitamin deficiency or gastrointestinal upset). The child will be in a social environment in which certain feeding habits and foodstuffs are the cultural norm. The control of feeding is to be understood as based upon a complex interaction of such factors (Booth, 1994). As an adult, there will be signals from depletion of nutrients detected somewhere in the body, memories of previous encounters with foods and knowledge of the availability of foods. The later development of satiety in adult feeding would be expected to depend to some extent upon patterns of satiety (e.g. gut filling, oral factors and hormone secretion) set up early in life.

There might be pressures on maintaining healthy eating habits by propaganda to avoid certain foods and to favour others. There might be peer pressure and social conformity factors (e.g. 'I want that product advertised on TV since all my classmates eat it'). Of course, there might also be economic and religious constraints on diet choice. There might be social pressures to reject food, as in the pressure some people feel to maintain a slim body line. All of these inputs to feeding control will play a role in determining appetite towards a certain food in a certain environment and in a certain physiological state (see Figure 6.6). There will be inhibitory effects upon appetite arising from such things as a full stomach and the detection of nutrients in the intestine. The strength of these signals will also be determined in part by the person's developmental history.

Figure 6.6   Some of the determinants of feeding motivation.

The task of this chapter is to consider some of these complex processes, and to look at the interactions between the factors summarized by arrows in Figure 6.6. The next section looks at the role of nutrients in the body, and subsequent sections consider some theories about which variables are involved in the control of the onset of feeding and subsequent satiety. The discussion will then consider how such signals play a role in conjunction with all of the other factors involved in ingestion.

Summary of Section 6.3

1   The new-born infant is equipped with a suckling reflex. Stomach filling inhibits this reflex.

2   As well as obtaining nutrients, suckling has important physiological consequences.

3   From this basic reflex, interacting with the external and internal environments of the body, there emerges the adult pattern of appetite and food intake.

6.4 Homeostasis and feeding

It is not difficult to appreciate the relationship between homeostasis and an important aspect of the control of food intake, and therefore to view feeding within the domain of physiological regulation. The role of feeding might seem to be analogous to switching on a heater in the temperature regulation of a room, in that behaviour can serve to maintain constancy of the internal environment. In terms of homeostasis, nutrient deficit is detected and this tends to trigger ingestion, which then corrects the deficit. Overeating *tends* to lower appetite and so a negative feedback control system is clearly implicated. However, although the principle of homeostasis captures an aspect of food intake control, it is not the whole story. Alas, if it were, we might have fewer problems of feeding and weight control. For this reason 'tends' is italicized, in order to emphasize that the regulatory factor should not be exaggerated.

Evidence will be presented to show that feeding can be understood only in terms of physiological factors taken in the context of the person's culture, social environment, developmental history and the availability of foods. For some fortunate individuals, given this complex of factors the regulation of their internal environment by feeding would seem to be good. In others, the combination of factors leads to such conditions as vitamin deficiency, obesity or anorexia. Thus, what might at first glance seem to be something of only physiological interest will in fact turn out to be an example of where a holistic approach involving sociology and psychology is needed. So this chapter will inevitably use different levels of analysis to gain further insight. The first topic will concern what is the internal cue to feeding that derives from some measure of our state of nutrient balance. It is here that insights can be gained from studying rats and dogs. Subsequent sections will then look at the role of that cue in the broader context of the controls of feeding, where more specifically human factors come into the picture.

Summary of Section 6.4

1   Homeostasis (negative feedback control) is an important aspect of feeding.

2   Food intake can only be understood in terms of a complex of interacting factors, only one of which is homeostasis.

6.5 The internal cue for feeding

6.5.1   Introduction

Exactly what constitutes the internal stimulus for feeding is a matter of great interest. Some researchers have tended to look for a single site for the **neural transducer** that generates a signal involved in feeding (i.e. a process by which a nutrient level gives rise to a neural signal). However, there is now a recognition that there are probably multiple sites involved. This section considers some of these possibilities.

6.5.2   Stomach filling

If you were to ask people what is the internal stimulus for hunger, some might answer that it is an empty stomach. Subjectively, it seems to feel that way, with a grumbling there telling us it is time to eat. Walter Cannon, an

American physiologist working in the early part of the 20th century, investigated the role of the stomach. His experimental technique is shown in Figure 6.7. For an objective measurement of stomach contractions, subjects were required to have a tube inserted down the oesophagus and to get used to its presence for several hours at a time. A balloon at the end of the tube was then partly inflated in the stomach. The tube was connected to a piece of apparatus that translated changes in pressure produced by contractions of the stomach muscles to a reading on a graph.

The results obtained suggested a causal link between contractions of the stomach and the sensation of hunger; hunger was reported at the peak of the contraction. Despite this theory being central to the discussions for a number of years, subsequent research using more sophisticated technology has found little correlation between contractions and subjective hunger. Also, as critics have pointed out, people with stomachs surgically removed still experience hunger. Although the stomach does not appear to be a prime site for the detection of physiological state, none-the-less, as you will see later, it is one of the multiple factors that determine food intake.

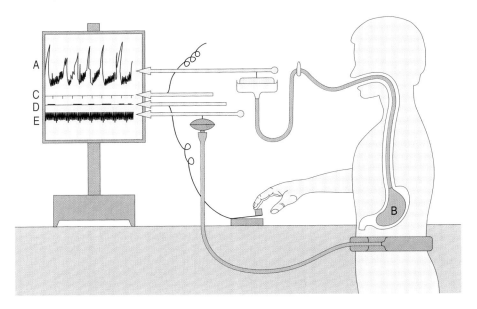

Figure 6.7   Apparatus used by Walter Cannon to investigate relations between stomach contractions and hunger, using a stomach balloon (B). Recordings show the increase and decrease in the balloon's volume (A), time in minutes (C), subject's own reports of hunger, indexed by key pressing (D) and movements of the abdominal wall (E) to demonstrate that these movements are not responsible for the changes in stomach volume.

6.5.3   Metabolic state

Following the demise of the idea that the stomach alone plays a crucial central role in food intake control, researchers focused upon the idea that somewhere in the body the level of a nutrient, or its metabolism by specific cells, gives rise to the signal underlying feeding and satiety. Currently the focus of interest is on two sites of such cells, in the brain and in the liver. It would appear that cells at both these sites are implicated. Exactly what constitutes the signal is still uncertain but researchers now have some promising leads. The detection of glucose and fatty acid levels or the metabolism of these substrates seem to be implicated.

One could imagine specialized neurons that are sensitive to the concentration of a particular nutrient in the fluid that bathes them. Figure 6.8a illustrates such an idea: here, it is assumed that a neuron is sensitive to the concentration of glucose, and changes its electrical state (e.g. generates action potentials) in response to the detection of glucose.

One early proposal was a **glucostatic theory** of feeding, in which the cue to feed was a fall in the blood glucose level. The rationale for this theory is not difficult to see since glucose can be utilized by any cell and is almost the sole source of energy for neurons. Figure 6.8a represents one version of the theory: that the activity of a neuron is sensitive to glucose concentration. Alternatively, or in addition, neurons might not be sensitive to the concentration of their energy source, as such, but rather to their ability to obtain fuel to metabolize. This is illustrated in Figure 6.8b.

❑　　Consider what you have already learned about diabetes and the role of insulin (Chapter 4 of the present book). On the basis of the theory represented in Figure 6.8a, what might you expect to be the situation in the case of diabetic individuals?

■　　Diabetics tend to have an excessively high blood glucose level for at least some of the time and, according to the glucostatic theory, such times would be those when hunger is not experienced.

In fact, diabetics can experience hunger even at times of abnormally elevated blood glucose. Thus the glucostatic theory cannot be the whole story, even if it turns out to provide part of the explanation.

Figure 6.8b shows an alternative theory: that a neuron is sensitive to the metabolism of glucose. Such a specialized neuron (unlike other neurons) might require insulin for transport of glucose across the membrane (analogous to opening channels as shown in the lower part of the figure), and such neurons appear to exist (Langhans and Scharrer, 1992). Thus, there might be a high level of glucose surrounding the neuron but if it cannot be transported across the membrane and utilized in significant amounts, this would trigger hunger. Such a process might then explain the hunger experienced by diabetics.

There are experiments that enable the ideas represented in Figure 6.8 to be tested. A substance which has important similarities to glucose is 2-deoxyglucose (or 2-DG, where a hydrogen atom replaces the 2-hydroxyl group of glucose). It crosses the membrane like glucose but competes with glucose for its passage across. Once inside the cell, it is not metabolized and also prevents the metabolism of any glucose that might be present. Injection of 2-DG stimulates feeding in many species including humans,

which suggests the involvement of a process of the kind shown in Figure
6.8c. In humans, the pleasantness rating of food is increased by injection of
2-DG, in spite of a rise in blood glucose level, suggesting the possibility of
the kind of process shown in Figure 6.8b and c over that shown in 6.8a.

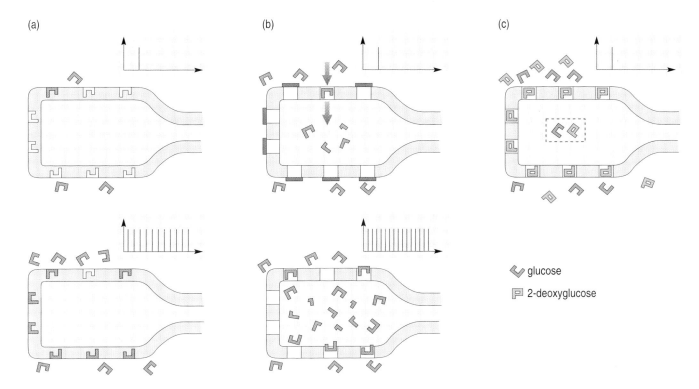

Figure 6.8   Possible mechanisms for neural detection of glucose levels. (a) A neuron sensitive to the glucose
concentration in the fluid that bathes it. Note the glucose receptors on the membrane which are specific for glucose
molecules. Above, glucose concentration is low, few sites are occupied and action potential frequency is low. Below,
glucose concentration is higher, as signalled by a higher frequency of action potentials.
(b) A neuron that is sensitive to its ability to obtain glucose for metabolism, shown as breaking apart the glucose
molecule. Above, as a result of a lack of insulin, most glucose transport proteins in the membrane are unable to
transport glucose and there is a low action potential frequency. Below, as a result of the presence of insulin they are
able to transport glucose, there is a high rate of glucose metabolism and a high frequency of action potentials.
(c) The situation when 2-deoxyglucose (2-DG) is injected. Note the occupation of glucose transport proteins by 2-DG
and blocking of the metabolism of glucose, indicated by enclosing 2-DG and glucose within the dashed rectangle.

In addition to neurons sensitive to the metabolism of glucose, there appear
to be those that are sensitive to fatty acid metabolism (Langhans and
Scharrer, 1992). In rats, there is evidence that blocking of this metabolism
can stimulate feeding. It appears that neurons, sensitive to both glucose and
fatty acid metabolism, act in combination to determine feeding tendency.
As metabolism at either neuronal site falls, so feeding is aroused.

What is the evidence on where such glucose- and fatty-acid-sensitive
neurons are located? Low doses of 2-DG injected into the brain are
effective at stimulating feeding, suggesting the involvement of neurons
there (Langhans and Scharrer, 1992). Some special neurons in the brain are
able to metabolize fatty acids and these might also be involved, but the

evidence is not strong. There is reliable evidence for neurons whose firing rate is especially sensitive to local glucose level/metabolism in both the hypothalamus and the liver. These neurons are sometimes termed glucose receptors or **glucoreceptors**, the implication of the description being that they play some role in the organization of metabolism and/or feeding control. The effect of glucose on some of these neurons tends to be the opposite of the effect of insulin (Mei, 1994). Mei suggests that the metabolic state of such neurons is the trigger to feeding.

There is considerable evidence to show that animals (humans included) monitor energy exchanges in the liver and that a signal from here plays a role in feeding motivation (Friedman and Stricker, 1976; Booth, 1978). Figure 6.9 will remind you of what happens after nutrients leave the digestive tract. In the wall of the intestine there are capillaries. Nutrients (apart from lipids) are absorbed across the intestine wall into these capillaries. They then travel to the liver via the hepatic portal vein. So the liver is ideally situated to monitor what is leaving the gut. According to some theorists, when a signal indicates a low level of nutrient availability at the liver, there is a tendency for feeding to be initiated.

Injections of glucose into the hepatic portal vein are particularly effective in inducing satiety in dogs. The same injection made elsewhere in the circulation is relatively ineffective. As Chapter 4 showed, the liver is strategically placed to be informed of all the metabolic changes occurring in the body. It can also derive nutrients from sources other than the digestive tract. Metabolic fuels (carbohydrates, fats and proteins) are converted here from one form to another. It seems that a signal derived from the liver is able to convey information on the general metabolic state, taking into account nutrients arriving from the gut as well as those being converted internally in the liver itself. At times the latter conversions are sufficient to restrain feeding even when no nutrients are arriving at the liver from the gut (Booth, 1978).

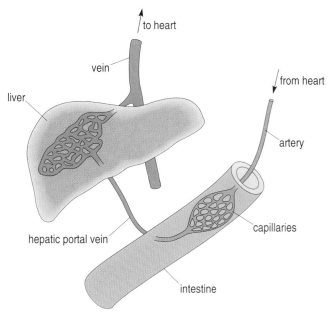

Figure 6.9   The liver, the intestine and the absorption of nutrients. Nutrients (other than lipids) are absorbed from the intestine into the capillaries in its walls. These capillaries drain into the hepatic portal vein, which is joined to the liver.

Of course, the final decision to feed or not is made at the brain and so neural pathways carrying information from the liver to the brain are implied. Such pathways do indeed exist and Russek (1971) found that if neural transmission along them is blocked then the satiating effect of hepatic portal vein glucose infusions is lost.

To summarize, it is probable that the signal to feed derives from metabolic information at various locations (e.g. gut, liver and brain). An integration of this information occurs in the brain together with other sources of information, such as the sensory quality of available food, in determining whether or not to feed.

Summary of Section 6.5

1   Stomach emptiness appears to play little or no role in arousing feeding.

2   Evidence suggests that the detectors of nutritional state ('neural transducers') are located in the brain and liver.

3   Evidence suggests that the detectors are neurons sensitive to their own glucose metabolism. Other types might also be involved.

6.6 The interacting mechanisms of satiety

The last section considered mainly those intrinsic factors that contribute to the initiation of feeding, though in considering the evidence satiety was sometimes described. The present section looks more closely at satiety.

In considering the processes that switch off eating, one might at first suppose that it is simply a reversal of the triggering events (e.g. restoration to normal of either glucose levels in the brain, or the flow of glucose to the liver). However, this is unlikely to be so since, by the time a meal is finished, most of it remains inside the digestive tract. So are there factors that help to terminate feeding but which do not necessarily play a role in its initiation?

In both the initiation and termination of meals, the evidence suggests that multiple factors are at work, acting in complex combination (Booth, 1994; Logue, 1991; Mei, 1994). Perhaps it is safest to think of some of these being more strongly involved in satiation (e.g. stomach bulk, chewing) and others being more involved in initiation (e.g. length of time since last meal, social factors) but both initiation and termination of feeding involve an overlapping complex of factors.

Before any food gets to the stomach it will be chewed and swallowed. Such mechanical actions might, in addition, provide signals for satiety. Receptors inform the central nervous system (specifically, the hypothalamus, which is known to have an important role in ingestion) of the pressures exerted on the teeth in the chewing process (Mei, 1994).

In normal feeding, these mechanical acts will be followed shortly by the detection of stretch within the stomach. The stomach contains stretch receptors whose firing rate increases with increased gastric contents (Read, 1992). People commonly say that they feel 'full' or 'bloated' at the end of a meal suggesting an effect of bulk. This belief is reflected in the behaviour of people keen to lose weight who commonly include a large percentage of bulky, low-calorie foods such as lettuce and carrots in their diet or who drink large amounts of liquid in association with the meal.

The evidence suggests that only a combination of factors such as oral stimulation by taste, mechanical action of chewing and stomach stretch, together with post-absorptive events, determines normal satiety (Read, 1992; Toates, 1986). Normal satiety therefore cannot be broken down into a simple sum of component parts and it might prove impossible to study the role of any given factor in isolation. For example, one could try loading human subjects with bulk in the stomach and then asking them about their feelings of satiety. However, there is the possible experience of nausea following a sudden load of unchewed and untasted material appearing in the stomach. Such nausea might have little in common with normal satiety and yet might be confused with it. Even in the absence of nausea, such an abnormal stimulus might say little about the conventional role of any stomach stretch signal. Evidence from animal studies suggests that stomach distension on its own plays rather little role in switching off feeding, unless it is extreme and induces nausea.

The presence of food in the intestine causes the release of hormones and these play a role in satiety (Mei, 1994). One in particular is cholecystokinin (CCK), which is synthesized in the epithelium of the upper part of the small intestine and its secretion into the bloodstream is stimulated by the presence of nutrients there (Read, 1992). Amongst other functions, it suppresses food intake in humans; CCK antagonists, however, increase food intake (Book 2, Chapter 3). Again, the role of CCK is perhaps best understood in the context of other factors. For example, it might well act to sensitize gastric stretch receptors (Read, 1992).

❑   What is meant by the expression 'to sensitize gastric stretch receptors'?

◼   For a given amount of gastric stretch, the frequency of action potentials arising is higher as a result of the presence of CCK.

The role of CCK, acting in combination with other factors, was indicated by an experiment on rats in which animals were trained to associate one flavour (X) with an energy-rich drink and another flavour (Y) with a non-energy-rich drink. It was found that CCK would suppress ingestion of solutions containing X but not Y (Logue, 1991).

Following absorption of food from the digestive tract, glucoreceptors in the liver (see Section 6.5) fire according to glucose concentration and so would be able to provide a contribution towards satiety (Mei, 1994).

Summary of Section 6.6

1   Multiple factors (e.g. taste, chewing, gastric contents, CCK released into the bloodstream) appear to determine satiety.

2   It is likely that satiety can only be understood in terms of a combination of contributory factors.

6.7 The role of external sensory factors in the intake of food

6.7.1   Introduction

A food that might be rejected in one energy state might be sought when more deprived. States within the body play a role in triggering feeding but, of course, they do so in combination with external stimuli, i.e. the sensory properties of food and its associations. These involve visual cues (e.g. the colour and presentation of food), auditory cues (e.g. crackling of certain breakfast cereals), and, perhaps above all, taste and smell. Taste and smell are not independent as inputs to the control of feeding.

❏   Think of an example from your own experience that would support this claim.

■   You might well have had a blocked nose and found that food had no smell, but also did not taste the same any more.

The flavour of a food is a complex of different components: taste, smell, temperature and even, in some cases, e.g. very spicy foods, an input to the pain system. Researchers have described so-called *taste primaries*, salt, sweet, sour and bitter, from which other more complex tastes can be derived, and for which the tongue contains receptors.

From evolutionary considerations, it is perhaps not surprising that the tongue should contain receptors sensitive to such primary qualities. In nature, sweetness is indicative of a source of carbohydrates and a salt taste is indicative of sodium chloride, both essentials for the body. Conversely, the bitter sensation is often indicative of poisons to be expelled from the mouth and avoided in the future.

6.7.2   Likes and dislikes

Likes and dislikes involve the intrinsic properties of foods but also involve interactions with bodily states. Even a strongly favoured food will usually become less attractive immediately following substantial ingestion (Cabanac, 1971). This points to the interaction of internal and external factors in the control of intake.

There exists a preference amongst large sections of the population for sweet tastes (Logue, 1991). Even after achieving a state of 'satiety' on a main course, many are able to squeeze in something sweet, a good example of the sensory-specific nature of satiety, discussed later. Humans are not unique in this regard; to researchers, rats are famous for their sweet tooth. Sense can be made of this in an evolutionary context since, in nature, sweetness is usually indicative of energy-rich carbohydrates. It is believed that we evolved in an environment in which there was a scarcity of such nutrients. For example, ripe fruits taste sweet. They are not only a source of energy, but also of vitamins and minerals and should be ingested. Today, in Western society, there is an over-abundance of sweet foods, especially for those with the money to buy. Today's high sugar intake is associated with dental caries, obesity and coronary heart disease, amongst other things.

The fact that, within as little as 24 hours following birth, babies show a preference for sweet fluids as compared to water, strongly suggests that there is a genetically determined preference (Logue, 1991). However, we cannot rule out the possibility that information is transferred to the fetus whilst it is still in the womb and thereby establishes a preference for certain substances. We have some interesting evidence of when cultures that lack a supply of sugar-containing foods (e.g. Inuit people of Alaska) contact cultures where there is an abundance of such foods. Such people rapidly acquire the bad habits of the new culture. This raises the possibility that a preference for sweetness might be genetically coded and common to all people. The evidence then suggests the existence of innate sensitive neural pathways between sweet detectors on the tongue and the motivational processes underlying ingestion. This conclusion is supported by the facial expressions of new-born babies to contact with sweet stimuli on the tongue, prior to any feeding, which is similar to that of adults.

It is interesting to note that in many species, a disproportionately large number of the neurons making up the nerve that transmits information on taste from the tongue respond to sweetness. There might be a developmental effect at work that would reinforce any genetically determined bias towards sweetness. Thus stimulation of sweet detectors might result in recruitment of relatively many neural pathways or increase the input from such pathways onto motivational processes.

Sodium and chloride ions are lost in urine and in sweat. Normally the kidney serves to conserve such ions so that the rate of loss is not excessive. However, in cases of renal disorder or a failure to secrete the hormones involved in sodium retention at the kidney (ADH and aldosterone), there can be excessive loss and the subject assumes a state of sodium deficiency. When this happens there is a craving for salt and large amounts are ingested. The implication here is that the messages from salt detectors on the tongue to motivational processes are sensitized by the depleted sodium level.

❏   This is an example of what process?

◼   Homeostasis.

As with sweet-tasting foods, there is reason to believe that in our evolutionary history, salt was often in scarce supply. These days, at least in the West, there is usually an abundance of salty foods and indeed consumption is commonly greatly in excess of need. The surplus is excreted by the kidney but there can be a risk of hypertension as a result of excessive levels of salt intake (see Chapter 5).

In general, deprivation enhances the attractiveness of the required commodity. Salt is craved in sodium deficiency and water is craved in a state of dehydration. This is how homeostasis is maintained: by bodily states making appropriate changes in the reaction to appropriate tastes and smells. There is some suggestion in the literature (Logue, 1991) that, when given a choice between carbohydrates and proteins, the choice is determined by need for the particular nutrient. Thus, if breakfast was rich in protein, people tend to prefer carbohydrate for lunch. It might be that ingested nutrients affect neural transmission in specific appetite circuits in the brain so as to cause relative satiation to the substance ingested. However, not all researchers are convinced that this effect really occurs.

Whereas subjects crave and avidly ingest some substances, others are rejected by their sour or bitter tastes. Even in new-born infants, the facial expression on confronting a sour or bitter taste is unambiguously one of rejection and spitting out. This would presumably serve to protect against toxic substances.

Exposure to a particular food tends in the long-term to increase the liking for that food (Logue, 1991). However, in the short-term, ingestion decreases the attraction of the food, an effect termed **sensory-specific satiety**. Sensory-specific satiety is a consequence of the taste properties of a substance as it is ingested. It is of rapid onset following the start of a meal. As Logue expresses it:

> For food preferences, familiarity does appear to breed (some) contempt, while absence makes the heart grow (somewhat) fonder. (Logue, 1991)

❏   Does a combination of short-term satiety and a longer-term preference make sense adaptively?

◼   Following a period of deprivation, by favouring the familiar, the choice is biased towards that known not to have harmful consequences. Conversely, by short-term satiety specific to an ingested food, a bias is given in favour of other familiar foods that might be present and so would lead to a richer variety of substances ingested. One consequence of sensory-specific satiety is that as the variety of foods available increases so will the amount eaten, something of obvious health implications in a society such as ours.

Quite apart from the intrinsic power of given substances to engage feeding or rejection, substances tend to be favoured or disfavoured according to the consequences (e.g. gain of nutrients, intestinal upset) of their ingestion, an example of a learned association (Booth, 1994). The next section briefly looks at this.

6.7.3   Conditioning of preferences and aversions

Foods can vary in attractiveness, not only as a function of their intrinsic make up and the nutrient state at the time of ingestion but also as a function of the consequences of ingestion. For example, relief of a vitamin deficiency can increase the attractiveness of the food responsible.

A novel taste paired with an established and preferred taste can take on some of the properties of the established taste (Logue, 1991). This might explain why someone tasting tea of coffee for the first time will tend to take sugar with it. However, after having experienced the combination of sugar and, for example, tea, the tea may later become acceptable even without the sugar.

Some of the best-known results showing links between ingestion and its consequences concern **taste-aversion learning**, also sometimes termed the Garcia effect. In a number of species, it has been shown that if a distinctive flavour is ingested and the consequence is then gastrointestinal illness, the flavour is subsequently avoided. Many people have their own story of their experience of this effect. It appears that the previously acceptable flavour is now not only shunned but actually tastes bad (Dickinson and Balleine, 1992; Berridge, 1995). This is of obvious survival value since generally, if illness follows feeding, the food is the culprit.

In humans, taste-aversion learning is a good example of where a basic learning process, common to most if not all animals, can override rationality. A patient may be informed by their doctor that there is no connection between a food ingested and an illness experienced somewhat later. For example, even if a stomach upset was caused by flu, the patient could imagine that it was due to a recently ingested food.

As Logue (1991) notes, taste-aversion learning in childhood might explain some strong dislikes that humans exhibit. Children often eat novel foods and are often ill for various reasons and so there is the opportunity for chance pairing between taste and illness. The child might not even be aware of having developed an aversion until next in the presence of the food (Dickinson and Balleine, 1992).

6.7.4   The role of conditioned situational cues

There is evidence, both in rats (Weingarten, 1984) and in humans (Logue, 1991), that cues associated with previous feeding events can come to arouse feeding in the future. These are further examples of conditioning.

❏   In Pavlov's terms, what would such cues be termed?

■   Conditional stimuli. The potency of the cues is conditional upon the earlier pairing with food presentation.

Thus researchers gave pre-school children items of food to eat in a particular location and in the presence of specific auditory and visual stimuli. As a control condition they were also exposed to another location with other auditory and visual stimuli but without having food to eat there. Later it was found that children, even after having recently eaten, were likely to eat in the feeding-associated context rather than another.

There is some evidence that likes and dislikes can be created or changed in young children by the psychological attitude of the food giver. A pleasant attitude with associated friendly facial expression can increase liking for foods given in that context.

6.7.7   Social and habit factors

In non-human animals, there is a positive correlation between (a) the size of a meal and (b) the length of time elapsing between that meal and the next. In humans, there is normally no such relationship. Rather, the timing of the onset of a meal tends to depend upon habit and the presence of such social factors as other people getting a meal ready (Langhans and Scharrer, 1992). The presence of other people eating tends to increase the size of a meal taken. This shows the importance of cultural factors; insight cannot be gained simply by looking into the physiological events in the body.

Imitation can play an important role. Children can sometimes grow to acquire a taste for a food that other children are obviously enjoying (Logue, 1991). The implications of this for television advertising are alarming. Many commercial advertisements are for foods poor in nutritional value and yet children's preferences for them seems to grow simply as a result of exposure (Logue, 1991).

Summary of Section 6.7

1   Sensory stimuli (e.g. taste) play an important role in food intake.

2   Sweetness is a powerful factor in the ingestion of certain foods.

3   Satiety is to some extent a function of the particular food ingested, so-called sensory-specific satiety.

4   Associations are formed between taste and the consequences of ingestion, an example being taste-aversion learning.

5   Social factors can promote food intake.

6.8 Abnormalities of food intake

6.8.1   Introduction

Problems of inappropriate intake, eating either too much or too little, are of fundamental importance for health. One of the rationales for research on the *neuropharmacology* of appetite is to discover drugs that can reduce or increase appetite, e.g. in the case of overeating, antagonists to the neurotransmitters involved in the appetite system or agonists to neurotransmitters involved in satiety. Of course, we need caution here. A drug might reduce appetite indirectly and have nothing to do with the specifics of appetite and feeding. For example, it might make the person feel sick and thereby depress all active behaviours. This section attempts to see where the basic processes of food intake control might go wrong.

6.8.2   Inadequate intake

The term 'anorexia' refers to a lack of appetite, for whatever reason it is caused, e.g. as a part of depression or as the condition **anorexia nervosa**. Anorexia nervosa might be accompanied by *bulimia nervosa*, consisting of binges followed by getting rid of the excess food ingested by means of vomiting or laxatives. Anorexia nervosa is a serious condition and has been described as 'the relentless pursuit of thinness through self-starvation, even unto death' (Logue, 1991). The disorder usually afflicts females in the period from their teens until their 30s. Only some 5% of anorexic individuals are male (although anorexia is on the increase in this group). Whether the expression 'anorexia' is an accurate one for describing this condition is not entirely clear since the sufferer might at some level experience appetite, which is overridden by other factors.

The explanations offered for anorexia nervosa have been many and have been based at different levels. Some have been based upon the idea that the sufferer compares herself (or himself) with society's ideal forms and expectations. Through the media, young women are exposed to 'perfect' slim bodies as a kind of role model. Other theorists have proposed physiological explanations for the disorder. At this point we need to be rather cautious in our interpretation of the theories.

Think about the following issue. Does postulation of a sociological explanation mean that the physiological explanation has to be wrong? Could a sociological explanation involve a physiological explanation as well?

As you should realize by now, these are not necessarily mutually exclusive explanations. There might be different causes for the disorder in different subjects or it might be the case that both sociological and physiological factors play a role in complex interaction. Even if one allocates responsibility to society, human beings are still flesh-and-blood beings and any effects of society are presumably mediated through the nervous system.

Anorexic individuals have distorted perceptions of their body image, judging themselves to be larger than they actually are. They are also abnormal in the interpretation that they place upon sensations from the stomach (Robinson, 1989). There are reports of abnormalities of the hypothalamus in anorexic people but we cannot be certain that these are the cause or consequence of the disorder. Since anorexic women fail to start to menstruate or cease menstruation with onset of the disorder, there are various possibilities for complex brain–endocrine system interactions. When starvation is severe, there is a slowing of the rate of gastric emptying (Robinson, 1989). This might well contribute to the maintenance of the condition by inducing an abnormally high satiety effect.

Turning the discussion to a very different group of patients, cancer is commonly a cause of anorexia, which in some cases might play a contributory role towards death (Logue, 1991). The explanation for such anorexia might be in terms of changes in taste sensitivity and food preference. There are also likely to be metabolic and hormonal changes. In some cases the cancer itself contributes to the anorexia whereas in other cases the treatment might be the major factor. Taste-aversion learning (see Section 6.7.3) would appear to have an important role in such anorexia. Cancer represents a fundamental disturbance to the body and for the sufferer it is one which is bound to be present after any given food has been ingested. Thus every meal provides the potential for learning an aversion to the flavour of the meal. In addition, chemotherapy appears to play a role. Experiments have shown that both adults and children who are presented with a novel-flavoured ice-cream just before undergoing chemotherapy acquire an aversion to the taste. A significant percentage of cancer patients experience nausea, and in some cases vomiting, in anticipation of chemotherapy (Logue, 1991). Such nausea might then form a link with food ingested hours earlier.

6.8.3   Obesity

Obesity might seem a simple issue: the obese eat too much relative to normal-weight controls. However, hormonal and metabolic abnormalities can be involved. There is evidence that some obese people eat considerably more than non-obese people, particularly in the period during which they are actually increasing in weight. However, the difference between intake and metabolic expenditure need only be very small to produce a cumulative weight increase over a period of months. Researchers have found few reliable differences in feeding behaviour when comparing obese and control individuals (Logue, 1991), except that the obese tend to be more prone to eat beyond satiety with highly palatable foods.

Think back to the discussion of sensory-specific satiety in Section 6.7.2. What do you think that the relevance of this phenomenon might be in a contemporary Western society? Relate your thoughts to the evolutionary significance of this process.

Sensory-specific satiety would be a useful process for ensuring that a human selects from amongst various available foods, rather than ingesting just one. However, evolution did not occur in the context of today's abundance of highly palatable foods. Hence, the factor could now be maladaptive in that it persuades us to ingest too much. Another factor, which might well play an important role in obesity, is the anticipatory rise in insulin secretion that occurs as a result of the taste of sweet substances in the mouth (see Section 6.2). Such insulin secretion would promote fat synthesis. Frequent 'snacking' on desirable morsels between main meals might well over-excite such a link.

It is known that obese children are likely to be the product of obese parents. In this context, think of the kind of explanation that might be given for this effect. What kind of research could be done to test the hypothesis?

Either a genetic or environmental factor could be involved or both. One way to attempt to tease these apart is to compare identical and fraternal twins as well as adopted children. Surveys of this kind suggest that there is a genetic factor at work in the determination of obesity. However, there is also an environmental factor (Logue, 1991). Postulation of a genetic factor raises the issue of what is the underlying physiological process that mediates such an effect.

The term 'metabolic rate' refers to the rate at which energy is utilized (Chapter 4). All other things being equal, the lower the metabolic rate, the more prone the person is to obesity. Herein lies one of the complications in this area; when food intake is reduced there is a tendency for the metabolic rate also to fall (Johnsgard, 1989). This is why the reduction in energy intake does not match the loss of weight. Worse still, the reduction in metabolic rate can continue for months after the normal intake has been restored. This indicates one of the hazards and paradoxes of dieting. It underlies the importance of developing stable healthy-eating patterns as early as possible and trying to maintain them. It also points to the futility and health risks of start–stop ('yoyo') dieting.

One way in which metabolic rate can be increased is by exercise and so this is to be encouraged. In some cases the increase can extend for hours beyond the termination of exercise. One long-term advantage of exercise can be an increase in the ratio of lean/fat body weight, with subsequent advantages for keeping metabolic rate high. There is evidence that the obese exercise less than controls (Logue, 1991). The danger is that subjects can get into a vicious circle: as weight increases so exercise decreases. This means that later, even with the will to do it, the subject might not be able to perform enough exercise to increase metabolism sufficiently to lose weight (Kolata, 1987). Of course, there will be various social, economic and environmental factors that will play a role in how much exercise a person is able to take. Such factors include: ability to walk or cycle to a place of work or study as part of the normal day; the amount of free leisure time and the availability of a suitable and safe environment (such as parkland, moorland, gymnasium, swimming pool, etc.) for sporting activities. One of the worst factors for obesity in children would seem to be television. Many children fail to take enough exercise and tend to take frequent snacks of the sweet foods that they see advertised.

There are ways of overcoming serious and chronic adult cases of obesity. Probably the most drastic, is surgically to remove part of the stomach (Logue, 1991). This appears to be a successful procedure and patients commonly recover even an ability to engage in vigorous activities. It is interesting, in the context of theories of feeding, to know why this procedure results in loss of weight. It might be the result of a reduced rate of absorption of nutrients from the gut. However, there is evidence of a significant reduction in food intake post-operation. This might be caused by a stronger signal deriving from distension of what remains of the stomach in response to a given quantity of food. Other surgical procedures that have been tried include jaw wiring, such that only liquid foods can be ingested. Perhaps not surprisingly, this can result in too much weight loss, although some weight is restored when the wiring is removed. Such examples will probably cause you to wonder whether really a better solution than this cannot be found. Should we not be taking a long hard look at the social factors that promote obesity? You might like to reflect on this issue.

A pharmacological intervention that has been used to control overeating is the use of amphetamines. Such drugs tend to lower food intake but the process that it targets to do so is not entirely clear. In part, amphetamines might have a general disorganizing effect on behaviour (Logue, 1991). There are some dangerous side-effects of amphetamine, and so its use is not generally recommended. Researchers have looked into the possibility of harnessing some of the body's own satiety agents (Section 6.6). Both glucagon (see Chapter 4) and CCK are released following ingestion and appear to play a role in satiety. However, there are problems in artificially exploiting such substances. A form that can be taken orally has not yet been devised. This means injections are needed. Additionally, the natural profile of release of these substances might be important. They would normally be released following a meal and their satiating effect might well be due to a joint action with other factors such as gut distension.

Some people specifically crave certain unusually sweet foods (e.g. chocolate) and there is some reason to believe that a deficit in the brain neurotransmitter serotonin underlies this (Logue, 1991). Drugs that increase serotonin level can sometimes help to alleviate such craving.

Behavioural therapists try a variety of stimulus-control techniques to help obese patients to lower their intake (Logue, 1991). For example, patients can be taught techniques to avoid being in a situation of overeating; taking only a limited amount of money to the supermarket would be one such technique. Patients can be taught to take small bites and thereby slow the rate of intake.

❑   Can you see any theoretical rationale to explain why slowing the rate of intake might work, based upon an understanding of satiety mechanisms discussed in Section 6.6?

■   If food is ingested more slowly, it might give satiety hormones more time to be secreted and play a larger part in switching off feeding at a lower level of intake.

As Logue (1991) notes, there is no single magic formula for weight loss applicable to all people. Indeed, one has reason to imagine that there is a wide variety of different factors that underlie obesity in different people. One subject might have a chronically low metabolic rate, possibly arising in part from earlier dieting attempts. Another might have an over-reactive insulin response to the taste or even sight of food.

Summary of Section 6.8

1   The nervous system is the target for drugs designed to alter appetite.

2   Anorexia nervosa is a disorder that involves rejection of food in the pursuit of a slimmer body.

3   Obesity is the outcome of an interaction between food intake, metabolism and lifestyle. An abundance of energy-rich foods contributes to obesity.

6.9 Brain mechanisms and eating

Our knowledge of the brain mechanisms underlying feeding has been largely gained from studies of non-human animals and has involved making lesions to the brain, chemical stimulation and electrical recording from neurons. Extrapolation to humans is therefore fraught with some difficulty. However, work on non-human primates (Rolls, 1994) offers perhaps the best opportunity. In the macaque monkey, there exist neurons whose responses are closely related to feeding. Specifically, they respond to either the taste or the sight of food or, in some cases, to both. In terms of taste, they specifically 'fire' a response in the presence of a nutritive solution (e.g. glucose), but not a saline solution or pure water, on the tongue. Firing of the response is related to the concentration of nutrients present.

It was found that such neurons responded to food only if the animal had been deprived of food at the time. Thus the neural response is an index of motivation. It was found that, if a monkey had been fed to satiety on a particular food, this would be reflected in a cessation of firing of the hypothalamic neuron from which recordings were being made. However, the activity of the neuron reflected the phenomenon of sensory-specific satiety (Section 6.7.2).

❑   What could be meant by this?

■   Changing the available food caused a recovery in activity of the neuron. It also stimulated ingestion whereas the previous food was not ingested.

Rolls (1994) believes that similar neural processes operate in human and non-human primates. This belief is based on the observation that, in humans, sensory-specific satiety relates to both the taste and sight of foods, whose attraction decreases with ingestion of the specific food. In the macaque monkey, such neurons also came to respond to stimuli paired with food, such as the syringe from which glucose was applied. Such a stimulus was ineffective prior to its pairing with feeding. This would seem to be a neural embodiment of a conditioning process in which food-related stimuli can arouse the tendency to feed. Such neurons would seem to represent part of the neural basis underlying preparatory reflexes such as salivation and insulin secretion.

❑   Describe Rolls' experiment in the terms used for Pavlov's experiment, as described in Section 6.2 (though bear in mind that such conditioning is anything but simple and so we can only hope for a first approximation to the truth).

◼   The taste of food would be the unconditional stimulus and the response of the neuron to this, the unconditional response. The sight of the food would be the conditional stimulus and the response of the neuron to this would be the conditional response.

Figure 6.10 shows a simple representation of the kind of neural operations that are implicated in these findings. The motivation neuron (1) is influenced by the taste and sight of food. That is, neurons that are sensitive to the taste and sight of food make excitatory synapses upon neuron 1. However, there are also inhibitory influences upon neuron 1. These derive their inputs from: (i) a measure of internal nutrient level and (ii) a memory of recently ingested foods. Thus, a surfeit of nutrients will exert an inhibitory, in this case satiety, effect. Also, inhibition/satiety that is specific to a given food will arise from a memory of a recent ingestion of that food.

Thus, activity in the neurons that detect the presence of substances in the mouth and those in the visual pathways is not dependent upon energy state or ingested food. However, the capacity of these neurons to trigger the motivation neuron is inhibited by nutrient-related factors. (Sensory inputs are *gated*, meaning inhibition can be exerted on the pathway, before the inputs get to motivation neurons in the hypothalamus.)

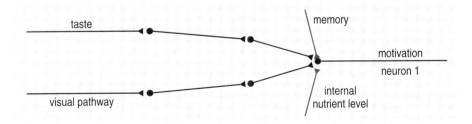

Figure 6.10   The kind of neural processes that are suggested by the recordings of Rolls (1994). The black triangular input represents excitation and the red triangular input represents inhibition to neuron 1.

This completes the main discussion of feeding. It must be borne in mind that there are powerful interactions between feeding and drinking, the latter of which will be discussed in Section 6.10.

Summary of Section 6.9

1   Knowledge about brain mechanisms in human feeding must necessarily depend upon a cautious extrapolation from non-humans.

2   There are neurons in the brain that are sensitive to, on the one hand, the taste and the sight of food and, on the other, to nutrient levels in the body.

6.10   Drinking

6.10.1   Introduction: the body fluids

The intake of water and the associated sensation of thirst are somewhat easier to understand than food intake, largely because water is a single substance. Drinking is, of course, closely connected with the state of hydration of the body.

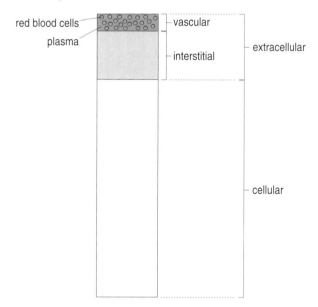

Figure 6.11   The distribution of water in the body.

As you saw in the previous chapter, for some purposes, it is convenient to consider the water of the body to be divided into compartments, as shown in Figure 6.11. The largest compartment is the **cellular compartment** (also termed 'intracellular compartment'), consisting of the water in all of the cells of the body. With reference to the somewhat more realistic Figure 6.12, the cellular compartment consists of the sum of water in all cells, whether they be heart, brain or skin cells or whatever. By exclusion, all of the water that is not in the cells constitutes the **extracellular compartment**.

❑   Can you recall an important difference between the environments on the two sides of the cell membrane?

■   The inside is rich in potassium ions and the outside is rich in sodium ions. (Book 2, Chapter 3.)

❑   Look at Figures 6.11 and 6.12. How can the extracellular compartment be subdivided?

■   Into the plasma (fluid of the blood) and **interstitial compartment**. The interstitial compartment is that part of the body water that is outside of the bloodstream, lying in the spaces between the cells. It is, therefore, the interface between the cells and the bloodstream.

❑   Suppose a concentrated solution of sodium chloride is injected into the bloodstream (sodium ions are largely confined to the extracellular fluid). What will be the effect on the body fluids?

■   As a result of osmosis, water will tend to move out of the cells into the extracellular fluid (so the cells will shrink).

To take the converse situation, sodium deficiency will tend to result in a movement of water in the opposite direction, resulting in swelling of the cells.

Water is lost from the body by a variety of routes, as urine, sweat, evaporation from the skin and from the lungs in the process of breathing. In each case, it is lost from the extracellular compartment. Water is gained as a result of drinking water and other liquids, from the water content of food (e.g. lettuce is mainly water) and from the metabolism of food (see Chapter 4).

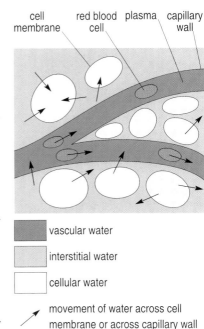

Figure 6.12   Fluid in the body showing some tissue cells (containing cellular water), red blood cells, the interstitial fluid and vessels of the bloodstream (capillaries).

6.10.2   Negative feedback processes involved in initiating drinking

Introduction

The term 'negative feedback', which you have met already in several contexts, refers to a system in which a deviation from a given state tends to cause action to restore the state. In other words, deviations from the state tend to be self-eliminating, hence the adjective 'negative' to describe such a system. Drinking clearly has features of a negative feedback system. Loss of body fluids tends to trigger drinking such as to correct the loss. The losses that trigger drinking can be from either the cellular or extracellular compartment.

❑   Could the kidney also be described as part of a negative feedback system?

■   Yes. An excess of water in the body fluids tends to instigate action to correct the excess, i.e. an elevated urine production rate. A deficiency tends to slow up the rate of urine formation.

The cellular compartment

If a human is injected with a solution of sodium chloride that is more concentrated than the blood (hypertonic saline), he or she will experience thirst. This is a result of cellular dehydration, caused by the movement of water out of the cells into the extracellular fluid. Similarly, if you have ever eaten a salty meal or tried drinking seawater (not something to be recommended!), you will have experienced a strong thirst. The presence of sodium chloride at a high concentration in the gut will cause the movement of water from the plasma of the blood into the gut as a consequence of a process of the kind represented in Figure 6.13.

❑   What will be the consequence of this movement for the distribution of fluids in the cellular and extracellular compartments?

■   The movement of water into the gut will increase the concentration of sodium and chloride in the extracellular fluid. This will cause a movement of water from the cells into the extracellular compartment.

On a closely related theme, it is important that artificial milks for human infants are formulated correctly, such that they do not cause dehydration (of the extracellular fluid), with subsequent diarrhoea and vomiting.

This section concerns thirst caused by the injection of concentrated substances (e.g. sodium chloride) into the blood, where a loss of water from the cells is the trigger. (The following section looks at the extracellular stimulus to drinking.) It appears that stimulation of cells in the brain, termed osmoreceptors, is the trigger for such drinking. Minute injections of hypertonic saline into the hypothalamus are followed by copious drinking. Such injections made elsewhere do not cause drinking. This suggests that a local cellular dehydration underlies drinking and that, at least to some extent, the injection mimics the normal drinking stimulus.

Alternatively, hypertonic saline could trigger neurons in a way unlike that by which normal drinking operates, just because of its ionic (that is, electrically active) content. However, drinking can be induced by substances other than sodium that dehydrate the osmoreceptors. Also, in response to sodium chloride injections, the only behaviour that is consistently observed is drinking (McKinley, 1991). This suggests that the result is not simply an artefact of sodium chloride having an unnatural stimulating effect upon neurons, but that it is similar to the normal arousal of drinking. There is further evidence, obtained in dogs, to suggest that receptors in the brain are specifically the trigger for drinking. In dogs deprived of water, the urge to drink can be stopped by the infusion of pure water into the region of the postulated receptors, even though the remainder of the cellular compartment remains dehydrated (Thrasher, 1991).

Three situations that provoke drinking are deprivation of water over a period of time, injection of sodium chloride and potassium deficiency (Fitzsimons, 1991).

Figure 6.13a–c shows the state of the cellular and extracellular volume of the body under these three conditions, indicating the normal state and the abnormal state that these procedures induce. Also shown are the changes in ion concentration that these procedures induce. For clarity, whilst both Na^+ and K^+ are present in each compartment, only the predominant ion is shown.

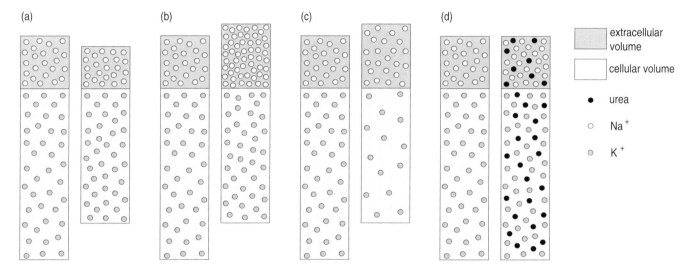

In Figure 6.13a, water deprivation is associated with a reduction in both extracellular and cellular fluid volumes. There is a rise in the concentration of K^+ in the cellular compartment and of Na^+ in the extracellular compartment. Water would be lost first from the extracellular compartment but, by osmosis, some water will move from the cells into the extracellular compartment. In (b) there is a rise in extracellular sodium concentration which causes water to be drawn out of the cells. Thus there is cellular dehydration and increase in cellular K^+ concentration similar to that induced in (a).

Figure 6.13   The state of the body fluids under three thirst-provoking situations. In each case, the representation to the left is the normal state and that to the right the disturbed state: (a) water deprivation; (b) hypertonic sodium chloride injection into the blood; (c) potassium deficiency. Part (d) represents an extracellular urea injection.

❏   Look carefully at Figure 6.13a and b. Can you see a difference between (a) and (b)?

■   In (a) there is a loss of both extracellular and cellular water, whereas in (b) there is no loss of extracellular water. Rather there is an expansion.

❑   Injecting hypertonic saline into the blood causes a swelling of
         extracellular volume but is a particularly potent thirst stimulus. What
         does this suggest about any possible role of extracellular swelling in
         thirst?

■   That the swelling does not inhibit the drinking caused by the
         corresponding shrinkage of cellular volume.

As with sodium, there is a continual loss of potassium from the body in the
urine. This is normally replaced from the diet. If only a potassium-deficient
diet is available, there will be a loss of potassium from the cells. This means
that the cells will be unable to retain as much water as normal, a situation
illustrated in Figure 6.13c. In each of three situations you can see why thirst
should be triggered by loss of cellular water. It is assumed that cells in the
brain are representative of events throughout the body fluids, as shown in
Figure 6.13, and thereby trigger thirst and drinking.

Injection of a substance such as urea, which can easily cross the cell
membrane, triggers relatively little drinking even though the concentration
of the substance in the blood increases. Figure 6.13d shows the effect of such
an injection on body fluids. Note that it does not cause a depletion of cellular
water since, within a very short time, it is distributed evenly throughout the
body fluids. This contrasts with a solute such as sodium chloride which
cannot cross the cell membrane and is largely confined to the extracellular
compartment, as shown in Figure 6.13b.

The existence of cellular detectors located in the brain has been clearly
shown. However, there might also be detectors of the body's fluid state at
other locations within the central nervous system or at sites such as the liver
(Fitzsimons, 1991), analogous to the situation for feeding (Section 6.5.3).
The signals arising from any such detectors would be expected to be
conveyed to the brain, where they would be integrated with those already
arising from detection of the fluid state in the brain.

The extracellular stimulus

In addition to the cellular stimulus to drinking, where human thirst seems to
be rather similar in its organization to that of other species, there is evidence
for an extracellular stimulus to thirst (Ramsey and Booth, 1991). Depletion
of the extracellular volume also arouses an appetite for sodium.

❑   Maintenance of extracellular sodium concentration is important for
         the maintenance of extracellular volume. Why is this?

■   Without maintenance of extracellular sodium concentration, water
         ingested will tend to move into the cells, causing cellular overhydration
         (swelling) but leaving an extracellular deficit.

The extracellular detector of fluid volume is specifically a detector of blood
volume; when this falls, thirst tends to be aroused. There is no evidence for a
detector of interstitial volume (i.e. the fluid in the spaces between the cells).

However, interstitial and blood volumes are closely interdependent so that a major loss from the interstitial space would be expected to be reflected in a depletion of blood volume. Gain of water by the bloodstream is rapidly shared with the interstitial space.

In regard to thirst triggered by an extracellular fluid deficit, extrapolation to humans from rat experiments is more fraught, as humans appear to be less sensitive to extracellular fluid loss than are other species, except possibly under extreme loss (Rolls, 1991). **Haemorrhage** (loss of blood) is a relatively weak stimulus in humans compared to other species. However, haemorrhage might well be accompanied by shock and experienced in a reclining position which, because of circulatory readjustments, could mask any potential effect on the stimulation of drinking (Rolls, 1991). At some location in the circulation, a signal (relatively weak or strong, depending upon the species) on the state of blood volume is detected. This plays a role in generating thirst. It is interesting to speculate as to how exactly it plays this role. From animal experimentation we know that, under conditions of fluid balance, the signal detecting the state of filling of a blood vessel exerts inhibition upon the thirst-generating processes in the brain (Fitzsimons, 1991).

❑   What then would be the consequence of a reduction of extracellular fluid volume?

■   The signal detecting the state of filling would diminish in strength. This would lower the level of inhibition exerted and arouse the thirst processes in the brain. A representation of the kind of neural process that is implicated is shown in Figure 6.14.

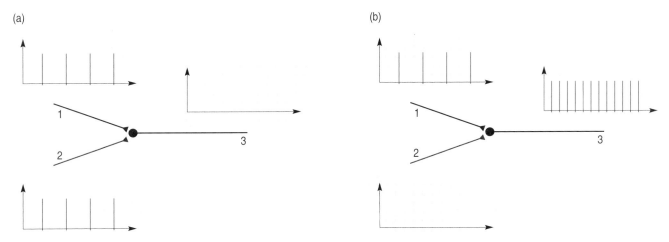

Figure 6.14   Representation of a possible process underlying the generation of a thirst signal. An excitatory neuron (1) monitors the state of the osmoreceptor (fluid loss increases action potential frequency), whereas activity in the neuron sensitive to stretch in a blood vessel (2) exerts inhibition. (a) The state of fluid balance: the osmoreceptor generates a low 'background' level of action potentials as does that detecting blood vessel stretch; these effects cancel out so that neuron 3 is not activated. (b) The result of haemorrhage: the inhibitory neuron (2) is *silent* and hence the motivation neuron (3) is activated.

Changes in the circulation are also detected by cells in the kidney, which then proceed to secrete renin in response. In the blood, renin acts to produce angiotensin II (see Chapter 5). Depending upon the species, angiotensin acts in the brain to arouse thirst, apparently more strongly in rats than in humans (Rolls, 1991). It also acts on the physiology of the body in three ways that are functionally related to its effects upon thirst:

1   Angiotensin constricts blood vessels, and so raises the blood pressure.

2   Both directly and by an effect mediated by aldosterone, angiotensin helps to conserve sodium by the kidney. This is crucial for maintaining extracellular volume.

3   Angiotensin increases the rate of release of ADH.

As you know, ADH acts on the kidney to conserve water, and it might also serve to sensitize the processes underlying thirst (Fitzsimons, 1991).

Termination of drinking

As with the discussion of feeding, an entirely analogous argument concerns the factors that switch off drinking. When drinking is complete, most of the ingested water is still in the gut. The original state of cellular dehydration that might have initiated the drink will still be uncorrected.

❑   What does this imply about the processes that switch drinking off?

■   That pre-absorptive processes are involved.

Mechanisms of inhibition deriving from the mouth and stomach are implicated in satiation. Subjective reports of humans drinking following a period of prior water deprivation indicate a reduction in thirst within some 2.5–5 minutes after the onset of drinking (Verbalis, 1991). Yet significant changes in cellular fluid composition take considerably longer than that to occur, e.g. 20 minutes. Figure 6.15 shows a representation of the strength of the contributory factors towards satiety, following the onset of drinking (Verbalis, 1991).

Figure 6.15   Factors that contribute to satiety of drinking. Note the rise in strength of oropharangeal (mouth) and gastrointestinal factors, corresponding to mouth detection and stomach filling and emptying, respectively. Note the slow rise in strength of post-absorptive factors as water is absorbed from the digestive tract.

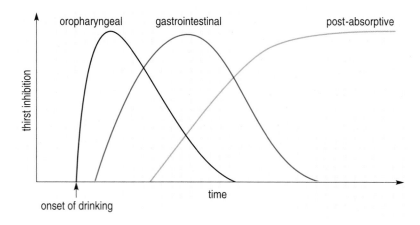

The evidence suggests that the oral contribution to satiety consists of a combination of information from (a) receptors that detect the presence of water in the mouth and (b) the mechanical act of swallowing. Gargling with water can offer some temporary relief to dehydrated humans as can having an ice cube in the mouth (Verbalis, 1991).

6.10.3   Normal drinking in humans

The message of the previous sections is that (a) drinking serves to regulate the volume of the body fluids and (b) reductions from the normal volume of fluid trigger drinking. However, the evidence suggests that a large fraction of drinking by humans occurs in the absence of the kinds of deficits discussed. In practice, in Britain, given an abundance of available fluids and a temperate climate, such deficits rarely arise (Kraly, 1991; Rolls, 1991). Feeding is a particular trigger to drinking and although some of this fluid intake might well be due to stimulation from the presence of food in the stomach or from extracellular dehydration, much of it appears to be attributable to habitual and social factors such as always drinking tea or coffee at breakfast time. Some drinking might well be a learned association with dehydration and be triggered by the presence of food in the mouth. The amount of fluid ingested each day can vary by a great amount, depending upon how tasty it is and how easily available without effort.

6.10.4   Disorders associated with drinking

Normally a certain amount of over-drinking is not a major problem since the kidney can rapidly excrete the surplus. However, when **hyponatremia** (low extracellular sodium concentration) is the result of overdrinking, this can present a problem in humans (Verbalis, 1991). This is associated with an inappropriate secretion of ADH and hence a retention of water that would otherwise be excreted as a result of ADH suppression. Patients sometimes continue to drink in spite of being in such a state, indicative, it would seem, of a rather weak inhibition on drinking from cellular over-hydration.

The two very different pathological conditions of dehydration and hyponatremia can be seen at any age. However, they are particularly likely to be seen in elderly people, where they can contribute significantly to mortality (Phillips *et al.*, 1991). In the elderly, dehydration can result from a combination of an abnormally low sensitivity of the thirst mechanisms to loss of water and a diminished ability of the kidney to conserve water. The latter is due to a loss of the sensitivity of the kidney to ADH. Figure 6.16 shows the result of depriving young and old healthy male human subjects of water for a period of 24 hours and then allowing water for 60 minutes.

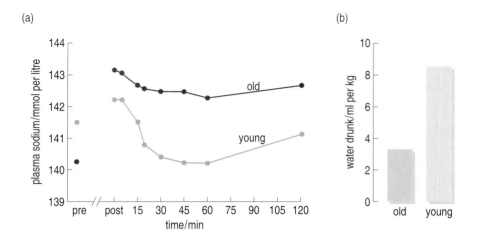

Figure 6.16 Graph showing: (a) plasma sodium concentration in young and old males pre- and post-deprivation and in the period post-deprivation after water was available; (b) quantity of water drunk (ml per kilogram of body weight) in the 60-minute period following deprivation.

It can be seen that, in the young but not the old subjects, drinking returns plasma sodium concentration to very near its pre-deprivation value within 2 hours of providing water. The elderly did not experience the oral dryness reported by the younger subjects. The result should alert those concerned with the care of elderly people to the increased possibility of dehydration that might occur as a result of, say, physical incapacity or illness.

It is interesting to speculate as to the site of abnormality in the processes underlying thirst in the elderly. Could it be a decreased sensitivity of the osmoreceptors? This is possible though unlikely since ADH secretion depends upon similar if not identical osmoreceptors in the brain and the ADH response to dehydration is not diminished. This suggests that in some way the pathway that links the osmoreceptors to the thirst motivation process, involving cognition, is diminished. Alzheimer's disease is associated with reduced cognitive processing and Alzheimer patients might be particularly susceptible to dehydration. Carers for the elderly can be in a difficult situation of trying to get the right balance. On the one hand, elderly people are advised to drink over and above what is suggested by their thirst signal in order to preempt dehydration. On the other hand, excess water intake needs to be avoided since, if there is a reduced capacity to excrete a surplus, the dangers of overhydration and hyponatremia can appear.

Summary of Section 6.10

1   Drinking is triggered by the loss of fluid from either the cellular or extracellular compartments or both.

2   The cellular loss is monitored by osmoreceptors in the brain.

3   The extracellular loss is monitored by detectors of blood volume.

4   Pre-absorptive factors (e.g. stomach fullness and oral detection) play a role in satiety.

5   In humans, social and habitual factors play an important role in
     drinking.

6   Regulation of body-fluid state in older humans is sometimes poor.

6.11   Overview

There are some important similarities in the two systems of feeding and
drinking. Both depend upon taking a local measure of a physiological
variable and it is suggested that in both cases receptors are in both the brain
and liver. In both cases, switching the behaviour off depends upon an
interaction of various factors, oral, gastric and post-absorptive.

An important message to come from the discussion of feeding is the
complex interaction of factors, internal and external, that contributes to
both appetite and satiety. Perhaps the surprise is that the feeding and
nutrient system works so well for so much of the time, in spite of the
abnormal challenges to which it is exposed. Although there are vital
negative feedback effects at work, food intake and body weight are the
outcome of factors that often seem in a precarious balance. Feeding
depends upon arousing a motivation by the availability of appropriate
energy-containing nutrients. It would seem that this balance can be shifted
by a change of diet. Very high-fat foods and very high sugar-content drinks
are a relatively recent phenomenon in terms of evolutionary time and it is
not surprising that the system cannot always cope adequately with them.

Looking back over the chapter, it is appropriate to draw some comparisons
and contrasts between drinking and feeding. Like heat, water cannot be
stored and so any excesses are lost, mainly as urine. Ingested energy-
containing nutrients taken in excess of immediate metabolic needs are
stored and available for later utilization as fuel.

To some extent it is true that we are what we eat. The proteins that
constitute the structure of our bodies can only be derived ultimately from
ingested nutrients. Vitamins and minerals, essential for our bodies, are
obtained in what we eat. However, much of what we eat is simply used as
fuel, like the petrol in a car which doesn't contribute to the car's structure.
If we do not eat enough food to maintain our metabolism, the body must
quite literally start to consume itself. A crucial factor is the maintenance of
blood glucose level, such that there is sufficient glucose for the nervous
system. Thus an important factor is the availability of fuels for use in
metabolism.

Fluid intake and body water regulation have some parallels with this.
Sufficient water must be obtained in order for loss through the urine, sweat
and respiration to occur. However, even if all of these losses were to halt we
would still need a constancy of the internal fluid environment for the body
to function. The blood can only be pumped around the body if the plasma
composition is maintained. Ionic exchanges across membranes as in the

action potential can only occur within a fluid matrix. Therefore, it seems logical that drinking would arise as a result of deviations from some fixed value of body fluid state and this is indeed how it works. Feeding is rather different since there does not seem to be a value of body energy reserves that are held constant, despite the belief that some used to hold that body weight is held at a regulated value and feeding depends upon this value (Booth, 1978). Rather, the evidence suggests that in some way the supply or availability of fuels for metabolism is monitored and used to generate a feeding signal.

It can also be useful to compare, on the one hand, food intake and energy balance and, on the other, temperature regulation. Differences are apparent. For temperature regulation, there is a biological imperative to maintain a fairly uniform temperature throughout, with only a slight day–night variation. Deviations from the norm can quickly be lethal. For energy balance, wide fluctuations are not only tolerated but are part of the 'evolutionary design'. The maintenance of successful energy balance has depended upon a capacity for variations in amount of energy stored, both in terms of bodily location (e.g. in fat storage sites at particular locations) and in time (e.g. storage at times of abundance), and this is the process that can so easily be compromised in obesity. Excess heat can readily be lost (if you doubt this, try taking a sauna, but not for too long), whereas excess fat is lost with difficulty. In temperature regulation, there is clearly an exquisite sensitivity of the negative feedback process to deviations from a normal state. Maintenance of nutritional state and body weight has more of a rough-and-ready feel to it, so it is surprising that things generally function as well as they do.

Objectives for Chapter 6

After reading this chapter, you should be able to:

6.1   Define and use, or recognize definitions and applications of, each of the terms printed in **bold** in the text.

6.2   Explain how the regulation of physiological variables can be achieved by the control that is exerted over other internal physiological variables and over behaviour. (*Question 6.1*)

6.3   Explain what is meant by the term 'anticipation' and how conditioning can produce such a process. (*Question 6.2*)

6.4   In the context of ingestive behaviour, explain what is meant by a reflex. (*Question 6.3*)

6.5   Explain why homeostasis can only explain some aspects of food intake control. (*Question 6.4*)

6.6   Describe the internal and external factors that are involved in food intake control. (*Question 6.4*)

6.7   Give some indication of how food intake control can 'go wrong' in such conditions as anorexia and obesity. (*Question 6.5*)

6.8   Explain how combinations of neurons are thought to underlie the processing of information concerned with food intake. (*Question 6.4*)

6.9   Explain how body fluid levels contribute to drinking. (*Question 6.1*)

6.10 Explain why, for both feeding and drinking, satiety is thought to be a function of several events. (*Question 6.7*)

Questions for Chapter 6

Question 6.1   (*Objective 6.2 and 6.9*)
Suppose two groups of rats are injected with a small amount of concentrated sodium chloride solution. One group is allowed immediate access to drinking water and drinks an average of 10 ml of water. The other group is injected with the identical amount but access to water is delayed by 40 minutes. This group drink an average amount of 7 ml. Can you suggest why there is a difference in the groups?

Question 6.2   (*Objective 6.3*)
Consider Pavlov's salivary conditioning experiment and the language of conditioning. If the conditional stimulus of the bell is presented a number of times without the unconditional stimulus, the conditional response declines in amplitude. Relate this to the more familiar terms for the physiological events that take place.

Question 6.3   (*Objective 6.4*)
In the expression 'unconditional reflex', as applied to salivation, what is reflex-like about this reaction?

Question 6.4   (*Objectives 6.5, 6.6 and 6.8*)
Please refer to Figure 6.10. Suppose that activity within the neuron marked 'internal nutrient level' inhibits neuron 1 so that it fires less easily. When nutrient levels fall the inhibition is lifted. What might be the significance of a neuron (neuron 1) that is sensitive to both the presence of food and the nutrient level?

Question 6.5   (*Objective 6.7*)
Relate Figure 6.10 to the fact that some people overeat and become obese, particularly on attractive foods.

Question 6.6   (*Objective 6.8*)

Neural pathways carry information from the liver to the brain and play a role in satiety. If we know the neurotransmitter employed by the neurons whose axons form this pathway and inject an antagonist to its receptors, what would be the expected effect upon the amount ingested in a meal?

Question 6.7   (*Objective 6.10*)

In the case of both feeding and drinking, why do we believe that the variables that switch off behaviour must be different from a reversal of the variables that switch it on?

References for Chapter 6

Berridge, K. C. (1995) Food reward: brain substrates of wanting and liking, *Neuroscience and Biobehavioural Reviews*, **20**, 1–25.

Booth, D. A. (1978) *Hunger Models: Computable Theory of Feeding Control*, Academic Press, London.

Booth, D. A. (1979) Metabolism and the control of feeding in man and animals, in K. Brown and S. J. Cooper (eds) *Chemical Influences on Behaviour*, pp. 79–134, Academic Press, London.

Booth, D. A. (1994) *Psychology of Motivation*, Taylor and Francis, London.

Bruner, J. S. and Bruner, B. M. (1968) On voluntary action and its hierarchical structure, *International Journal of Psychology*, **3**, 239–55.

Cabanac, M. (1971) Physiological role of pleasure, *Science*, **173**, 1103–7.

Dickinson, A. and Balleine, B. (1992) Actions and responses: the dual psychology of behaviour, in N. Eilan, R. A. McCarthy and M. W. Brewer (eds) *Problems in the Philosophy and Psychology of Spatial Representation*, pp. 277–93, Blackwell, Oxford.

Fitzsimons, J. T. (1991) Evolution of physiological and behavioural mechanisms in vertebrate body fluid homeostasis, in D. J. Ramsey and D. A. Booth (eds) *Thirst: Physiological and Psychological Aspects*, pp. 3–22, Springer-Verlag, London.

Friedman, M. I. and Stricker, E. M. (1976) The physiological psychology of hunger: a physiological perspective, *Psychological Review*, **83**, 409–431.

Johnsgard, K. W. (1989) *The Exercise Prescription for Depression and Anxiety*, Plenum Press, New York.

Kolata, G. (1987) Metabolic catch-22 of exercise regimens, *Science*, **236**, 146–47.

Kraly, F. S. (1991) Effects of eating on drinking, in D. J. Ramsey and D. A. Booth (eds) *Thirst: Physiological and Psychological Aspects*, pp. 297–312, Springer-Verlag, London.

Langhans, W. and Scharrer, E. (1992) Metabolic control of eating, *World Review of Nutrition and Diatetics*, **70**, 1–67.

Logue, A. W. (1991) *The Psychology of Eating and Drinking*, W. H. Freeman, New York.

McKinley, M. J. (1991) Osmoreceptors for thirst, in D. J. Ramsey and D. A. Booth (eds) *Thirst: Physiological and Psychological Aspects*, pp. 77–92, Springer-Verlag, London.

Marchini, G., Lagercrantz, H., Feuerberg, Y., Winberg, J. and Uvnäs-Moberg, K. (1987) The effect of non-nutritive sucking on plasma insulin, gastrin, and somatostatin levels in infants, *Acta Pediatrica Scandanavica*, **76**, 573–78.

Mei, N. (1994) Role of the digestive afferents in food intake regulation, in C. R. Legg and D. A. Booth (eds) *Appetite – Neural and Behavioural Bases*, pp. 86–97, Oxford University Press, Oxford.

Phillips, P. A., Johnston, C. I. and Gray, L. (1991) Thirst and fluid intake in the elderly, in D. J. Ramsey and D. A. Booth (eds) *Thirst: Physiological and Psychological Aspects*, pp. 403–11, Springer-Verlag, London.

Ramsey, D. J. and Booth, D. A. (eds) (1991) *Thirst: Physiological and Psychological Aspects*, Springer-Verlag, London

Read, N. W. (1992) Role of gastrointestinal factors in hunger and satiety in man, *Proceedings of the Nutrition Society*, **51**, 7–11.

Robinson, P. H. (1989) Gastric function in eating disorders, *Annals of the New York Academy of Sciences*, **575**, 456–65.

Rolls, B. J. (1991) Physiological determinants of fluid intake in humans, in D. J. Ramsey and D. A. Booth (eds) *Thirst: Physiological and Psychological Aspects*, pp. 391–99, Springer-Verlag, London.

Rolls, E. T. (1994) Neural processing related to feeding in primates, in C. R. Legg and D. A. Booth (eds) *Appetite – Neural and Behavioural Bases*, pp. 11–53, Oxford University Press, Oxford.

Russek, M. (1971) Hepatic receptors and the neurophysiological mechanisms controlling feeding behaviour, *Neurosciences Research*, **4**, 213–82.

Thrasher, T. N. (1991) Volume receptors and the stimulation of water intake, in D. J. Ramsey and D. A. Booth (eds) *Thirst: Physiological and Psychological Aspects*, pp. 93–109, Springer-Verlag, London.

Toates, F. (1986) *Motivational Systems*, Cambridge University Press, Cambridge, UK.

Uvnäs-Moberg, K. and Winberg, J. (1989) Role for sensory stimulation in energy economy of mother and infant with particular regard to the gastrointestinal endocrine system, in E. Lebenthal (ed.) *Textbook of Gastroenterology and Nutrition in Infancy* (2nd edition), pp. 53–62, Raven Press, New York.

Verbalis, J. G. (1991) Inhibitory controls of drinking: satiation of thirst, in D. J. Ramsey and D. A. Booth (eds) *Thirst: Physiological and Psychological Aspects*, pp. 313–34, Springer-Verlag, London.

Weingarten, H. P. (1984) Meal initiation controlled by learned cues: basic behavioural properties, *Appetite*, **5**, 147–58.

Widström, A.-M., Marchini, G., Matthiesen, A.-S., Werner, S., Winberg, J. and Uvnäs-Moberg, K. (1988) Nonnutritive sucking in tube-fed preterm infants: effects on gastric motility and gastric contents of somatostatin, *Journal of Pediatric Gastroenterology and Nutrition*, **7**, 517–23.

Woods, S. C. (1991) The eating paradox: how we tolerate food, *Psychological Review*, **98**, 488–505.

CHAPTER 7
DIET AND HEALTH

You are advised to watch TV programme 3, *Food: whose choice is it anyway?*, before beginning your study of this chapter.

7.1 Introduction

An essential aspect of maintaining the body is the consumption of food. The range of foods we eat is known as our **diet** and the components of food which are eaten, absorbed by the body and produce energy, promote growth and repair of the body, or control these processes are called *nutrients* (defined in Book 2, Chapter 2). In earlier chapters of this book, you learnt how the complex mixture of substances found in food is broken down into simple components which are then used as a source of energy and of molecular 'building blocks'. You also learnt about psychological aspects of feeding and drinking. In this chapter, we turn to the subject of diet itself. Our health is dependent upon the nature and quantities of the foods we eat (also known as *nutrition*) and the consumption of what is commonly called a *balanced* diet, which contains the full complement of nutrients, in amounts appropriate for our individual needs.

❑   List some examples, that you have met in the course so far, of the importance of an adequate diet for the maintenance of good health.

■   Poor maternal nutrition is linked to low birth weight, which may be linked to health problems in later life (Book 1, Chapter 2). Good nutrition is linked to more rapid wound healing (Book 1, Chapter 3). Adequate levels of vitamins, particularly folic acid, in the diet of pregnant women are important for normal embryonic development, and may reduce the incidence of neural tube defects (Book 1, Chapter 6). You might have remembered the role that diet has in the healthy growth of the musculo-skeletal system (Book 2, Chapter 2). Diets that contain plentiful fibre may be linked to reduced incidence of cancer, diabetes and cardiovascular disease (Chapter 3 of this book). High salt intake can lead to high blood pressure (Chapter 5 of this book). You may well have thought of other examples.

Most of us feel that we have some idea of what constitutes a healthy diet, and we will look at the components of diet in some detail in the next section of this chapter. However, other factors can have profound effects upon diet, e.g. geography, sociological factors, religion, culture, financial circumstances, and also psychological factors.

The major changes that have occurred in the way human populations have lived, from prehistory up to the present day, have greatly influenced human diets. Around 40 000 years ago the global human population was very small, probably no more than two million individuals (Book 1, Chapter 4). Food was obtained by hunting and killing animals and gathering fruits, nuts or seeds. Where animals were plentiful, hunting was an extremely energy-efficient activity; short bursts of activity were rewarded with high-energy food. These early hunter–gatherers are estimated to have obtained 10 000–15 000 kcal per hour of work (Cohen, 1989). Accurate determinations are obviously difficult to calculate from scant prehistoric evidence so these energy estimates are calculated from observations of present-day hunter–gatherer peoples.

As human populations increased, animal populations decreased and hunters were forced to travel further to obtain their food. This, along with the extinction of large animals such as mammoths, made the life of the hunter–gatherer less energy-efficient. Archaeological evidence shows that humans switched from food collection to food production via agriculture. In this type of life, people began to live together in larger groups, plant crops and domesticate animals. Energy efficiencies of 3 000–5 000 kcal per hour of work have been estimated for primitive farming, using present-day populations for comparison. Agriculture meant that humans could avoid starvation from the lack of available game, and that food surpluses could be stored for later use. Settled communities became hierarchical and people became specialists in certain tasks such as pottery or weaving.

There were drawbacks to this new lifestyle. Greater gatherings of people meant that infectious diseases became a significant cause of ill-health. In the previous, sparse hunter–gatherer populations, there were insufficient numbers to maintain an ever-present (*endemic*) infection. Another drawback was that the varied diet of hunter–gatherers was now replaced with a more monotonous one (for example one in which the main component might be rice or wheat) and was thus more likely to be nutrient-deficient.

The human population continued to increase, although there were periods of slow growth as plagues and wars took their toll. Additional influences on diet were brought about by the development of different cultures and religions. More recently, advances in agricultural and industrial technology have increased food production to meet the demands of the rising population.

Today the global population is around 5.5 billion. Within this population there is a sharp divide between the nations that have an industrial economy (the so-called 'developed' countries such as the industrialized 'Western' countries of Europe, North America, Japan, Australia, etc.) and those that do not (the so-called 'developing' countries). Other countries have a rapidly developing industrial economy and in some ways fall between these two groups. The majority (over three-quarters) of the human population live in developing countries.

In developed countries, food and its influence on health has become an issue of increasing concern. This concern is mainly focused around issues such as the possible links between over-consumption and disease, and the effects of intensive farming practices on food safety. In developing countries, food is also an issue of concern, but the issues are those of under-consumption, and in some cases limited access to any food at all; large numbers of people suffer from hunger and starvation and, at best, may only expect to live to their mid-50s. In countries that are developing an industrial economy, there is a mix of concerns. Rapid changes in patterns of food consumption often accompany industrial development; the adoption of the Western diet rich in fat, salt and sugar, appears to be associated with the acquisition of Western patterns of ill-health.

This chapter cannot possibly cover all aspects of diet and human health, so we have chosen to focus on four main areas. First, we concentrate on the current view of what actually constitutes a healthy human diet, and on aspects of the study of links between diet and disease. Second, we take a brief look at how, in the UK, our ideas of a healthy diet have changed during the last century or so. Thirdly, we consider some of the sociological factors which affect food consumption and food choice and finally we look, briefly, at how humans influence the food chain.

Summary of Section 7.1

1   An adequate diet is essential for health, but diet is influenced by many things, such as geographical factors, sociological factors, wealth, culture, and religion.

2   Changes in the human lifestyle since prehistoric times have had profound influences on diet.

3   The concerns of developed countries over diet and health are focused on issues of over-consumption and methods of food production, while those of developing countries are focused on under-consumption and food availability. Countries with a rapidly developing industrial economy are in transition between these two positions, and are often faced with both types of problem.

7.2 Components of a healthy human diet

You have already learnt quite a lot in this course about the main nutrients in the human diet.

❑   List the six main types of nutrient in the human diet. (Think back to Chapter 3.)

■   The six major types of nutrient are carbohydrates, proteins, lipids, vitamins, minerals and water.

A lack of an adequate supply of any of these nutrients is known as **malnutrition**, and leads to poor health. If deficiency continues, it can lead to disease, starvation (or, in the case of water, to dehydration) and eventually to death. There is also an absolute requirement for some specific molecules in the diet. This is because, although the body can manufacture most of the molecules it needs (providing that it is supplied with enough energy and 'starting materials' in the diet), some essential molecules *cannot* be made by the body. These molecules are called **essential nutrients**, and must be supplied in the diet. The essential nutrients include a number of amino acids, fatty acids, vitamins and minerals.

Other components of the human diet are not nutrients at all, as they do not perform the functions of producing energy or promoting growth and repair, but are eaten for other purposes. For example, spices and other flavourings help make some food more palatable, whilst the nutritional value of tea and coffee comes from any added milk and sugar, not from the plant products in these drinks.

Foods, then, are generally a complex mixture of nutrients and human diets are extremely varied, but all diets must contain adequate amounts of the six nutrient types to sustain a healthy body. What are these 'adequate' amounts, and how have they been determined?

Information about the influence of nutrients on the human body comes from the branch of scientific research known as **nutrition**. Much research has been done to try to establish the nature of the 'optimum' diet. (We will consider how this research is performed later in the chapter.) Our current understanding of what constitutes a healthy diet is based on reports made by committees of experts in nutrition, set up by various governments and organizations such as the World Health Organization (WHO) and the European Union (EU). These committees review the evidence from nutritional research. In the case of some nutrients, however, there is relatively little research data on which to base recommendations on intake values. In the UK, the current recommended intake of the different nutrient types comes from the 1991 report of the Committee on the Medical Aspects of Food (COMA), *Dietary Reference Values for Food, Energy and Nutrients for the UK*.

The 1991 COMA report was the first to set intake levels for the major nutrients (carbohydrates, proteins and lipids) as well as for vitamins and minerals. The committee also decided to replace the previous recommendations which were known as the *recommended daily intake* (RDI) and the *recommended daily amount* (RDA) with a range of values for each nutrient, known as **dietary reference values (DRVs)**.

❏   Suggest why the COMA committee members decided to recommend a *range* of intake values for each nutrient.

◼   Not all of the population will require the same amounts of nutrients. Some individuals will require more and others less of any particular nutrient than most other members of the population.

Thus the COMA Panel decided to set a range of DRVs in order to emphasize that the recommendations were population estimates and not recommendations for daily intakes by groups or individuals. Individual requirements for nutrients vary considerably depending on factors such as age, sex, size, metabolic rate and occupation, as well as on the rest of the diet, which may alter the efficiency of absorption or utilization of a certain nutrient (as mentioned for iron, in Chapter 3). The body also has stores of certain nutrients (fat-soluble vitamins, for example) so variations in daily intake of such nutrients can be accommodated. Thus it could be misleading to recommend a particular daily intake level.

The COMA Panel set four levels of DRVs:

1   The level at which 50% of a population would need more of that nutrient and 50% would need less. This level is referred to as the **estimated average requirement (EAR)**.

2   The level that would be enough only for the few people (2.5%) in a group with low needs for that nutrient. This level is known as the **lower reference nutrient intake (LRNI)**.

3   The level that would be enough, or more than enough, for 97.5% of people within a certain group; at this level, deficiency would be unlikely. This level is the **reference nutrient intake (RNI)**. (Confusingly, RNI values are still often quoted as RDA or RDI on food packaging.)

4   Where there was insufficient information about the human requirements for a particular nutrient (vitamin E, for example), a **safe intake** level was set which was sufficient for most people's needs but would not be too high an amount to cause undesirable effects.

How are we to interpret and use these DRVs to help us eat a healthy diet? (In this respect, it is perhaps interesting to note that the recommendations of other committees such as those set up by the WHO and in the USA, have arrived at values that are somewhat different to the the DRVs set by the COMA Panel.) Clearly, public awareness and food labelling are of key importance; we will return to these issues later in this chapter. Let us now look at each type of nutrient in more detail.

7.2.1   Carbohydrates

You have already learnt that carbohydrates are the major source of energy in the human diet. The amount and type of carbohydrate in the diet, however, vary considerably, particularly between populations living in different parts of the world. There can also be considerable variation in the amount and types of carbohydrate in the diets of different groups *within* populations. At one extreme, for a small proportion of the affluent peoples of the developed world, fat rather than carbohydrate is now the main source of energy, while at the other extreme, some populations in the developing world have a staple diet composed almost entirely of cereals such as rice, and carbohydrate provides the overwhelming source of energy, as shown in Figure 7.1.

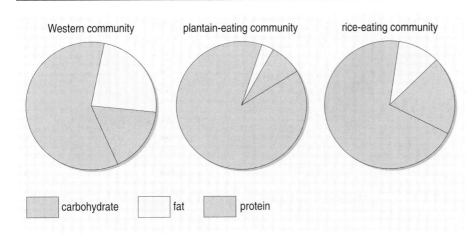

Figure 7.1   Percentage intake of the main nutrient types in three types of community characterized by different diets.

Types of dietary carbohydrate

You will recall from Book 1, Chapter 3, and also from earlier chapters of this book, that there are two major types of dietary carbohydrate. These are the polysaccharides and the so called simple sugars (sometimes also called free sugars), which include monosaccharides and disaccharides.

❑   Give examples of polysaccharides, disaccharides and monosaccharides and their dietary origins.

■   Polysaccharides include starch and cellulose obtained from plants, and glycogen, which is stored in the liver and skeletal muscle (Chapter 4). Disaccharides include sucrose (table sugar) and lactose (milk sugar). Monosaccharides include glucose (mainly obtained by the digestion of polysaccharides and disaccharides, but also present, in small amounts, in fruit and vegetables) and fructose (which is found in ripe fruit and many vegetables, especially root vegetables such as beetroot, carrots and parsnips).

Simple sugars, or monosaccharides, such as glucose and particularly fructose are made by plants as sources of energy and stored around their seeds, in the flesh of fruits. Both these monosaccharides are also found in honey. Fructose contains the same amount of energy as glucose (17 kJ or 4 kcal per gram), but tastes twice as sweet and so can be used by those who like sweet foods but are trying not to take in too much energy (slimmers or diabetics, for example). The most common disaccharide in the diet is sucrose, which is obtained from sugar beet or sugar cane. This sugar is used extensively in manufactured foods. The disaccharide lactose forms about 7% of human milk and about 5% of cows' milk.

The most common digestible dietary polysaccharide is starch. Starch is the main storage material for plants and can be found in potatoes and in seeds, e.g. cereal grains, and peas and beans (pulses). Starch forms the main dietary carbohydrate for much of the world's population. However, in the developed world, simple sugars have become an increasing proportion of carbohydrate intake (as shown in Figure 7.2), especially during the 20th century. We will return to the significance of this later in this section.

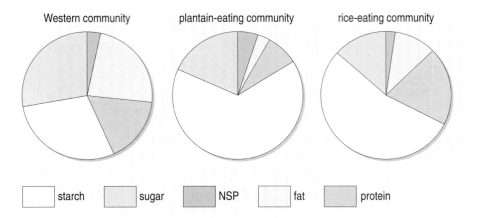

Figure 7.2 Percentage nutrient intake in three communities with different diets.

Another important plant polysaccharide present in food is cellulose which contributes to the non-digestible part of our food and is often called *fibre*, *roughage* or **non-starch polysaccharide (NSP)**. NSP is defined as plant material which cannot be digested by the enzymes of the human gut. NSP is the preferred term because components of dietary fibre do not always look fibrous and the term roughage could conjure up ideas of internal abrasion. Cellulose is insoluble in water (and is hence known as *insoluble* NSP). The two other types of NSP – *pectins* from fruit and *mucilages* from pulses (peas and beans) – form a jelly-like structure in water; these are *soluble* types of fibre. Both insoluble and soluble NSP are thought to be important to a healthy diet.

❑   Diets that contain plentiful insoluble NSP result in bulkier gut
      contents, which travel more quickly through the digestive system.
      From what you learnt in Chapter 3, explain why this happens, and
      which cell types in the gut are involved.

■   Distension of the gut is detected by enteric neurons which stimulate
      peristaltic activity of the smooth muscle in the gut wall. Bulky gut
      contents provide increased stimulation and so peristalsis is
      accelerated.

Food with a high insoluble NSP content spends less time passing through the gut; the food has a reduced *transit time*. The transit time for food that is low in fibre can be several days or longer, whereas a meal that is high in insoluble NSP can pass through the gut in about a day. Bulky food also reduces the need for straining at defaecation which itself can cause haemorrhoids or piles. Diets containing high levels of insoluble NSP have also been reported to have a protective effect against some other gastrointestinal disorders, including formation of gallstones (the small stone-like structures formed when cholesterol solidifies in the gallbladder), appendicitis (inflammation of the appendix), and *diverticular disease*.

Diverticular disease is a gastrointestinal disorder in which areas of the gut wall are deformed into small 'pockets' or *diverticula*, and it has been linked to low–NSP diets. It is thought to occur when the walls of the intestine are pushing against gut contents which are hard and compacted, as occurs with low–NSP diets. Gut contents/chyme become stuck in these pockets, so infections can begin there and eventually sections of the gut become painful and inflamed.

❑   From what you have learnt earlier in this book, what are the other possible advantages to health of a diet high in insoluble NSP?

■   Shortened transit time reduces the amount of contact between intestinal tissue and potentially harmful substances in the diet. NSP may also actually bind potentially toxic substances, and hence aid their excretion. For this reason, it is thought that diets high in insoluble NSP are protective against conditions such as bowel cancer, and indeed, the incidence of bowel cancer is lower in populations with a higher intake of insoluble NSP (Chapter 3). Diets high in NSP are also associated with a lower incidence of diabetes and heart disease (Chapter 3). However, diets high in insoluble NSP also tend to be low in fat and sugar, and in some cases have higher levels of some vitamins, all of which may have beneficial effects. Thus much more research needs to be done before the nature of the protective effects of diets high in insoluble NSP can be firmly established.

❑   What are the *disadvantages* of a diet high in insoluble NSP?

■   Insoluble NSP may bind some vitamins, and thus reduce their absorption from the gut.

So far in our discussion of NSP we have focused on *insoluble* NSP. However, it is now thought that *soluble* NSP (found in fruit, vegetables and pulses) is also likely to be beneficial to health. We do not have space to go into all the details here, and indeed the mechanism by which the soluble NSP exerts its effects has not been firmly established, but there is evidence that soluble NSP causes a significant reduction in circulating cholesterol levels.

We now return to starch and the simple sugars. You will remember from Chapter 4 that any absorbed monosaccharides that are not immediately used by cells to produce energy are converted into the storage molecules glycogen and triacylglycerols (fats). These, in turn, can be utilized to provide energy when glucose is not entering the circulation from the gut. If the need is great, proteins can also be catabolized to provide energy. Although carbohydrates are the main source of energy in the human diet, fats also make a significant contribution to energy production in the developed world (as do proteins, where these form a large proportion of the diet). The energy yields of carbohydrates, fats and proteins are shown in Table 7.1.

Table 7.1   The energy yields of different nutrients.

Nutrient type	Available energy	
	/kcal per gram	/kJ per gram
carbohydrate	4	15–17
fat	9	37
protein	4	16

The energy content of foods is assessed by electrically igniting carefully measured quantities of the foodstuff in oxygen and then measuring the heat output. This heat energy released by burning the food in oxygen is equivalent to the energy released in the body when the food is catabolized completely.

The *total energy intake* in the diet is of key importance to health. A diet containing insufficient energy-producing nutrients leads to a loss of weight, and eventually to malnutrion and an increased susceptibility to ill-health. Over-consumption of energy-producing nutrients, on the other hand, leads to weight gain (largely because of an increase in body fats) and eventually to **obesity**. This can be defined as body weight which is elevated above the desirable level to an extent which is associated with serious increased risk to health. The range of body weights for individuals of different heights are shown in Figure 7.3.

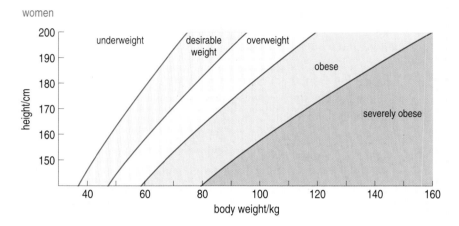

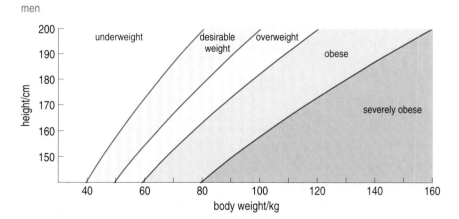

Figure 7.3 Relationship between body weight and height for women and men. The range of weights classified as desirable, overweight and obese for individuals of different heights are indicated.

Both overweight and obesity are associated with increased incidence of serious conditions such as high blood pressure (hypertension), cardiovascular disease and diabetes mellitus (non-insulin-dependent, type II), as well as conditions which are not life-threatening, but which do affect well-being, such as varicose veins and arthritis. On the gloomy side, both underweight and overweight individuals have an increased risk of premature death, as shown in Figure 7.4.

Clearly, the energy requirements for different individuals will vary.

❑   What factors will influence the energy requirements of different individuals?

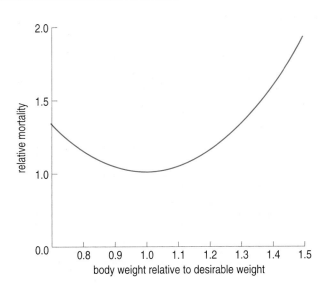

Figure 7.4   The relationship between actual body weight relative to desirable weight and relative mortality.

■   Age, body size, sex, occupation, metabolic rate (Chapter 4), pregnancy, lactation.

DRVs for energy are shown in Table 7.2 (you may like to compare this table with Table 4.4, which shows the energy used by a typical adult during different activities).

Table 7.2   Dietary reference values (estimated average requirements, EAR) for energy through the lifespan. Also shown are the extra (+) amounts of energy required during pregnancy and lactation.

Age	EAR/kcal per day	
	Males	Females
0–3 months	545	515
4–6 months	690	645
7–9 months	825	765
10–12 months	920	865
1–3 years	1 230	1 165
4–6 years	1 715	1 545
7–10 years	1 970	1 740
11–14 years	2 220	1 845
15–18 years	2 755	2 110
19–50 years	2 550	1 940
51–59 years	2 550	1 900
60–64 years	2 380	1 900
65–74 years	2 330	1 900
over 75 years	2 100	1 810
pregnancy		+200*
lactation		+450–480

* During the last trimester.

The *source* of energy in the diet is also of considerable importance. Since fats are a much more concentrated source of energy than carbohydrates, it is easy to exceed the DRVs for energy when eating a high-fat diet. Diets containing high proportions of fats have also been linked with disease (e.g. cancer of the colon and cardiovascular disease). However, as you have learnt, fats are an essential component of the human diet. Proteins, too, are essential; a minimum intake level is required simply to replace proteins lost in secretions and during turnover, which occurs constantly. However, if other energy sources in the diet are insufficient, proteins are catabolized to provide energy. Unless protein intake is very high, this is clearly an unsatisfactory situation, as the body would not be able to maintain its levels of essential proteins and would undergo wasting. (We will discuss both fats and proteins in more detail shortly.) These factors have been taken into account in the DRVs which recommend the relative contributions which carbohydrates, fats and proteins should make to the daily total energy intake. These are shown in Table 7.3.

Table 7.3   Summary table showing the proportion of energy (as per cent of total) obtained from the three main types of energy source, compared with COMA guidelines. (Alcohol is not included.)

Energy source	Average	Range	Guidelines
carbohydrate	42	30–55	50
fat	39	27–50	35
protein	15	9–20	15

So, the recommendations are that carbohydrates should form the major source of dietary energy. However, the proportions of the different types of carbohydrate in the diet are also believed to be of considerable importance to health. Moreover, it is not simply the relative amounts of starch and the simple sugars, but the *source* of the simple sugars in the diet which are considered to be important. Simple sugars can be classified into two groups:

> **Intrinsic sugar**, defined as sugar that is contained within the structure of the foodstuff (i.e. in the tough, polysaccharide walls of the plant cells which make up the food material).

> **Extrinsic sugar**, defined as any sugars not incorporated into the structure of the food, such as sugars extracted from fruits and those in honey and table sugar.

Lactose (milk sugar) in milk and milk products can be excluded from the latter group as it does not seem to have the same effects on human health as sucrose. For dietary recommendations, the term **non-milk extrinsic sugar** is therefore used for free sugars excluding lactose. This classification may seem to be confusing but the two types of sugar (intrinsic and non-milk extrinsic) are thought to have different effects on human health. Intrinsic sugars are thought to have no adverse effects on health, whereas consumption of large amounts of non-milk extrinsic sugars is associated with health risks. Such risks include: obesity, tooth decay and elevated levels of blood glucose, insulin and cholesterol, which may lead to increased incidence of non-insulin-dependent diabetes and cardiovascular disease. In the UK, the main non-milk extrinsic sugar is sucrose; most of the sucrose consumed has been added to processed food already by the manufacturer but some is added to food during preparation by the consumer.

The current dietary reference values and actual average intake for carbohydrates are shown in Table 7.4.

❑   How does the current UK dietary carbohydrate intake compare to the COMA recommendations?

■   The average British dietary intake of carbohydrates is lower than recommended, while the intake of non-milk extrinsic sugar is higher than recommended.

The intake of non-starch polysaccharide (NSP) is recommended at an average of 18 g per day (12 g being the minimum intake and 24 g being the maximum). Actual intake of NSP is around 11–13 g per day. (To give you some idea of what this means, a medium-sized apple weighing 100 g contains 2 g of NSP and 100 g of uncooked wholewheat spaghetti contains 9 g of NSP.) Thus NSP intakes are at or just below the minimum recommended levels.

As already mentioned, the ability of individuals to relate DRVs to actual intake of nutrients relies upon both awareness of what the guidelines actually are, and also informative labelling of foods.

Table 7.4   Dietary reference values (DRVs) and average actual intakes of digestible carbohydrates. (Values are per cent of total dietary energy intake.)

Carbohydrate type	DRV/% total	Average intake /% total
intrinsic sugar, milk sugar and starch	39	24
non-milk extrinsic sugar	11	18
total	50	42

Look at the labels on some food products. For example compare the contents of wholemeal and white bread, biscuits, pies, baked beans, fish fingers, etc. Do you think that the labelling is detailed enough to enable consumers to make informed choices about the foods that they eat?

❑   From your own experience, and from your observation of food labels, suggest likely sources of the excess extrinsic sugars in the average British diet.

■   Sugars are a major component of many processed foods, but in many cases, food labels do not distinguish between intrinsic and extrinsic sugars. Fewer people today add sugar to tea or coffee and the shift to consumption of processed rather than home-made foods has meant that less sugar is used for food preparation and cooking in the home. Thus the sources of extra extrinsic sugars have shifted from 'visible' sucrose added by the individual to food and drink to the 'invisible' sources found in processed and manufactured foods.

❑   What are the possible reasons why humans (and other animals!) enjoy sugary foods so much?

■   A 'taste' for sweet foods may have evolved as an adaptive characteristic because fruits were a good source of energy, vitamins and minerals for the hunter–gatherers (Book 1, Chapter 1, and

Chapter 6 in this book). Sociological and cultural factors encourage those in the developed world, particularly children, to eat sweet foods. Human breast milk is very sweet, so babies may learn to associate satiety and comfort with a sweet taste, an example of *conditioning* (Chapter 6).

The rapid rise in blood glucose levels which occurs after consumption of sugary foods leads to rapid changes in metabolism of glucoreceptors which may be involved in the control of feeding. This brings us to another aspect of carbohydrates in the diet; the *rate* at which they are absorbed from the gut.

Clearly, ingested monosaccharides and those derived from disaccharide sugars are likely to be more rapidly absorbed from the gut than those from most polysaccharides, despite the digestive action of salivary amylase. Thus sugary foods will tend to produce a larger and more rapid rise in blood glucose levels than meals containing little sugar, but more polysaccharide. However, the *physical form* of the polysaccharide also has a significant effect on the rate at which its component monosaccharides are absorbed. Starch in whole grains or seeds for example, is inaccessible to digestive enzymes in the gut. Milling of grain improves access, but food manufacturing processes have the greatest effect, producing small granules of starch which allow easy access of the digestive enzymes. Cooking further increases the digestibility of starch, the starch granules swelling and taking up water. A few processed foods, particularly pasta, contain very little water so the carbohydrate in these foods is very dense, even after cooking. These foods are digested more slowly than other processed carbohyrate foods, such as bread. Some foods contain starch which is actually undigestible unless cooked, such as that in some fruits (e.g. unripe bananas) and some vegetables (e.g. potatoes); this undigestible starch passes out of the body in the faeces.

Starch can thus be classified into **rapidly digestible starch, slowly digestible starch** and **resistant starch**. The relative amounts of different types of starch in a meal can have a significant effect on blood glucose levels after eating that meal; this is one reason why porridge oats or muesli may be a better breakfast cereal than the highly processed and sugared cereals which are so appealing to children. The relatively unprocessed wholegrain cereal will take longer to be digested than the processed alternative, and will therefore produce a less rapid and smaller rise in blood glucose levels. However, it will continue to be digested and monosaccharides will be absorbed over a longer period of time. A similar effect will occur for pasta (white pasta contains 43% slowly digestible starch), in comparison with white bread (4% slowly digestible starch).

The proportion of the different types of starch in the diet is very important for diabetics, who cannot regulate blood glucose levels. You have already learnt that elevated levels of glucose in the circulation can be harmful; a major reason for this is that when glucose is present at a high levels, it can bind to proteins (this is known as protein *glycation*). This causes irreversible structural changes to the protein and the formation of what is known as

Amadori product. Amadori product can bind irreversibly to other proteins, exacerbating the damage caused by excess glucose. It is important to note that although protein glycation is a major problem for untreated diabetics, it also occurs in non-diabetic individuals, and may be the cause of the increased incidence of cataracts, peripheral nerve damage and connective tissue damage in the elderly.

It is also possible that the elevated levels of blood glucose that occurs in individuals who regularly *overeat* very sugary foods, may lead to over-stimulation and, in the long-term, a disruption of the normal control system which regulates blood glucose levels (the insulin/glucagon and autonomic nervous systems – see Chapter 4). This may be one of the reasons why overweight individuals are more prone than those of 'desirable' weight to develop non-insulin-dependent diabetes.

Now let us return to the problem of relating the recommended guidelines on nutrient intake with the food that most people actually eat. The rather complex percentage recommendations given in the guidelines can seem remote from everyday diets, so in 1994 the COMA report on Nutritional Aspects of Cardiovascular Disease tried to translate its recommendations into actual portions. For example, it was advised that potato intake rise from one small portion daily (defined as two egg-sized potatoes) to one medium portion (three egg-sized potatoes). However, this advice was seen by some as prescriptive and a sign of governmental intervention in individual diets. The recommendation that cheese sandwich consumption be reduced brought particular criticism (Figure 7.5).

Figure 7.5   How the *Guardian* newspaper reported the findings of the 1994 COMA report on 10 August 1994.

The report's overall recommendations were that people increase their consumption of vegetables, fruit, potatoes and bread by 50%, thus increasing the amount of energy they obtained from those carbohydrate sources. This increase should be at the expense of energy from fatty and sugary foods.

Summary of Section 7.2.1

1   Carbohydrates that can be digested and assimilated by the body are simple sugars, disaccharides and polysaccharides such as starch.

2   Polysaccharides from plant material that cannot be broken down and digested by digestive enzymes in the gut are called non-starch polysaccharides (NSP).

3   NSP exists in soluble and non-soluble forms. An adequate intake of NSP is linked to rapid and effective peristalsis and a reduced incidence of colon cancer and other disorders. A diet low in NSP is linked with various digestive and metabolic disorders.

4   Consumption of intrinsic sugars does not seem to have the same effects on health as over-consumption of non-milk extrinsic sugars. The most common non-milk extrinsic sugar consumed in excess in developed countries is sucrose.

5   Starch can be classified as slowly digestible, rapidly digestible and resistant (to digestion). The rate at which starch is digested varies with the physical form of the foodstuff; processing and cooking produces starch granules which allow digestive enzymes greater access. Consumption of foods with a larger proportion of slowly digestible starch produces a slower and smaller rise in blood glucose levels, which is likely to be beneficial to health, as well a providing a more prolonged source of energy.

6   Excess levels of sugar in the blood, even high levels that occur normally in non-diabetic individuals, leads to binding of sugar to protein (glycation) which causes protein damage and the formation of Amadori product. In the long-term this is thought to result in damage to a number of tissues of the body, including the eye, the peripheral nervous system and connective tissue.

7   Dietary recommendations in relation to carbohydrates are to increase consumption of starch and intrinsic sugars and reduce the consumption of non-milk extrinsic sugars.

8   Food labelling may sometimes be incomplete, and it may be difficult to calculate the amounts of any particular nutrient in a portion of food from the information given. This makes it difficult to keep closely to dietary guidelines.

7.2.2   Lipids

The major dietary lipids are the triacylglycerols, or fats and oils, which are made up of three fatty acid molecules combined with one molecule of glycerol (Book 1, Chapter 3). Fats occur in the diet in both 'visible' forms such as butter, margarine, cheese and lard, and 'invisible' forms such as in milk and eggs (where the fat is held in suspension as an emulsion) and in ready prepared or processed foods.

Fats are concentrated sources of energy, each gram containing 37 kJ or 9 kcal (Table 7.1). Excess dietary fats are stored in adipose tissue which, as you learnt in Chapter 4, provides a source of energy-providing molecules at times of need. Adipose tissue also has a role in protecting vital organs and insulating the body. Although an excess of fat in the diet leads to increased body fat, weight gain and associated health problems, fats are an essential component of the human diet. As already mentioned, some fatty acids are essential nutrients, e.g. linoleic and α-linolenic acid. Both these fatty acids are needed as components of cellular membranes and for the synthesis of important signalling molecules called *eicosanoids*, which include the *prostaglandins* (Book 1, Chapters 4 and 6). Dietary fats also contain vitamins (vitamins A, D, E and K) which are essential for good health.

Fatty foods taste very pleasant to humans and are thought to be involved in satiety (Chapter 6). This is why humans are attracted to foods rich in fats. Fat is often seen as the 'baddie' in modern diets but, as you can see from the range of functions it has in the body, a healthy diet must contain a proportion of fat. Table 7.5 shows the fat content of a range of foods.

Table 7.5   The fat content of a range of foods (listed in descending order of fat content).

Food	Fat content /%	Food	Fat content /%
lard	99	beef (rump steak)	14
margarine	81	eggs	10.9
butter	82	milk	3.8
cream cheese	47	bread (white)	1.7
cheddar cheese	34	rice	1
pork sausage	32	haddock	0.6
herring	19	potatoes	0

Cholesterol is another lipid which has received a particularly 'bad press', because elevated levels of cholesterol in plasma have been found to be a risk factor for cardiovascular disease. However, cholesterol has vital roles in the human body.

❏   What are the functions of cholesterol in the body?

■   Like some of the fatty acids, cholesterol is a component of cell membranes. It is also a precursor molecule for the manufacture of other molecules such as vitamin D, steroid hormones and bile salts (Chapter 3).

As you learnt in Chapter 4, cholesterol is manufactured by the body (particularly in the liver) and only 20–25% comes from dietary sources (cholesterol is found at high levels in eggs and animal products such as kidney and liver). Under normal circumstances, if dietary intake is high, there is a corresponding reduction of cholesterol synthesis by the liver. Thus, for most individuals, the amount of cholesterol consumed is unlikely to result in an elevated level of plasma cholesterol. However, the *total* fat intake, and also the *types* of fat in the diet do have an effect on plasma cholesterol levels. This is because saturated fatty acids (i.e. those with no double bonds between their carbon atoms) increase the amount of circulating cholesterol, while unsaturated fatty acids (i.e. those with one or more double bonds) reduce the amount of circulating cholesterol. For this reason, the recommendations for fat intake specify not only the total amount of fat in the diet, but also the relative amounts of the different types of fatty acid, as shown in Table 7.6.

Table 7.6 Dietary reference values for fats and fatty acids and actual intakes as a percentage of total daily energy intake (adult, population average). (The difference in the values for total fats and total fatty acids is accounted for by the energy derived from glycerol.)

	Recommended intake/% total (no alcohol)	Recommended intake/% total (assumes 5% alcohol)	Average actual intake (and range) /% total
total fats	35	33	39 (30–50)
total fatty acids	32.5	30	35
saturated fatty acids	11	10	17 (10–23)
cis-polyunsaturated fatty acids	6.5	6	6 *(3–12)
cis-mono-unsaturated fatty acids	13	12	12 *(8–17)
trans-fatty acids	2	2	

* Includes actual intake of *trans*-fatty acids (approximately 2% of total)

On inspection of Table 7.6, you will notice two points that we have not yet discussed. First, alcohol is taken into account in the current guidelines for energy intake. (Similar reductions in the recommended contribution of carbohydrates to the total energy intake are made if alcohol is consumed.) This is because alcohol yields a considerable amount of energy; 29 kJ (or 6.9 kcal) per gram. Those of you who indulge in the occasional or more regular alcoholic drink may be interested to know that alcohol (molecular formula C_2H_5OH) is oxidized to acetyl CoA, which is metabolized via the TCA cycle (Chapter 4).

The second point to note from Table 7.6 is that recommendations about the amounts of different *types* of unsaturated fatty acids are made. Unsaturated fatty acids can be classified in several ways. One important division is between the fatty acid isomers: *cis-* and *trans*-fatty acids. (Isomers were defined in Book 1, Chapter 3.) The *cis*-fatty acids have both parts of the hydrocarbon chain on the *same* side of the molecule whilst *trans*-fatty acids have parts of the hydrocarbon chain on opposite sides. Figure 7.6 shows the *cis*- and *trans*-forms of the mono-unsaturated fatty acid, oleic acid.

Although this may seem a mere structural detail, it has relevance for the effects that the two types of fatty acid might have on human health. Most naturally occurring fatty acids are in the *cis* form. Some *trans*-fatty acids are found in fats from ruminant animals (such as sheep and cows) and *trans*-fatty acids are also generated by the food industry in the commonly used process of *hydrogenation*. This is the addition of hydrogen atoms to poly-unsaturated fatty acids (i.e. their reduction, Chapter 4) to make them more saturated and therefore more solid. In this way, an oil is turned into a fat. Hydrogenation increases an oil's stability and also makes it possible to use hardened vegetable oils instead of animal fats for baking, etc. Deep-frying foods in oil also generates *trans*-fatty acids.

❑   What effect might an increased intake of *trans*-fatty acids have on cell membrane structure?

■   Cell membranes are composed of a bilayer of phospholipids, together with cholesterol and proteins (see Figure 3.31 in Book 1, Chapter 3). Increased incorporation of *trans*-fatty acids into cell membranes could distort their normal structure.

Recently, some nutritionists have voiced concerns over increasing intake of *trans*-fatty acids (because of the current move away from the use of butter to hydrogenated vegetable oils). However, since this increase has only relatively recently occurred, it could be argued that it is too soon to be sure about the effects of increased intake of *trans*-fatty acids on health. The concerns are partly based on some evidence that *trans*-fatty acids may be linked to coronary heart disease (CHD); some evidence suggests that *trans*-oleic acid, which is found in margarines, raises plasma LDL levels, but lowers plasma HDL levels, a similar effect to that of saturated fatty acids. You will recall from Chapter 4 that the ratio of LDL to HDL is thought to be an important factor associated with an individual's risk of suffering cardiovascular disease; the greater the proportion of HDL, the smaller the risk.

For these reasons, COMA recommends that *cis*-polyunsaturated fatty acids should make up 6% of total dietary energy, while *trans*-unsaturated acids should make up no more that 2% of dietary energy (Table 7.6).

The influence of fats and cholesterol on human health is a complex area of intense research and debate. The 1994 COMA Report made many recommendations for further research, including nine separate topics related to dietary fats. There is still much we do not know about the interactions and effects of fats on the body. The result of this can be seen in the seemingly contradictory results coming from dietary studies into fat and health which are reported in the media. Table 7.7 shows the common dietary sources of saturated and unsaturated fats.

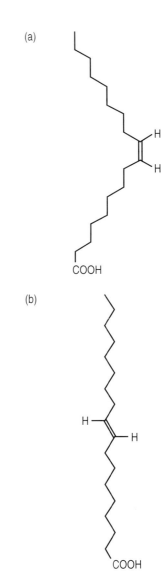

Figure 7.6   Skeleton formulae of oleic acid isomers: (a) *cis*-oleic acid; (b) *trans*-oleic acid. Skeleton formulae show the shape of organic molecules and only identify atoms or chemical groups of interest; so here the carboxyl (–COOH) groups and the H atoms at the double bonds are shown. (You met the skeleton representations of steroids in Book 1, Chapter 4.)

Table 7.7 Common dietary sources of saturated and unsaturated fats.

	Type of source	Examples
High in saturated fats	dairy products	butter, cream, milk, cheese
	meat	liver, lamb, beef, pork
	others	coconut oil, palm kernel oil, palm oil, hard margarine, lard
High in polyunsaturated fats	vegetable oils	corn (maize) oil, soya bean oil, safflower seed oil, sunflower seed oil
	nuts	most, except coconut and cashew nuts
	margarines	many soft varieties especially those made from soya bean and sunflower seed oils
	fish	all types

❑   Is it correct to generalize that animal fats are saturated and vegetable oils are unsaturated?

◼   No. Although most vegetable oils are high in polyunsaturated fats, oils from plant sources such as palm and coconut contain high levels of saturated fats. Thus a product labelled 'made from blended vegetable oils', without specifying which oils it uses, may be misleading the consumer into thinking the product is high in polyunsaturates.

Many consumers are confused about the links between dietary fat intake and health. Overall, as with the other COMA recommendations, the advice is not to make drastic changes to your diet but to shift consumption from animal to polyunsaturated and mono-unsaturated plant and fish oils and to reduce total fat intake in favour of carbohydrates as energy sources.

Summary of Section 7.2.2

1   Fats are a concentrated form of energy which give food a pleasant and satisfying taste. They include the essential fatty acids and also contain fat-soluble vitamins, A, D, E and K.

2   The lipid cholesterol is an essential component of cell membranes and is also the precursor of steroid hormones and bile. It is made in the liver, as well as being present in foods. In normal circumstances, cholesterol in the circulation is kept at appropriate levels by modification of the amount synthesized by the liver. Dietary fatty acids, however, can influence the levels of circulating cholesterol; saturated fatty acids raise, and unsaturated fatty acids lower, levels of cholesterol in the blood.

3   The structure of fatty acids is thought to be important in determining their actions in the body, and thus may have implications for human health. For example, a high intake of *trans*-fatty acids may affect cell

membrane structure and also affect the balance of the different types of circulating lipoproteins (which is important in relation to an individual's risk of developing cardiovascular disease).

4   Dietary recommendations are to shift consumption away from saturated animal fats towards unsaturated plant and fish oils and to reduce overall fat consumption in favour of carbohydrate energy sources.

7.2.3 Proteins

As you can see from Table 7.1, proteins yield about the same amount of energy per gram as carbohydrates but proteins are not primarily used by the body as an energy source. Their main use is in the growth, repair and maintenance of body tissues.

❑   Proteins are macromolecules made from repeating subunits. Can you recall what those subunits are?

■   Proteins are made up of long chains of amino acids.

There are 20 different amino acids, of which eight are essential; that is, they cannot be made by the body and thus have to be obtained from the diet. There are two others, which can only be synthesized from particular essential amino acids, and a further one (histidine) which is made in small amounts, so must also be included in the diet. Arginine is only essential for young children. (See Table 7.8.)

Table 7.8   Essential and non-essential amino acids.

Essential amino acids	Amino acids synthesized from essential amino acids	Non-essential amino acids
lysine	tyrosine*	glycine
methionine	cysteine†	alanine
threonine		serine
leucine		proline
isoleucine		glutamic acid
valine		glutamine
phenylalanine		aspartic acid
tryptophan		asparagine
(histidine)		
(arginine – for young children)		

* Synthesized from phenylalanine.

† Synthesized from methionine.

As you saw in Book 1, Chapter 3, and in many other parts of this course, proteins perform a wide variety of functions within the body. Proteins in the diet are broken down by the digestive system and the absorbed amino acids are used to make new proteins. There is a constant process of protein synthesis and degradation going on throughout the body.

❑   Why do we need a constant supply of protein? Couldn't the body
    simply keep recycling the amino acids in its own proteins?

■   Protein is constantly lost from the body, e.g. via the shedding of skin
    cells and through bodily secretions (such as digestive juices).

Table 7.9 shows the protein content of some common foods. Note that
protein can be obtained from both plant and animal sources.

Table 7.9   The protein content of some common foods.

Animal-derived foods	Protein content/%	Plant-derived foods	Protein content/%
cheese (cheddar)	26	soya flour (low fat)	45
bacon (lean)	20	soya flour (full fat)	37
beef (lean)	20	peanuts	24
cod	17	bread (wholemeal)	9
herring	17	bread (white)	8
eggs	12	rice	7
beef (fat)	8	peas (fresh)	6
milk	3	potatoes (old)	2
cheese (cream)	3	bananas	1
butter	less than 1	apples	less than 1

Some foods, such as eggs, milk and beef, contain all the amino acids
necessary for the human diet, but some other sources of protein contain
levels of particular amino acids that are below human requirements. Wheat,
for example, is low in the amino acid lysine. For people whose diets contain
a variety of protein sources, these individual deficiencies in particular foods
are not important. For those whose diets are restricted in the variety of
protein sources that are used, these deficiencies can cause illness. Maize (or
corn) is low in the essential amino acids lysine and tryptophan. Tryptophan
is used by the body to make niacin (see Section 7.4.4); so populations whose
staple food is maize, such as those in parts of Africa and South America,
can suffer from niacin deficiency, a condition called *pellagra*. Pellagra
causes skin lesions, diarrhoea and eventually death if left untreated. In the
developed world, maize is eaten (mainly in the form of cornflakes) as part
of a *varied* diet; niacin deficiency is therefore very rare in the developed
world.

Protein intakes in Britain are more than adequate for our needs. Table 7.10
shows the recommended daily intakes of protein for individuals of different
ages. Extra dietary protein is needed by people who are suffering from
injury, infection, burns and cancer, as all these can result in an increased
loss of protein. This again stresses the need for good nutrition in hospitals
(as discussed in the section on wound healing in Book 1, Chapter 3).

❑   At what stage of life might there also be a requirement for extra
    dietary protein?

■   Women who are pregnant or breastfeeding need a plentiful supply of protein.

In the developing world, however, human diets are often deficient in protein as well as having an overall inadequate energy content. *Protein–energy malnutrition* (or protein–energy *deficiency*) is a condition where the diet of adults and children are lacking in a range of nutrients and overall food intake is too low for their bodily requirements. **Marasmus** is a severe form of protein–energy malnutrition and is a condition that results from a long-term insufficiency in energy intake. It is a condition often seen in famines, although low-level marasmus can occur throughout a vulnerable population, only the most severe cases being noticed. Once the body's fat stores are depleted, muscle and organ protein is broken down to provide energy. The epithelial cells and villi of the gut are also affected by marasmus and this can lead to poor absorption of nutrients from the inadequate diet. This cycle of inadequate diet and poor absorption of nutrients leads to the severe body wasting that is seen in the victims of famine. Women who are malnourished also tend to produce low birth weight babies (Book 1, Chapter 6) and this can lead to health problems in the next generation. Intestinal parasites, prevalent in many developing countries, can also exacerbate malnutrition by interfering with nutrient absorption.

Protein deficiency in children can also cause a condition called **kwashiorkor**. It can occur when children are weaned from breast milk onto protein-poor foods such as cassava (a root vegetable) or green bananas. Repeated childhood infections and a lack of vitamins and minerals exacerbate the condition, which is characterized by oedema (swelling due to fluid retention) and a general lack of energy for any activity. Table 7.11 shows 1990 estimates of the extent of malnourishment world-wide in children under 5 years old.

Table 7.10   Dietary recommendations for protein intakes throughout the lifespan. (The data are reference nutrient intake (RNI) values.)

Age	RNI/g per day
0–3 months	12.5
4–6 months	12.7
7–9 months	13.7
10–12 months	14.9
1–3 years	14.5
4–6 years	19.7
7–10 years	28.3
males:	
11–14 years	42.1
15–18 years	55.2
19–50 years	53.3
more than 50 years	46.5
females:	
11–14 years	41.2
15–18 years	45.0
19–50 years	46.5
more than 50 years	46.5
during pregnancy	+6
during lactation:	
baby 0–4 months	+11
baby more than 4 months	+8

The '+' signs indicate that these values are to be added to the adult requirement.

Table 7.11   Estimates of the numbers and percentages of children under 5 years old in different parts of the world who suffered from malnourishment in 1990.

Region	Number/millions	Prevalence/%
North America	0.3	2
South America	4.3	12
Caribbean	0.5	21
African continent	23.6	23
South Asia	91.0	69
East Asia	47.4	35

The 1989 United Nations report on nutritional trends in 33 countries concluded by saying that 'The nutritional status of young children is probably the most sensitive indicator of sudden changes in food security and health status, acting as an early signal of distress, ill-health, famine and, eventually, death'.

Summary of Section 7.2.3

1   Protein is an essential component of the diet. The essential dietary amino acids (together with amino acids synthesized in the body) are used to produce new proteins which replace those continually lost via the shedding of skin cells and in bodily secretions.

2   A range of protein sources ensures an adequate intake of all the necessary amino acids and the avoidance of deficiency diseases.

3   Extra protein intake is required by those suffering from injury, infection, burns or cancer, as well as at certain times of life, i.e. during pregnancy and when breastfeeding.

4   Protein deficiency is rare in developed countries but common in other parts of the world. Protein and energy deficiencies cause the conditions marasmus and kwashiorkor, which are particularly prevalent in malnourished children.

7.2.4   Minerals and vitamins

In addition to the major nutrients, which act as metabolic fuels and provide the building blocks for the synthesis of new macromolecules, there is also an important dietary requirement for two other groups of molecules. These are the minerals and vitamins, and because only small amounts of these are required in the diet, they are sometimes known as **micronutrients.**

Minerals

As you learnt in Book 1, Chapter 3, the most abundant elements in our diet are carbon, hydrogen and oxygen (which are found in carbohydrates, fats and proteins) and nitrogen (which is present in proteins). However, many other elements must also be included in the diet: these are the **minerals** and they perform a number of important roles in the body.

❑   Can you recall the particular minerals that influence skeletal growth and development?

■   Calcium and phosphorus are minerals that are needed to build and maintain healthy bones.

❑   What other minerals have you encountered during the course which are essential to health?

■   Iron and sodium are two examples, although you will probably have thought of several others. Iron is a component of haem, and thus essential for oxygen transport in the body (Chapter 2). Sodium, in its ionic form (Na^+), is the major positively charged ion in the body and plays an essential role in the conduction of nerve impulses (Book 2, Chapter 3) and in the transport of small molecules across cell membranes (Chapters 3 and 5 of this book).

Although the dietary requirements of these minerals are relatively low compared to those of the nutrient macromolecules, other minerals are needed in even smaller amounts. These are called **trace elements**, and include copper, iodine and zinc.

Minerals have many different roles in the body; these can be summarized as follows:

1   They form essential *structural* components of cells and tissues; for example, sodium, potassium, calcium and chlorine, in their ionic forms, are found in all cells and extracellular fluids, while calcium, phosphorus and magnesium salts are major components of bones and teeth.

2   The ions of several minerals (Na^+, K^+, Ca^{2+}) play a essential role in *intercellular communication* (for example in the action potential), and in the *transport* of small molecules across cell membranes by active transport. Ca^{2+} also acts as an *intracellular* messenger which, among many other things, triggers neurotransmitter release at nerve terminals.

3   Minerals are also essential components of many important molecules including some *hormones* (for example iodine is an essential constituent of the thyroid hormones), *haemoglobin* (in which iron is bound to haem) and many *enzymes*.

❑   What is the name given to non-protein molecules which are associated with enzymes and which play an essential role in their catalytic activity?

■   These are called coenzymes (Chapter 4).

Some coenzymes are very loosely associated with enzymes, e.g. coenzyme A (which carries acetyl groups) and NAD^+ and FAD (which carry hydrogen atoms/electrons). Others, however, are tightly bound, in some cases by covalent bonds (Book 1, Chapter 3), in which case they are known as **prosthetic groups**.

Many mineral ions, or minerals that are part of organic molecules such as haem, act as as prosthetic groups. An enzyme complex in which copper is a prosthetic group is *cytochrome oxidase*, which is one of the components of the electron transport chain (Chapter 4). Haem, in which iron is bound, also acts as a prosthetic group in other protein components of the electron transport chain. Zinc is an essential part of many enzymes, including carbonic anhydrase (Chapter 5), carboxypeptidase (Chapter 3), DNA polymerase and RNA polymerase. (These last two enzymes are responsible for the fundamental processes of DNA replication and mRNA synthesis, which you first encountered in Book 1, Chapter 3.)

It is important to note that, because only small amounts of minerals are needed in the diet, and because minerals are abundant in foods, people who eat a varied diet are unlikely to develop mineral deficiency. However, there are exceptions to this. For example, people who eat food grown in a local region in which there is a mineral deficiency in the soil may have an inadequate intake of that mineral. This is a problem for people in many mountainous areas (particularly the Himalayas and Andes, but also in the Alps and other areas) where iodine is leached from the soil by high rain and snowfall. *Iodine deficiency* (sometimes known as *goitre*) has serious consequences; iodine is an essential component of the thyroid hormones (thyroxine and tri-iothyronine – Book 2, Chapter 2), which are essential for normal growth and for development of the central nervous system. Nowadays, people in the developed countries are very unlikely to be deficient in iodine, because iodine supplements are added to foods, particularly table salt. However, iodine deficiency is still a serious problem for millions of individuals in the developing world.

A very common mineral deficiency world-wide, which also affects individuals in the developed world, is that of iron. Infestation with intestinal parasites such as hookworm, which leads to loss of blood in the faeces, is a major cause of iron deficiency in the tropics. Iron deficiency is common in women, because of losses during menstruation. Vegetarians are also more likely to experience iron deficiency than are meat-eaters.

❑   Why might some vegetarians be deficient in iron?

■   Haem iron (the form of iron in meat) is more readily absorbed than the iron salts found in vegetables. Vegetables and fruits contain substances which bind iron salts and thus reduce iron absorption (Chapter 3).

The recommended daily requirements (for a woman between 25 and 50 years of age), functions and dietary sources of minerals and trace elements are shown in Tables 7.12 and 7.13.

A number of other minerals (e.g. silicon and vanadium) are known to be essential in the diet, although their roles have not been established. Yet other minerals, such as fluorine (present as the fluoride ion, F^-, in seafood and some water supplies), have beneficial effects (at appropriate levels), but are not thought to be essential. It is also important to realize that excess intake of many minerals can have toxic effects.

Vitamins

The other dietary components that are required in very small amounts are the **vitamins**. Vitamins are a chemically diverse group of organic molecules which are found in a variety of foods. They were named before their detailed chemical structures were known, and so they tend to be referred to by a letter as well as by a chemical name; for example vitamin D is cholecalciferol and vitamin C is ascorbic acid.

The importance of certain types of foods to health was recognized early in human history. More recently, during the 15th century, the necessity for a diet containing fruit and vegetables to prevent scurvy in sailors was realized.

Table 7.12   The major mineral elements required by the body. The recommended intakes (RNI) for a woman between 25 and 50 years of age are listed. The approximate adult body content, functions and common food sources of the minerals are also shown.

Element	RNI/g	Body content/g	Functions	Main food sources
calcium (Ca)	0.7	1000	major structural component of bones and teeth; necessary for blood clotting, muscle contraction and conduction of nerve impulses	milk, cheese, bread and flour (if fortified), cereals, green vegetables
phosphorus (P)	0.55	700	present in bones and teeth; essential for energy storage and transfer by ATP	milk, cheese, bread and cereals, meat and meat products
sodium (Na)	1.6	100	major positive ion in extracellular fluids; Na^+ also present inside cells; essential for conduction of nerve impulses and active transport of small molecules across cell membranes (e.g. absorption from gut)	main source is salt (sodium chloride, NaCl) used in food processing, cooking and at the table
chlorine (Cl)	2.5	100	major negative ion (as Cl^-) in body fluids; present in gastric secretions (as HCl)	salt
potassium (K)	3.5	140	main positive ion inside cells; K^+ also present in extracellular fluids; essential for conduction of nerve impulses, also for the maintenance of ion concentration gradients across cell membranes (by the Na^+–K^+ ATPase), hence indirectly for other forms of active transport	widely distributed in vegetables, meat, milk, fruit and fruit juices
iron (Fe)	0.015	4	essential component of haemoglobin in red blood cells	meat and offal, bread and flour, potatoes and other vegetables
magnesium (Mg)	0.3	25	present in bone, inside cells and in body fluids; needed for activity of some enzymes	milk, bread and other cereal products, potatoes and other vegetables

Table 7.13   Trace elements required by the body. The functions and common food sources of the trace elements are shown.

Element	Functions	Main food sources
cobalt (Co)	required for formation of red blood cells	liver and other meat
copper (Cu)	prosthetic group of many enzymes; necessary for haemoglobin formation	green vegetables, fish, liver
chromium (Cr)	involved in interaction between insulin and insulin receptors	liver, cereals, beer, yeast
iodine (I)	essential constituent of thyroid hormones	milk, seafood, iodized salt
manganese (Mn)	essential component of some enzymes	cereals, pulses, nuts
molybdenum (Mo)	essential component of some enzymes	kidney, cereals, vegetables
selenium (Se)	essential component of some enzymes; associated with vitamin E activity	cereals, meat, fish
Zinc (Zn)	essential component of many enzymes and also of receptor proteins for steroid and thyroid hormones	meat and meat products, milk and cheese; bread flour and cereal products

Scurvy is a disease caused by a deficiency of vitamin C; the sailors could have died of this disease if their diet had not been supplemented with fruit and vegetables containing the vitamin. The active substances present in food that prevented scurvy and other disorders were unknown until vitamins were isolated and chemically characterized in the early part of the 20th century.

Like minerals, vitamins have a large variety of functions in the body, some of which are outlined below. Many are precursors of coenzymes.

❑   What are the two coenzymes which are involved in the transfer of hydrogen atoms/electrons during cell respiration?

■ NAD^+ (nicotinamide adenine dinucleotide), which is derived from niacin, and FAD (flavin adenine dinucleotide), derived from vitamin B_2 (also known as riboflavin).

Other vitamins and vitamin derivatives are important in *signalling* inside cells. Examples are vitamins A and D, which bind to intracellular receptors and thereby regulate gene transcription and so influence cell function. The activated form of vitamin D promotes transcription of the gene coding for calcium binding protein. This protein is present on the lumenal surface of intestinal epithelial cells, and thus promotes absorption of calcium from the gut (Chapters 3 and 5).

Another major role played by some vitamins is that of an **antioxidant**. Vitamins E, A and C and the plant pigment β-carotene (which can be converted in the body to vitamin A) are also antioxidants. Antioxidants play an important protective role, by limiting the action of harmful substances produced by some of the chemical reactions that take place in the body. These harmful substances are known as **free radicals**, which are atoms (or groups of atoms) which contain unpaired electrons and so are unstable and highly reactive. They acquire electrons from other molecules that are around them, thus creating another unpaired electron in that molecule and so on, causing a *chain reaction*. This chain reaction can cause considerable damage to living material. Antioxidants 'mop up' (i.e. supply electrons to) free radicals before they can cause too much damage. Free radicals have been implicated in many human diseases and disorders although their exact role in many of these has still to be fully understood. Many pollutants generate free radicals, as does smoking, and it is this that is thought to be their link with diseases such as cancer. Recent research has also found that many smokers eat a diet low in dietary antioxidants even though their need for these nutrients is higher than that of non-smokers (Margetts, 1993).

The vitamins, their functions within the body and main food sources are listed in Table 7.14.

Vitamins A, D, E and K are fat-soluble vitamins whilst the others are water-soluble. The body can build up stores of fat-soluble vitamins in the liver but excess water-soluble vitamins are removed from the body via the urine, so regular intake is necessary.

Table 7.14   Vitamins essential for human health, including their functions in the body and dietary sources.

Name	Main sources	Functions in the body and effect of shortage
Fat-soluble vitamins		
vitamin A (retinol)	milk, dairy products, margarine, fish-liver oil; also made in the body from carotenes found in green vegetables and carrots	necessary for healthy skin and also for normal growth and development; deficiency will slow down growth and may lead to disorders of the skin, lowered resistance to infection and disturbances of vision such as night blindness; antioxidant
vitamin D (cholecalciferol)	margarine, buttermilk, fish-liver oils, oily fish	necessary for the formation of strong bones and teeth; shortage may cause bone diseases or tooth decay
vitamin E (tocopherols)	plant-seed oils	antioxidant
vitamin K (naphthoquinones)	green vegetables	assists blood clotting
Water-soluble vitamins		
B_1 (thiamine), B_2 (riboflavin), niacin, B_6 (pyridoxine), pantothenic acid, biotin	bread and flour, meat, milk, potatoes, yeast extract, fortified breakfast cereals	function as coenzymes in many of the reactions involved in making use of food; a shortage causes loss of appetite, slows growth and development and impairs general health; a severe deficiency causes disease such as pellagra or beriberi
vitamin B_{12} (cobalamin)	offal, meat, milk, fortified breakfast cereals	necessary for formation of nucleic acids and red blood cells; a shortage may lead to certain types of anaemia
folic acid	potatoes, offal, green vegetables, bread, Marmite, fortified breakfast cereals	has preventative role in the occurrence of neural tube defects (Book 1, Chapters 5 and 6)
vitamin C (ascorbic acid)	green vegetables, fruits, potatoes, blackcurrant syrup, rosehip syrup	necessary for the proper formation of teeth, bones and blood vessels; a shortage slows growth in children and if prolonged may lead to the disease scurvy; antioxidant

Vitamin deficiencies, like mineral deficiences, are now rare in the developed world. However, in some cases, although there may be enough of a particular vitamin in the diet, inadequate amounts of that vitamin may actually be absorbed.

❑   What factors have you already met that interfere with vitamin absorption in the colon?

◼   Vitamin absorption can be reduced if there is too much fibre in the gut, as fibre can bind some vitamins (Chapter 3).

As you also learnt in Chapter 3, there are bacteria in the colon which produce several vitamins. Antibiotic treatment can destroy these bacteria, so this too can reduce the amounts of vitamins which are absorbed. Both a high-fibre diet and antibiotic treatment can thus have serious consequences for people who may have a low dietary intake of vitamins, e.g. some elderly individuals.

The lack of research information has led to confusion, particularly surrounding intake levels of minerals and vitamins needed by humans, and this has allowed the development of a huge market in vitamin and mineral supplements. Nutritional advice about mineral and nutrient pill supplementation has always been that it is unnecessary if a varied and balanced diet is being eaten. There are also those who promote the ingestion of very large doses of minerals and vitamins: the 'what must be good for you in small amounts must be better for you in large amounts' approach. However, there are serious side-effects of over-consumption of certain fat-soluble vitamins.

❑ Why are large doses of water-soluble vitamins not so dangerous?

■ Excess amounts of water-soluble vitamins are not stored in the body, but are excreted in the urine (Chapter 5).

However, over-consumption of some water-soluble vitamins can also be harmful. For example, excess vitamin B_6 can cause damage to the peripheral nervous system.

Taking large amounts of the fat-soluble vitamin A can cause liver and bone damage, hair loss, double vision, vomiting and headaches. Vitamin A overdose in pregnant women can cause birth defects in their unborn children. This is why the advice to pregnant women about eating liver has changed recently. At one time pregnant women were encouraged to eat liver as a rich source of vitamin A (and also iron). Animal feeds, in the developed world, are now routinely supplemented with vitamin A, which accumulates in high levels in animal livers. This means that pregnant women should be careful to watch their overall intake of this vitamin.

Although much research still needs to be done, it seems clear that a healthy diet should contain a wide variety of foods, with a high proportion of energy from carbohydrates, a low content of fat, particularly saturated fat and plenty of fresh fruit and vegetables. Advice on healthy eating often stresses the need to choose a balanced diet in which all major nutrients are present in varying amounts (Figure 7.7).

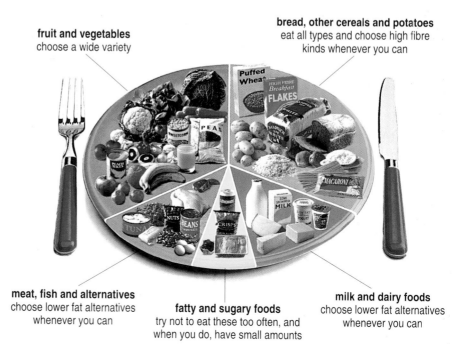

Figure 7.7 'The Balance of Good Health': A guide to choosing a healthy diet produced by the Health Education Authority in 1994.

fruit and vegetables
choose a wide variety

bread, other cereals and potatoes
eat all types and choose high fibre kinds whenever you can

meat, fish and alternatives
choose lower fat alternatives whenever you can

fatty and sugary foods
try not to eat these too often, and when you do, have small amounts

milk and dairy foods
choose lower fat alternatives whenever you can

Summary of Section 7.2.4

1   Minerals and vitamins, which are needed by the body in small amounts, are known as micronutrients. Some minerals, called trace elements, are needed in only minute quantities. Vitamins and minerals are essential to a balanced, healthy diet.

2   Vitamins are classified as either fat-soluble or water-soluble. Excess fat-soluble vitamins can be stored by the body, whereas an excess of most water-soluble vitamins is eliminated from the body in the urine. The over-accumulation of fat-soluble vitamins, which cannot be easily eliminated from the body, can lead to ill-health.

3   Although vitamin and mineral deficiencies are rare in the developed world, there is still a debate about the amounts of these nutrients needed to ensure good health throughout the lifespan.

4   Some vitamins act as antioxidants, which reduce the effects of the free radicals produced by the body and present in cigarette smoke and chemical pollutants. Free radicals are thought to cause certain diseases and disorders.

7.3 The study of diet and disease

Despite having ample access to an enormous range of foods and having a long life expectancy, people in the developed world have become increasingly concerned with their diets in the latter half of the 20th century. There are two important factors involved in this concern.

1   The shift away from infectious disease as the major cause of death and illness to disease conditions, such as cardiovascular disease and cancer, has led to an examination of the many factors that may be important in those diseases. Diet seems to be one of the most important factors and one over which people feel they may have some control.

2   There is the feeling that people living in industrialized countries have little control over the *quality* of the food they eat and that modern agricultural practices and food processing and additives (such as preservatives and colourings) alter their food for the worse. There are fears that our everyday diets may be contributing to the increased incidence of cancer and cardiovascular disease.

There are, however, a number of problems in making links between diet and disease. Firstly, studies on diet and disease have to involve large numbers of people and be long-term. This is because dietary effects on disease are only noticeable over long periods of time, especially in the case of slowly developing conditions such as cancer. These types of study are expensive and time-consuming and often the number of subjects involved in the project diminishes as individuals die as the years progress. Secondly, there are practical difficulties in the accurate analysis of an individual's diet. If you have ever tried to record all the food and drink you have consumed over even just a few days, you will know that it can be a very tedious business, especially if portions have to be weighed. This is often the reason why people find it hard to stick to calorie-counted diets. People also have the habit of 'forgetting' to record what they think the researchers will consider 'bad' foods, such as drinks, sweets and snacks. One research report, on a seven-day food diary analysis, mentioned that '...self-estimation of alcohol consumption is particularly prone to under-reporting...' (Livingstone *et al.*, 1990). Those people who do stick to the tedium of recording and weighing their food may also not be representative of the population under study. In other words, you may be left with those who are obsessed with food and health!

The effects of certain components of food on animal health has been studied extensively. This type of research has provided valuable information about the roles of different types of nutrients, and played an important part in the increased awareness of the importance of human nutrition that occurred during the first part of the 20th century, as you will learn later in this chapter.

❏   Think of some of the advantages and disadvantages of using animals to study human nutrition.

■   Animal physiology and reactions to food may be considerably different to those in humans, so the results may not necessarily be extrapolated from animals to humans. Moreover, animals cannot be used to study the complex interactions which occur between human diet, lifestyle and environment. Many nutritional studies on humans continue for years, as the effects of food on health may take considerable time to be seen. However, there are advantages to animal studies, for although *prolonged* effects of dietary components cannot be studied in animals, results can be obtained in a much shorter period than for humans. Furthermore, studies on animals can be performed very accurately and exact monitoring can be performed, avoiding the problems of working with the forgetful or self-deluding humans mentioned above.

Micronutrients, such as trace elements and vitamins, seem to be important factors in some diseases, but we still know relatively little about their reactions in the body or at what level they are protective to health. We also need to know more about the *interactions* between nutrients in food, and between nutrients and environmental factors. Looking at nutrients in isolation from other factors that may be important in ill-health has led to people becoming confused about the seemingly contradictory reports in the media about whether nutrient X causes cancer or whether nutrient Y is not as good for you as was once thought. It is unlikely that single foods, in isolation from other nutrients, lifestyle factors or environmental influences cause ill-health on their own.

There needs to be great caution in recommending great shifts in people's diets before the effectiveness of such changes has been evaluated. A change in diet that is meant to reduce the incidence of one condition may increase the risk for another.

However, the general dietary guidelines issued by such bodies as COMA present a balanced, varied diet that can be achieved by most people in the developed world and should promote good health. Not all members of industrialized societies, however, have equal access to a healthy diet and there has been increasing concern about the links between food, ill-health and poverty. We will return to food and poverty later in this chapter.

Summary of Section 7.3

1   The links between diet and disease have been extensively researched recently, due to the decline in the effects of infectious disease on human life and the examination of the role of diet in other major causes of ill-health, such as cardiovascular disease and cancer. Concerns have also been raised about the quality of diets in the developed world and the influence of agricultural and food processing techniques on food quality.

2   Studies on the relationship between various diets and dietary components and the incidence of certain diseases are hampered by the often long periods of time that any beneficial or harmful effects from diet take to become obvious or measurable. Accurate measurement of human diet is also difficult over long periods of time. Animal studies can help to some extent, but cannot replicate the complex interactions of food with human physiology, society and the environment.

7.4 Changing ideas about the UK's diet

It is interesting to note that in the UK our ideas about what constitutes a healthy diet have changed rapidly in the 20th century. At the beginning of the century, the state of the urban poor was highlighted by the poor state of health of the men called up to fight in the Boer War. Studies showed that 30% of the population in Edinburgh and 60% of that in Manchester were suffering from malnutrition. This sparked national concern (mostly about Britain not producing armies fit to fight or people able to run the Empire), so in 1906 the national school meals service was started. The school meals service increased public awareness of the need for children to eat foods that provided them with the energy and protein they needed for growth. In the 1920s, milk consumption was encouraged, and in 1933 the Milk Marketing Boards were set up. School milk was introduced in the 1930s and doses of cod liver oil were given to children to prevent rickets.

❑   Rickets is a condition caused by a deficiency of what dietary component?

■   Rickets is a condition in children in which bone growth is affected by the lack of vitamin D (Book 2, Chapter 2).

❏   How does rickets affect children, and why were children of the poor in industrial areas affected?

■   Vitamin D is essential to healthy bone growth and without it children's bones do not become strong enough. This means that their leg bones bow inwards under the weight of their upper bodies, giving them a characteristic 'knock-kneed' posture. Vitamin D is mostly obtained through the exposure of the skin to sunlight or from animal products in the diet. These children's diets were lacking vitamin D and they had little opportunity for exposure to sunlight, living in the dim slums of the industrial north of Britain.

During this time there had been an increasing awareness of the importance of certain other foods – particularly fruit and vegetables – for health. These were called *protective foods*, and were shortly afterwards found to contain vitamins.

An influential report in 1936 by John Boyd Orr called *Food, Health and Income* made links between poverty, poor diet and poor health. Boyd Orr was a physician who had set up the Rowett Research Institute in Aberdeen to study the nutrition of farm animals (there was no money in looking at human nutrition at the time). Having studied the effects of a varied, balanced diet on animal health, Boyd Orr made the connection between the nutrition of farm animals and that of humans and pointed to the neglect of the nutrition of children in poor families:

> *If children of the three social groups were reared like young farm stock, giving them a diet below the requirements for health would be financially unsound. Unfortunately, the health and fitness of the rising generation are not marketable commodities which can be assessed in terms of money.*
> *(Boyd Orr, 1937)*

However, there were others who put forward the idea that it was poor maternal care which accounted for childhood malnutrition. One Glaswegian physiologist suggested the remedy was simply to educate the poor about nutrition. This is an argument which recurs today and we will meet again in the next section of this chapter on poverty and diet.

The government was encouraged by Boyd Orr's proposals that the health of the nation could be improved by nutritional means and they put him in charge of developing a national food policy. The Second World War meant that there was strict food rationing and to avoid widespread malnutrition, Boyd Orr and his colleagues emphasized the need for home production of vegetables and consumption of sufficient (but not excess) quantities of milk, butter, meat and bread. The diet was one that was filling, avoided deficiencies and was available to everyone. There was intense nutritional education of the public to eat a balanced diet that incorporated 'protein foods', 'energy foods' (carbohydrates and fats) and 'protective foods' to avoid nutritional deficiencies. Many people now consider the wartime diet to be a healthy one which avoided excess consumption of any one dietary constituent.

After the war ended, it was felt that enough was then known about human nutrition; all the nutrition research units were closed except for the Rowett (which returned to animal nutrition) and the Dunn Centre in Cambridge (which still undertakes research into human nutrition). By the 1950s, people were released from food rationing and began to demand luxury items which they had not been able to obtain in the previous years, e.g. large amounts of meat, dairy produce, sugar and other sweet foods. Improvements in agricultural technology, intensive animal rearing and subsidies to farmers enabled large amounts of cheap food to be produced. The idea that Britain needed food in quantity to avoid deficiency persisted from the pre-war years. It was thought that eventually everyone would be able to choose an enjoyable, balanced and cheap diet. Western Europe and the United States began to produce food in excess of their needs and this was sold cheaply on world markets. Any that could not be sold was stored as food 'mountains' or 'lakes'. The continual discussion and renegotiation of the Common Agricultural Policy (CAP) in Europe and the General Agreement on Tariffs and Trade (GATT) world-wide is trying to address the problems of over-production, but progress is very slow. The concept of 'set aside' (paying farmers not to produce from their land) has also been implemented to cut down on food excesses, but paying farmers not to produce food cannot be a long-term solution.

❏   Can you think of how another major influence, the way we shop, has changed during recent years, and how this has affected food production and distribution, and the range of foods available in the UK today?

■   The advent of supermarkets has had a tremendous influence on the range of foods available and the way food is marketed today. Before there were supermarkets, local producers sold seasonal produce to local shops. Nowadays supermarket chains can buy food from many producers in both the UK and other countries, forcing down prices and encouraging intensive production. Large supermarkets stock a wide variety of foods and many types of fruit and vegetable are now available throughout the year.

❏   How might this change to supermarket shopping be expected to have affected our diet?

■   One might expect that it would be easier to obtain a balanced diet, as a wide range of produce is now available thoughout the year. However, in some cases, the price of imported foodstuffs is high. Also, people now tend to drive to supermarkets to do their shopping on a weekly, fortnightly or even a monthly basis, rather than every day. This can lead to increased consumption of processed and convenience foods.

As the UK became more affluent, the nation's diet changed rapidly to one high in animal fats, salt and sugar and low in starchy and fibrous foods. People had shifted their concept of food as a matter for survival and health to one of pleasure and an indication of social status. Changes in the way we shop, and the increased use of labour-saving kitchen appliances meant a shift towards convenience foods. Processed, preserved and packaged foods now account for 70% of all food consumed in Northern Europe. So now potatoes are consumed as chips, crisps and in other processed forms, which not only command a higher price than the original vegetable but also have a higher fat content. Food processing techniques also increase the amount of salt and sugar 'hidden' in foods. Sugary drinks are heavily marketed and sugar is used in many products to give the food a pleasant texture and feel in the mouth. Salt in foods enhances the flavour and can mask the use of cheaper ingredients.

❑   How might these changes in food processing have affected our diet?

■   The 'hidden' fats, salt and sugar in modern Western diets make it difficult for individuals to control their intake of these substances, which is thus likely to increase.

This is at a time when there is increased interest in the link between diet and health; newspapers and magazines carry articles about nutritional advice and research almost every day.

❑   Think about any recent articles that you have come across in news-papers and magazines about diet, food quality and health. What are the particular areas of concern reported?

■   There have been many reports on diet and disease, e.g. the relationship between food fat and particularly cholesterol content, and heart disease. The influence of salt consumption on blood pressure has been extensively reported. There have been food-poisoning scares such as *Salmonella* in eggs, *Listeria* in cheeses and cook–chill foods (meals for reheating supplied by outside caterers) and *E. coli* 157 in meat products. BSE (bovine spongiform encephalopathy) has made many people suspicious of beef and has also raised ethical concerns about intensively reared animals and the use of animal growth stimulants. There are many other environmental issues relating to present-day food consumption that are causing concern.

The main historical 'landmarks' in the changing ideas of the British people to diet are summarized in Figure 7.8.

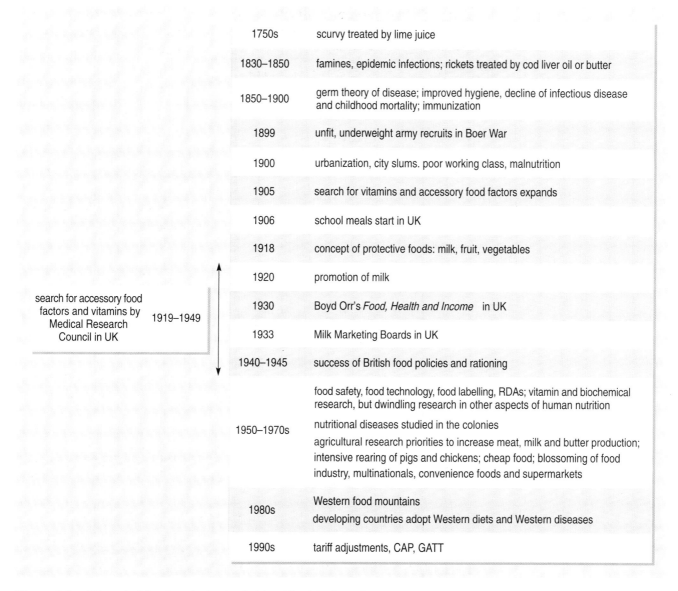

Figure 7.8 Historical landmarks in the fields of health, food from the 1750s until the late 20th century. (CAP = Common Agricultural Policy; GATT = General Agreement on Tariffs and Trade.)

In Britain, current concerns about diet are thus focused mainly on the quality of the foods we eat and avoiding over-consumption. However, there is also increasing concern that some groups of people in Britain cannot afford an adequately balanced diet (see Section 7.6), even though a recent (1996) survey showed that Britain still had the cheapest food and basic commodity prices in Europe.

Summary of Section 7.4

1   At the beginning of the 20th century, malnutrition was identified as a major health problem for a large proportion of the British population. Meals, milk and vitamin supplements were provided in schools to avoid deficiency diseases such as rickets.

2   Concerns about effects of an inadequate diet on the health of the nation were raised by Boyd Orr and his colleagues, who had studied animal nutrition. During the Second World War, rationing of sugar, bread and animal products, and increased consumption of vegetables provided a balanced diet, which avoided excess of any one nutrient, and prevented mass dietary deficiency.

3   After the war, public demand was for those foods once strictly rationed, e.g. meat, dairy produce and sugar. The emphasis, however, was still on producing cheap food, so intensive agriculture was subsidized to ensure that everyone had access to a 'luxury' diet.

4   These policies led to over-production and over-consumption which are only slowly being addressed. Diets now often incorporate too much fat, sugar and processed food, which are linked to various health problems. There is also concern over farming methods and food hygiene. However, on a positive note, the population as a whole are better informed about what constitutes a healthy diet, and a wide range of foods are now available throughout the year.

7.5 Food poverty in the developed world

We tend to think of lack of access to food due to poverty (sometimes called *food poverty*) as purely a problem for the developing world but there is increasing evidence which shows that the very poor in the developed world cannot afford to buy the constituents for what the rest of the population consider to be a healthy diet.

However, it has also been asserted by some critics that the bad nutrition of the poor is due to their ignorance and inability to prepare food. One recent study looked at how 48 families with children living on income support managed to eat on a low income (Walker *et al.*, 1995). This study also included setting a budget standard, i.e. a costed list of the bare essentials necessary to give children a basic standard of living. The families ate food that was filling, satisfying and appealing to children, i.e. high in sugar and fat, as they could not afford to waste food. Table 7.15 shows the cost of 100 kilocalories from different foods. Clearly, the cheapest 100 kcal come from filling foods that are also high in sugar and saturated fat.

Table 7.15   The approximate cost of 100 kcal in different foods, estimated in 1993.

Food item	Cost/pence per 100 kcal	Food item	Cost/pence per 100 kcal
biscuits (custard creams)	2	sausages (pork)	10
sliced bread (white)	3	meat pie	11
rolls (wholemeal)	4	pork (lean)	33
chips (frozen)	4	fish fingers	13
potatoes (boiled)	7	cod fillet (frozen)	95
carrots	20	chocolate bar	8
broccoli	74	corn snacks	12
lettuce	76	apples	19
tomatoes	80	oranges	30
celery	103	milk (full fat)	7
		milk (skimmed)	13

The families taking part in the study shopped once a week or more frequently, in local shops, relying on frozen food and convenience meals for ease of storage and to avoid waste. Fresh fruit, vegetables and lean meat were items that they could rarely afford, although all the mothers knew what made up a healthy diet. This led to feelings of frustration and isolation from the rest of the population around them. A group of 197 mothers from all social classes was then asked to agree on what a week's healthy diet for children should be. The cost of this food and the other basic weekly expenditures were then calculated and compared to the families' weekly money from income support (Table 7.16). The calculations showed that the cost of a minimum healthy diet cannot be afforded without affecting some other aspect of this tight budget.

Table 7.16   The minimum weekly budget for families with children in different age ranges compared with income support levels. Expenditure does not include transport, housing, fuel costs or any pocket money.

Items of expenditure	Expenditure/£ per week			
	Under 2 years	2–5 years	6–10 years	11–16 years
food	6.85	9.36	9.72	10.11
clothes (girl)	5.57	7.13	6.94	5.83
clothes (boy)	5.41	8.65	6.49	6.34
possessions and equipment	4.75*	3.13*	2.20	4.13
activities	1.75	7.53	7.45	7.36
furniture and decorating	0.17	0.54	0.54	0.54
laundry	0.86	0.86	0.62	0.62
toiletries (girl)	6.54†	2.18†	0.65	2.45
toiletries (boy)	6.54†	2.18†	0.65	1.99
total (girl)	26.49	30.73	28.12	31.04
total (boy)	26.33	32.25	27.67	31.09
Income Support	20.68	20.68	20.68	28.03

* Includes baby equipment such as pushchair, car seat.

† Includes disposable nappies.

A survey by the National Children's Homes charity (NCH) in 1991 found that, in the month before the survey, 20% of parents and 10% of children in the poorest families had gone hungry because they did not have sufficient money to buy food. Many mothers did not eat meals themselves, to ensure that their children did not go hungry. Another survey by the same charity found that many young people in poor families had eaten only one meal or no meals at all in the previous 24 hours, and that 90% had not eaten any fresh fruit during the previous day. A 1995 survey by the NCH found that the healthy diet recommended for pregnant women was unaffordable by those women living on benefits, especially young mothers aged 16–17 who were not entitled to full benefits. The NCH survey of 120 women estimated that the average cost of eating a realistic and nutritious diet of the kind recommended during pregnancy was £18.12 a week, almost half the income of a single 24-year-old on benefits and 65% of the income of a single woman aged 16–17. Nearly all those surveyed were eating a poor diet and 76% regularly missed meals. A survey of their diet during the previous 24 hours showed that 43% had eaten no vegetables, apart from potatoes, and 75% had eaten no fruit. At the same time, nearly 80% had consumed sugar-rich foods or drinks and nearly 90% had eaten fatty snacks. The implications of this poor maternal nutrition on the subsequent health of the child was discussed in Book 1. Poor maternal nutrition leads to low birth weight babies, who are more likely to experience high mortality and morbidity rates, poor intellectual and physical development and to have more disabilities than babies of average or high birth weight.

Another survey in 1995 of 400 homeless people carried out by the charity Crisis, found that they were only receiving one-fifth of the recommended intake of vitamin A and less than two-thirds of the recommended daily amount of vitamin C. The homeless also suffer high rates of the infectious disease tuberculosis, because of poor nutrition and living conditions.

This research shows that the poorest members of the population, even in present-day Britain, are unable to obtain the basics for a healthy diet, not from ignorance or disinterest but because of financial constraints.

Summary of Section 7.5

1   Many people in the developed world who have low incomes are unable to buy an adequate, healthy diet. The decision to buy filling, satisfying food that children will eat makes best use of limited incomes but does not provide a balanced, healthy diet as recommended by current dietary advice.

2   The gap between the knowledge of what constitutes a healthy diet and the ability to buy that diet causes frustration and malnourishment, as mothers often forego food in order to feed their children adequately.

3   Poor nutrition in pregnant women is thought to contribute to poor development of the fetus, and so cause problems for the child in later life.

7.6 Social aspects of food consumption

While media coverage tends to focus on the relationship between diet and physical health, it is important to remember that food also plays a major role in the social and cultural lives of humans. When talking about how poverty affects their lives, many poor families mention such social aspects – for example, their inability to invite friends over for meals or visit restaurants. All life events such as births, marriages and even death are accompanied by the sharing of food with others. Religions make use of the symbolism of sharing food in many of their ceremonies, such as the Christian act of sharing blessed wine and bread or the Friday night meal in the Jewish tradition. Abstaining from food (fasting) is also a powerful sign of religious devotion, e.g. in the Moslem fasting period of Ramadhan. Table 7.17 shows some of the dietary restrictions prescribed by certain world religions.

Table 7.17   Examples of religious dietary restrictions.

Food restrictions	
Judaism	eat only animals with cloven hooves and which chew the cud, i.e. cattle, sheep, goats, deer
	eat only forequarters of sheep and cattle
	eat only fish with scales and fins
	no blood, no pork, no game
	do not mix meat and milk
Islam	no blood
	no pork
	no alcohol
Sikhism	no beef
Hinduism	no beef
Days of the year	
Christianity	no meat on Fridays during Lent (Roman Catholics)
	fast on Wednesdays and Fridays (Greek Orthodox) (with the exception of two weeks)
	no food preparation on Sabbath (Mormons, Seventh Day Adventists)
Judaism	no food preparation on Sabbath
Time of day	
Islam	food may not be eaten between sunrise and sunset during Ramadhan
Buddishm	monks do not eat after midday
Preparation of food	
Judaism	ritual slaughtering of animals
	use of separate utensils for meat and dairy products
Islam	ritual animal slaughter
Hinduism	ritual bathing and donning of clean clothes by Brahmins before eating
Fasts	
Christian	40-day Lent fast before Easter and a 40-day Advent fast (Greek Orthodox)
Islam	month of Ramadhan
	13th, 14th, 15th of each month

Food is also linked with various emotions and some of us may overeat when we are unhappy, depressed or wanting comfort. Our ability to enjoy food has perhaps been diminished by the current focus on the control of diet in order to maintain good health. We should not forget that the enjoyment of food will have positive effects on our well-being (think back to nurturing oneself, in Book 1, Chapter 2). Figure 7.9 shows guidelines for a healthy diet from the Ministry of Agriculture, Fisheries and Food (MAFF). Note that the first of these is a direction to 'Enjoy your food'!

Poor people who have to balance food budgets very carefully often feel uninterested in food because the sense of fun has gone from their eating. Humans eat to survive, but eating also fulfils social, psychological and cultural needs. These complex needs affect our choice of food and will influence how readily we change our diets to those considered more healthy. There are many unanswered questions about how we choose our food and the complex interactions of factors that influence that choice. A £1.6 million, six-year study funded by the government through the ESRC (Economic and Social Research Council) was begun in 1992 in the UK and it aims to answer fundamental questions such as:

- How do we learn about food?

- What leads people to take up new types of diet?

- What part does concern with our health play in what we choose to eat?

- Does our diet change when we get married or as we grow older?

This research shows our need to understand quite basic processes in human food choice and eating patterns, as well as understanding the biological and physiological aspects of food consumption (as discussed in TV programme 3).

Food and food preparation has always been a particular concern of women, in all societies and throughout human history.

❑   What sort of links between women and food are you aware of in your own social setting?

■   Women are still the main buyers, preparers and servers of food, despite recent changes in working patterns for women. They are the main targets for food advertising, and articles about all aspects of food and diet form a large part of many magazines aimed at women. Women also worry more about the food they eat, and its effect on their body size and shape. They comprise the majority of those suffering from eating disorders such as anorexia and bulimia nervosa. Women are also seen as the main informal teachers of cooking and food preparation skills to their children. Women are also seen as those responsible for ensuring their families eat a healthy diet.

Figure 7.9   MAFF guidelines for a healthy diet.

Not surprisingly, then, women are viewed as the main targets for advice on healthy eating. The conclusion from one of the ESRC research projects is that mothers are to blame for the poor diets of their children: 'We know that mothers often do not follow the advice they are given by doctors, health visitors and other health professionals [about healthy diets]'. This is reminiscent of the statements made at the beginning of this century about the poor being uneducated or unwilling to eat a proper diet.

Promotion of a healthy diet in the UK today has, so far, concentrated on trying to influence and change the individual's diet but responsibility for a healthy diet also rests with the producers of the nation's food, the agriculture and food-processing industries. Individual consumers are part of a long chain that stretches from the farm to the dinner table. Humans, in the late 20th century, are distanced from the point of food production; so it is easy to forget that the food we eat is part of a set of complex interactions between plants, animals and their environment. You will learn more about this in the final book of the course.

Summary of Section 7.6

1   Eating is of social and psychological as well as physiological importance, and thus contributes to health in many ways.

2   Food, food preparation, and ceremonies involving food are of importance in all major religions.

3   Women are seen as the main purchasers, preparers and servers of food and are the target of the majority of food advertising. They are also the main sufferers of eating disorders and many are concerned with the influence that food intake has on their body size and shape.

7.7 Humans in the food chain

Occasionally we are reminded by events of the origins of the food we pick up from the supermarket shelves. One recent event in the UK was the food scare about beef and BSE (bovine spongiform encephalopathy). Deregulation of the animal feed business led to changes in the processing of material to be fed to farm animals. Intensive animal rearing has also meant that farmers can no longer rely on the animals' natural eating habits, i.e. grazing pasture, to supply them with all the nutrients they need for rapid growth. Animal feed is now supplemented with high levels of protein, which promotes rapid growth in muscle mass and so provides cheap and plentiful supplies of meat. To raise the level of protein in animal feed, the carcasses of dead sheep used to be rendered down and then added to the feed production process. Some of the sheep used had died from a disease called scrapie, which affects the animal's nervous system. The infective agent of scrapie (called a *prion* – Book 2, Chapter 2) is very heat-resistant. Following deregulation, rendering of sheep carcasses was often carried out at lower temperatures than had been used previously, with the result that the scrapie agent survived the rendering process. Cows fed with this infected feed then developed a disease similar to scrapie which was called BSE (commonly known as 'mad cow disease'). The infective agent caused a gradual degeneration in the animal's central nervous system. Cows would be seen staggering and acting in a 'mad' fashion before dying. The fact that this infective agent has apparently passed to another species as a result of animals eating contaminated food, has raised concerns that humans who eat beef and beef products from infected cows may also develop a BSE-like disease. There is a condition in humans called *Creutzfeld–Jacob disease* (*CJD*) in which the symptoms and effects on the central nervous system resemble those produced by BSE and scrapie in cows and sheep. However, CJD is a disease with a long incubation period, i.e. there may be many years between the time of contracting CJD and showing any symptoms. So if the BSE-causing agent can be passed into humans, it may be a long time before this is reflected in a rise in CJD cases. There is a great deal which is unknown about BSE and CJD, especially about the transmission and nature of the infective agent involved. The BSE scare has had a profound effect on the beef industry and the consumption of beef by the general public. The feed-processing practices have since been changed, but the long-term effects of the infection are still being investigated.

BSE is a good example of the effects for humans, as the end-consumers in our particular food chain, of changes in the health of animals lower down in that chain. It also serves to emphasize how food production practices can have potentially disastrous consequences.

❏   What other food scares have been linked to changes in agricultural practices?

■   *Salmonella* contamination of eggs was linked to battery or intensive food production techniques. The use of pesticides, herbicides and growth-promoting substances in animals (such as bovine somatotropin (BST) to promote milk production in cows and antibiotics added to calf feed) may all accumulate in the food we consume and affect our health. Nitrates in drinking water from agricultural fertilizers have been suspected of contributing to some digestive cancers.

As the final book in this course stresses, human health cannot be divorced from the health of other animal species or the condition of the environment generally. This has become most obvious in the recent concerns about the quality of the food we consume.

Summary of Section 7.7

Consumers in the developed countries often forget that they are part of a food chain that stretches from the farm to their table. Recent food scares have shown us that changes in agricultural practices can adversely affect our food quality and our environment.

Objectives for Chapter 7

After reading this chapter, you should be able to:

7.1 Define and use, or recognize definitions and applications of, each of the terms printed in **bold** in the text.

7.2 Describe the main historical changes in worldwide human diets. (*Question 7.1*)

7.3 Explain the role that the main nutrient groups play in the human diet. (*Questions 7.2 and 7.3*)

7.4 Describe how vitamins and minerals contribute to the body's health. (*Question 7.4*)

7.5 Outline the problems in making links between components of the diet and disease. (*Question 7.5*)

7.6 Describe the main concerns about the UK diet in the 20th century. (*Question 7.6*)

7.7 Explain the problems that those on low incomes have in eating a healthy diet. (*Question 7.7*)

7.8 Describe the social aspects of eating. (*Question 7.7*)

7.9 Explain the effects of changing agricultural practices on the human food chain. (*Question 7.8*)

Questions for Chapter 7

Question 7.1   (*Objectives 7.1 and 7.2*)

When humans moved from a hunter–gatherer existence to that of settled agriculture, what were the disadvantages?

Question 7.2   (*Objectives 7.1 and 7.3*)

Carbohydrates are the major source of energy in the diet. The two main types of digestible carbohydrates are starch and sugar. Both starch and sugar, however, can be further classified. What are the different types of digestible starch and the different types of sugar, and what is the significance to health of this further classification?

Question 7.3   (*Objectives 7.1 and 7.3*)

If NSP cannot be digested and assimilated, why is it important in the human diet?

Question 7.4   (*Objectives 7.1 and 7.4*)

Explain, giving examples, why minerals and vitamins can be considered to be important in communication within the human body.

Question 7.5   (*Objective 7.5*)

Why is it difficult to assess whether a certain component of the human diet is protective against a disease or disorder?

Question 7.6   (*Objective 7.6*)

How could the attitude to diet be summed up: (a) from the beginning of the 20th century and during the Second World War and (b) in the post-war period?

Question 7.7   (*Objectives 7.7 and 7.8*)

Why are women particularly affected by having incomes that are too low to provide an adequate diet for their families?

Question 7.8   (*Objective 7.9*)

What are the consequences of humans being at the top of the food chain?

References

Boyd Orr, J. (1936) *Food, Health and Income: Report on a Survey of Adequacy of Diet in Relation to Income*, Macmillan, London.

Cohen, M. N. (1989) *Health and the Rise of Civilization*, Yale University Press.

Committee on the Medical Aspects of Food Policy (COMA) (1991) *Nutritional Aspects of Cardiovascular Disease: Report of the Cardiovascular Review Group*, HMSO.

Committee on the Medical Aspects of Food Policy (COMA) (1994) *Dietary Reference Values for Food, Energy and Nutrients for the UK*, HMSO.

Health Education Authority (1994) *The National Food Guide: the Balance of Good Health*, HEA.

Livingstone, M. B. E., Prentice, A. M., Strain, J. J., Coward, W. A., Barker, M. E., McKenna, P. G. and Whitehead, R. G. (1990) Accuracy of weighed dietary records in studies of diet and health, *British Medical Journal*, **300**, pp. 708–712.

Margetts, B. M. and Jackson, A. A. (1993) Interactions between people's diet and their smoking habits: the dietary and nutrional survey of British adults, *British Medical Journal*, **307**, pp. 1381–1384.

Walker, R., Dobson, B., Middleton, S., Beardsworth, A. and Keil, T. (1995) Managing to eat on a low income, *Nutrition and Food Science*, 3 pp. 5–10.

ANSWERS TO QUESTIONS

Chapter 2

Question 2.1

(a) Blood from the body enters the right atrium via the inferior and superior venae cavae and flows through the tricuspid (atrio-ventricular valve) into the right ventricle. (Atrial contraction ensures that all the blood is pumped out of the atria and into the ventricles.) The blood is pumped from the right ventricle into the pulmonary arteries to the lungs. Backflow into the right side of the heart is prevented by closure of the pulmonary valve. Blood returns from the lungs to the heart via the pulmonary vein into the left atrium. It flows through the bicuspid (mitral) valve into the left ventricle and is pumped out of the heart into the aorta and then around the body. Backflow into the left side of the heart is prevented by closure of the aortic valve.

(b) The sino-atrial node, a group of specialized cardiac muscle cells, is the heart's pacemaker and generates rhythmical waves of electrical excitation which spread through the atrial muscle cells, each wave leading to contraction of the atria. The electrical activity reaches the atrio-ventricular node, where the speed of conduction slows temporarily, allowing the atria to complete their contraction before the ventricles contract. The conduction speed increases again when the electrical impulse reaches the bundle of His and is conducted through the Purkinje fibres to the base of the ventricles. Ventricular contraction follows the electrical depolarization of the ventricles, and blood is expelled from the base of the ventricles upwards.

Question 2.2

(a)   cardiac output $=$ heart rate $\times$ stroke volume

cardiac output $=$ 70 strokes per min $\times$ 70 ml per stroke

$=$ 4 900 ml per min

$=$ 4.9 litres per min

(b) Cardiac output can be altered by changes in heart rate or stroke volume or both. Heart rate is the major controlling factor and it is increased by increased sympathetic (noradrenergic) nervous activity stimulating the SAN; it is decreased by parasympathetic (cholinergic) innervation of the SAN. The heart rate can also be altered by humoral factors (e.g. circulating adrenalin and noradrenalin, the 'fight and flight' hormones). Stroke volume is dependent on the venous return (Starling's law), so an increase in venous return will increase stroke volume. Contraction of the smooth muscle in the walls of the veins and venules increases the venous pressure and forces a greater volume of blood back towards the heart, so increasing venous return.

Question 2.3

Peripheral resistance is the resistance to blood flow through the systemic circulation and is caused by the viscosity of the blood and the friction between the blood and the blood vessel walls. This in turn depends on the diameter of the blood vessels. Peripheral resistance increases when the lumen size of the arterioles is reduced by contraction of the smooth muscle in their walls (vasoconstriction). A decrease in peripheral resistance is brought about by relaxation of the smooth muscle in the arteriole walls (vasodilation). Vasoconstriction is initiated by the action of sympathetic (noradrenergic) nerves, and by circulating noradrenalin, angiotensin and antidiuretic hormone (humoral control). Vasodilation is initiated by the action of parasympathetic (cholinergic) nerves, bradykinin and histamine (local humoral control) and by a decrease in blood P_{O_2} or an increase in blood P_{CO_2} (metabolic autoregulation).

Question 2.4

(a) Air enters the body through the nose or mouth and passes via the larynx into the trachea. The trachea branches into two bronchi which divide into progressively narrower airways: smaller bronchi, bronchioles and terminal bronchioles; the terminal bronchioles divide further into respiratory bronchioles, alveolar ducts and finally alveoli. Contraction of the intercostal muscles causes an upward and outward movement of the ribs, and contraction of the diaphragm further increases the volume within the chest cavity. Since the pleural membranes covering the lungs are held against the chest wall by surface tension, the lungs are forced to expand by the expansion of the chest wall. Air rushes into the expanded lungs to fill the increased volume inside the chest cavity.

(b) Oxygen is carried in the blood in combination with the respiratory pigment haemoglobin, as oxyhaemoglobin. The majority of the CO_2 is carried in red blood cells as bicarbonate ions (HCO_3^-). The conversion of CO_2 to HCO_3^- ions in the red blood cell is catalysed by the enzyme carbonic anhydrase which speeds up the reaction between CO_2 and water; the product is carbonic acid (H_2CO_3) which dissociates into HCO_3^- ions and H^+ ions. The H^+ ions are buffered (neutralized) by haemoglobin, and the HCO_3^- ions diffuse out of the cell. An inward movement of chloride ions (Cl^-), known as the chloride shift, compensates for this loss of HCO_3^- ions from the red blood cell.

Question 2.5

During exercise, the working muscles require an increased supply of O_2, which demands simultaneous increases in cardiac output and ventilation. An increase in heart rate and stroke volume increases cardiac output. The heart rate is increased by a reduction in the tonic inhibition of the sino–atrial node. Stimulation by the sympathetic nervous system and the action of circulating adrenalin and noradrenalin cause vasoconstriction, which increases the peripheral resistance and venous return, resulting in increased stroke volume. Sympathetic nerve activity also increases ventilation by stimulating the contraction of the inspiratory muscles. Metabolic autoregulation in the muscle capillary beds increases the local blood supply; the increase in P_{CO_2} acts as a local vasodilator, increasing the blood flow through the tissues. A build–up of lactate during exercise shifts the oxygen–haemoglobin dissociation curve to the right so that O_2 is released from haemoglobin more easily. After the cessation of exercise, the alterations in ventilation and cardiac output persist until the oxygen debt caused by the lactate build–up is repaid.

Chapter 3

Question 3.1

Table 3.4. summarizes the digestive activities of structures A–J in Figure 3.16.

Table 3.4   Answer to Question 3.1.

	Gut region or digestive organ	Digestive secretions	Functions
A	mouth (jaw, teeth and tongue)		chewing; initiation of swallowing reflex
B	salivary glands	salts and water	moistens food
		mucus	lubricates food
		amylase	begins breakdown of polysaccharides
C	oesophagus		moves food to stomach by peristalsis
D	stomach		stores, mixes, dissolves and begins main digestion of food; regulates passage of partially digested food (chyme) into small intestine
		hydrochloric acid (HCl)	dissolves food; activates pepsinogen; kills microbes
		mucus	lubricates and protects epithelial surface
		pepsin (from pepsinogen)	begins protein digestion
E	pancreas	bicarbonate (HCO_3^-)	neutralizes HCl entering small intestine from stomach
		proteolytic enzymes, amylase, lipase and nucleases	digest proteins, polysaccharides, lipids and nucleic acids, respectively
F	liver		produces bile (contains bile salts, HCO_3^-, waste products)
		bile salts	emulsify lipids
		HCO_3^-	neutralizes HCl entering small intestine from stomach
G	gall bladder		stores bile between meals and releases it into small intestine as required
H	small intestine		mixing and propulsion of contents by peristalsis
		disaccharide-splitting and proteolytic enzymes which are not secreted but present in brush borders of epithelial cells	complete digestion of carbohydrates and proteins
		enzyme (enterokinase) that activates a pancreatic proteolytic enzyme (trypsin)	
			absorption of products of digestion
I	colon		storage and digestion of non-digestible matter; mixing and propulsion of contents by peristalsis
		mucus	lubrication of faeces
J	rectum		defaecation

Question 3.2

The epithelium has many finger–like projections, called villi, and the absorptive cell membrane of individual epithelial cells has many small projections, called microvilli, which form the brush border. These specializations greatly increase the surface area through which absorption can take place.

Question 3.3

Digestion of carbohydrates begins in the mouth, where they are mixed with amylase produced by the salivary glands. This enzyme breaks down starch into polysaccharide chains of shorter lengths. Soon after food reaches the stomach, the salivary amylase is denatured by hydrochloric acid (HCl). The HCl also assists in carbohydrate digestion by releasing carbohydrates from bulky foods. When the food reaches the small intestine, pancreatic amylase continues the digestion of the polysaccharide chains into disaccharides and short chains of glucose (called dextrins). The digestion of these into monosaccharides is completed by enzymes situated on the brush border of the intestinal epithelium. The monosaccharides are then absorbed by Na^+-coupled active transport. Non-digestible plant polysaccharides (fibre) pass to the large intestine, where some are digested by harmless bacteria, producing gases. The bulky undigested plant polysaccharides are important for the formation and movement of faeces, and possibly also in the excretion of toxins.

Question 3.4

Enteric neurons play an essential role in controlling smooth muscle activity and the production of digestive secretions, and in the coordination of intestinal reflexes, so motility (mixing of gut contents and peristalsis), secretion and the integration of digestive processes might be disrupted by such a drug.

Question 3.5

The three phases of control of digestion are known as the cephalic, gastric and intestinal phases. The cephalic phase is stimulated by the smell, taste and sight of food and results in an increase in saliva and stomach acid (HCl) production. The gastric phase is stimulated by distension of the stomach, decreased acidity of the stomach contents and the presence of peptides in the stomach, and results in the secretion of the hormone gastrin. Gastrin, in turn, stimulates acid secretion. The intestinal phase is stimulated by distension and by increased acidity and digestive products in the small intestine. These factors cause inhibition of gastrin and HCl secretion, and stimulation of production of the hormones secretin and cholecystokinin (CCK), which, in turn, stimulate the production of pancreatic secretions and bile.

Question 3.6

Sensory information on taste and smell leads to avoidance of 'dubious' foods. Vomiting is a means of eliminating the toxic agent and nausea may lead to its avoidance in future. The mucus produced by the mucosal epithelium has protective effects. Specialized immune system cells located in the epithelium, in Peyer's patches, allow antibodies against ingested pathogens to be generated, by sampling the contents of the gut lumen. Some of the digestive secretions themselves, particulary HCl, also destroy many pathogens.

Chapter 4

Question 4.1

(a) Oxidation is defined as the addition of oxygen atoms, the loss of hydrogen atoms or the loss of electrons. Reduction is the converse of oxidation, i.e. the loss of oxygen atoms or the addition of hydrogen atoms, or the addition of electrons.

(b) The two coenzymes that are reduced and later reoxidized during glucose catabolism are NAD^+ and FAD; these are reduced to NADH and $FADH_2$ respectively, and then reoxidized, ultimately by oxygen, via the electron transport chain.

(c) In the course of reoxidation of the reduced coenzymes, ATP is produced: two ATPs per $FADH_2$ and three ATPs per NADH. This is the the source of most of the cell's ATP (energy) supply. The NAD^+ and FAD thereby regenerated can then participate in further rounds of glucose oxidation (hydrogen removal).

Question 4.2

Completed Table 4.5.

Process	Starting molecule(s)	End-products (which proceed to the next stage)	No. and type of coenzymes reduced	Net no. of ATP molecules produced
glycolysis	glucose	2 pyruvate	2 NADH	2 ATP
link reaction	2 pyruvate	2 acetyl CoA	2 NADH	none
TCA cycle	2 acetyl CoA		6 NADH and 2 $FADH_2$	2 ATP
electron transport coupled to oxidative phosphorylation	8 NADH and 4 $FADH_2$			32 ATP

Question 4.3

(a) Blood glucose concentration is regulated, so although no new glucose enters the body during a day's fast, blood glucose concentration will not drop below the normal range in a healthy individual.

(b) As the concentration of glucose in the circulation falls to the lower part of the normal range (because no glucose is entering the bloodstream from the gut), the hormone glucagon is released into the circulation from the alpha cells of the islets of Langerhans in the pancreas. Insulin is no longer secreted from the beta cells of the islets of Langerhans. Glucagon acts to stimulate: release of glucose from stores of glycogen in the liver and skeletal muscle (glycogenolysis); release of fatty acids and glycerol from fat stores in adipose tissue (lipolysis); synthesis of 'new' glucose (gluconeogenesis) from glycerol, pyruvate, lactate and amino acids in the liver. The use of fatty acids, rather than glucose, as a source of energy (glucose sparing) is also stimulated.

(c) Fatty acids and some amino acids are used to generate energy during fasting. Fatty acids are converted to acetyl CoA, which enters the TCA cycle. Some amino acids are converted to TCA cycle intermediates, or to pyruvate, which can then be catabolized, by the link reaction, to acetyl CoA, which again enters the TCA cycle. (Note that ketones, produced from fatty acids in the liver, are not involved in the production of energy, except during *prolonged* fasting.)

Question 4.4

A diet high in animal fats and sugary foods will result in increased storage of fats in adipose tissue and, since animal fats contain a large proportion of saturated fatty acids, will cause an increase in the proportion of LDL (low density lipoproteins) relative to HDL (high density lipoproteins) in the circulation. Excess glucose is converted into triacylglycerols (fats) in the liver. Here, triacylglycerols are assembled, with proteins, into VLDL (very low density lipoproteins) which are exported into the circulation. Lipoprotein lipase, located on the surface of capillary endothelial cells, releases fatty acids from the VLDL (and also from the chylomicrons, which enter the circulation from the gut); the fatty acids then enter the cells and are stored as triacylglycerols.

Question 4.5

A new-born baby has a large surface area to volume ratio, so can lose heat rapidly. Babies are unable to take voluntary actions to control heat gain or loss. They also have poorly developed mechanisms for the involuntary control of heat gain and loss; they are unable to shiver, and heat loss is mainly by vasodilation. The new-born baby has a special mechanism for generating heat, called non-shivering thermogenesis, which takes place in the brown adipose tissue (BAT). In BAT, the reactions of the electron transport chain are uncoupled from ATP production, so more energy is released as heat. It is important that BAT is well supplied with blood vessels, for two reasons: to deliver oxygen needed for the reactions that take place in the mitochondria (aerobic respiration); and to transfer the heat generated there to other parts of the body via the circulating blood.

Chapter 5

Question 5.1
Substance X may be filtered at the glomerulus, and then partially reabsorbed. Alternatively it may not be filtered at all, but secreted into the filtrate. Clearance = amount excreted/amount in plasma. Thus, for X:

$$\text{clearance} = \frac{2 \text{ mg per min}}{8 \text{ mg per ml}} = 0.25 \text{ ml per min}$$

Question 5.2

(a) Glucose is reabsorbed by active transport coupled to sodium, in the proximal tubule.

(b) Sodium is reabsorbed by active transport, coupled to a number of other substances, including glucose, amino acids, bicarbonate and phosphate. It is also absorbed by diffusion through protein channels.

(c) Water is reabsorbed passively, by osmosis through protein channels in the membranes of the epithelial cells lining the kidney tubules, and by diffusion through the small spaces between these cells. In the collecting ducts, the number of protein channels through which water is absorbed is increased by ADH.

Question 5.3

See Figure 5.22. The regulated variables are the body fluid levels of water and sodium.

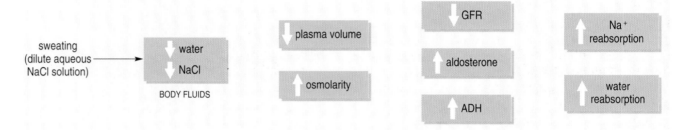

Figure 5.22   For answer to Question 5.3.

Question 5.4

It will result in acidosis, as, in the equation given on page 193, there will be a shift to the right, and hence an increase in the concentration of hydrogen ions. Under these circumstances, the amount of hydrogen ions secreted will be greater than the quantity of bicarbonate filtered, and hydrogen ions will therefore be excreted.

Question 5.5

A reduction in oxygen concentration stimulates the release of the hormone erythropoietin from capillary endothelial cells in the kidney. Erythropoietin, which is also produced by the liver, stimulates the proliferation of red blood cell precursors in the bone marrow.

Chapter 6

Question 6.1

In response to the rise in sodium chloride concentration in the extracellular fluid, the kidney would be expected to excrete a urine that is concentrated in sodium chloride. This would tend to reduce the disturbance to the intracellular compartment. The 40 minutes delay would give the kidney time to exert this control action.

Question 6.2

The unconditional stimulus is food in the mouth and the conditional response is the amount of saliva produced by the bell alone. If the bell is sounded a number of times but without food being given, the amount of salivation will decline.

Question 6.3

In a hungry dog, salivation is a relatively stereotyped and predictable reaction to a particular stimulus, that of food in the mouth. It is something that is common to all dogs.

Question 6.4

Motivation towards food can be aroused by the presence of food and this can happen particularly when nutrient levels are depleted. It is not difficult to appreciate that times of nutrient deficiency are times when attention needs to be drawn to food-related cues. It is logical to assume that this is mediated by the activity of neurons within the CNS.

Question 6.5

Note the excitatory inputs from the neurons triggered by taste and vision to the motivation neuron (1). Certain foods presumably have a particularly strong capacity to trigger activity in these pathways and hence in the motivation neuron.

Question 6.6

Since this pathway is assumed to play a role in satiety, injecting a receptor antagonist would be expected to lower the satiety effect and the subject would eat more than normal.

Question 6.7

In each case, we believe that there are variables within such sites as the liver and the brain that serve to trigger ingestion. However, at the time ingestion ceases, little water or nutrients will have got beyond the gut. Therefore, it is argued that pre-absorptive events (e.g. a memory of ingested material) play a role in satiety.

Chapter 7

Question 7.1

People had to work longer hours to produce a diet adequate in energy. Larger groupings of people in settled communities meant that disease could spread more rapidly than when people were living in small, isolated groups. Diets often relied on one or two staple crops and therefore became more monotonous and contained a smaller range of nutrient sources.

Question 7.2

Digestible starch can be classified as rapidly or slowly digestible, according to how quickly it is digested and its constituent glucose molecules absorbed. Rapidly digestible starch causes a rapid and relatively large rise in the concentration of glucose in the blood. Slowly digestible starch provides a smaller but more prolonged rise in blood glucose levels. This is an advantage for diabetics, and also for non-diabetic individuals, as the energy provided from a meal containing slowly digestible starch will be available for a longer period. Large rises in blood glucose levels may increase the chances of protein glycation and, if occurring often, may disrupt glucose regulatory systems.

Sugars can be classified as intrinsic sugars, which form part of the structure of plants, milk sugars and non-milk extrinsic sugars. It is thought that consumption of large quantities of non-milk extrinsic sugars is detrimental to health, and is associated with increased incidence of obesity, tooth decay, elevated levels of blood glucose and insulin, non-insulin-dependent diabetes and cardiovascular disease. Intrinsic sugars and milk sugars, however, are not thought to have adverse effects on health.

Question 7.3

NSP (non-starch polysaccharides, fibre) help to bulk up the food as it passes through the gut, aiding peristalsis, helping to prevent diverticulitis and minimizing transit times and contact time between any toxic substances in the food (which might trigger cancer) and the cells of the gut. Diets high in NSP are also usually low in fat and non-milk extrinsic sugars and high in micronutrients, thus helping to produce a balanced, healthy diet.

Question 7.4

Na^+, K^+ and Ca^{2+} ions all have a vital role in communication by neurons. They are involved in the generation of the action potential and thus the passage of nerve impulses. Ca^{2+} also serves as an intracellular messenger; for example, it triggers the release of neurotransmitter molecules at the synapse.

Other minerals are important for communication in the endocrine system, as they form an essential component of some hormones. For example, iodine is an essential component of thyroid hormones.

Vitamins are also important for communication in the body. Vitamin A and D derivatives act as signalling molecules inside cells, affecting gene transcription and hence the properties of cells. An example of this is the action of the active form of vitamin D, which promotes transcription of the gene encoding the calcium binding protein on the surface of intestinal epithelial cells, and hence promotes absorption of calcium from the gut.

Question 7.5

Human diseases and disorders are rarely caused by one single factor – diet is usually only one of many contributing factors. It is difficult to isolate any effect a dietary component may have from these other factors. Food is usually made from a complex mixture of different substances and it may be the interaction between these components, rather than an individual component, that is important. The complexity of food, in addition to the many interacting factors inside and outside the body, make nutritional research difficult. It may also take many years for any effect from diet to be seen in a population, i.e. coronary heart disease and cancer take many years to develop to the point where symptoms can be observed. There are also problems in accurately assessing people's diets for long periods of time.

Question 7.6

(a) An adequate diet was considered to be one in which there was enough energy and protein to allow proper growth and development, i.e. quantity was important to ensure against deficiency

(b) After the war, the concern was with luxury items that had previously been rationed, e.g. meat, dairy produce, sugar, and these items were provided as cheaply as possible to as many people as possible. More recently, the idea of quantity in the diet has begun to be replaced by concerns about over-consumption and lack of quality.

Question 7.7

Women are usually the main shoppers, providers and preparers of food; for this reason they feel the failure to feed their families more acutely. They may forego food themselves to allow their children to eat and so become malnourished. This malnourishment can affect their health, as well as the health of any children they bear, if the period of malnourishment is during their pregnancy.

Women make up the majority of one-parent families and so are often living on low-level, state benefits, which are insufficient for the purchase of a healthy family diet. Advice on healthy eating is targeted towards women and this can fuel their feelings of inadequacy in managing the household food budget.

Question 7.8

Humans are the final consumers of the food chain and so will ingest and may accumulate toxins or infectious agents present in that food, e.g. chemicals used on crops that are then fed to animals destined for human consumption. If the harmful substances are not removed from the body, then continual consumption of the affected food will lead to raised levels in human tissue and possible ill-health.

ACKNOWLEDGEMENTS

We are grateful to Jean Macqueen who prepared the index for this book.

Grateful acknowledgement is made to the following sources for permission to reproduce material in this book:

Covers

Front: Copyright © 1995 Comstock Inc. ; *back*: Robert Harding Picture Library.

Figures

Figures 2.1 (b), 2.3, 2.7, 2.13, 2.16 and 2.17: Adapted from *Biology*, 2nd edn, by Claude A. Villee, copyright © 1989 by Saunders College Publishing, reproduced by permission of the publisher; Figures *2.5 (a), (b) and 2.20 (d):* Ganong MD, W. F., Lange, J. and Lange, D. (1983) *Review of Medical Physiology*, 11th edn, Appleton and Lange, by permission of Professor W. F. Ganong MD and the publisher; *Figures 2.8, 2.19, 2.20 (b) and (c):* van Wynsberghe, D., Noback, C. R. and Carola, R. (1995) *Human Anatomy and Physiology*, 3rd edn, McGraw-Hill, Inc., by permission of The McGraw-Hill Companies; *Figure 2.20 (a):* Comroe Jr, J. H. *et al.* (1962) *The Lung: Clinical Physiology and Pulmonary Function Tests*, Mosby-Year Book, Inc.; *Figures 3.9, 3.10, 3.11, 3.13, 3.15, 4.20, 4.21, 4.22, 4.23, 5.16, 5.17 and 5.18:* Vander, A. J., Sherman, J. H. and Luciano, D. S. (1994) *Human Physiology*, Sixth International Edition, copyright © 1994, 1990, 1985, 1980, 1975, 1970 by McGraw-Hill, Inc., with permission of The McGraw-Hill Companies; *Figure 4.4:* Alberts, B., Bray, D., Lewis, J., Raff, M., Roberts, K. and Watson, J. D. (1994) *Molecular Biology of the Cell*, Garland Publishing, Inc.; *Figure 4.24:* © Margaret L. Estey, in Dawkins, M. J. R. and Hull, D. (1965) 'The production of fat', *Scientific American*, **213**, August 1965, p. 63, Scientific American, Inc.; *Figure 6.7:* Logue, A. W. (1991) *The Psychology of Eating and Drinking*, W. H. Freeman Inc.; *Figure 6.15:* Verbalis, J. G. (1991) 'Inhibitory controls of drinking: satiation of thirst', in Ramsay, D. J. and Booth, D., *Thirst: Physiological and Psychological Aspects*, © 1991 Springer-Verlag GmbH & Co. KG; *Figure 6.16:* Phillips, P. A., Rolls, B. J., Ledingham, J. G. G. *et al.* (1984) 'Reduced thirst following water deprivation in healthy elderly men', *New England Journal of Medicine*, **311**, pp. 753–759, © 1984 Massachusetts Medical Society; *Figures 7.2 and 7.8:* Garrow, J. S. and James, W. P. T. (eds) (1993) *Human Nutrition and Dietetics*, 9th edn, Churchill Livingstone; *Figures 7.3 and 7.4*: Bender, D. A. (1993) *An Introduction to Nutrition and Metabolism*, Taylor & Francis; *Figure 7.5: The Guardian*, 10 April 1994, Guardian News Service Limited; *Figure 7.7: Balance of Good Health*, reproduced by permission of the Health Education Authority; *Figure 7.9:* Reproduced with permission of the Ministry of Agriculture, Fisheries and Food, © Crown Copyright 1993.

Tables

Tables 3.3, 4.2 and 5.1: Vander, A. J., Sherman, J. H. and Luciano, D. S. (1994) *Human Physiology*, Sixth International Edition, copyright © 1994, 1990, 1985, 1980, 1975, 1970 by McGraw-Hill, Inc., with permission of The McGraw-Hill Companies; *Table 7.10:* Committee on the Medical Aspects of Food Policy (COMA) (1991) 'Dietary reference values for food energy and nutrients for the UK', © 1991 Crown Copyright, reproduced with the permission of the Controller of Her Majesty's Stationery Office; *Table 7.11:* Kelly, A. W. (1991) 'Estimates of the numbers and percentages of children under 5 years old in different parts of the world who suffered from malnourishment in 1990', *Subcommittee on Nutrition Technical Working Paper for UN Administrative Committee on Coordination*, United Nations; *Tables 7.15 and 7.16:* Walker, R., Dobson, B., Middleton, S., Beardsworth, A. and Keil, T. (1995) 'Managing to eat on a low income', *Nutrition and Food Science*, MCB University Press.

INDEX

Note: Entries in **bold** are key terms. Page numbers in *italics* refer to figures and tables.